W9-DEB-003

Lands and People

Written by Philip Steele
Illustrated by John James

First published in Great Britain in 1998 by
Dempsey Parr
13 Whiteladies Road
Clifton
Bristol
BS8 1PB

ISBN: 1-84084-201-6

Printed in Spain

Produced by Miles Kelly Publishing Ltd
Unit 11
Bardfield Centre
Great Bardfield
Essex
CM7 4SL

Designer: Diane Clouting
Editor: Linda Sonntag
Artwork commissioning: Branka Surla
Project manager: Margaret Berrill
Editorial assistant: Lynne French
with additional help from Jenni Cozens and Pat Crisp

Contents

6 billion people live on Earth.

How many people live in the world?
Billions! In 1997 there were about 5,840,000,000 human beings living on our planet. That's more than twice as many as 50 years ago.

Are there more and more people?
Every minute, 167 babies are born around the world. Imagine how they would cry if they were all put together! By the year 2025 there will probably be 8,036,000,000 people in the world.

Have people always lived where they do now?
During history many peoples have moved huge distances, or migrated. The Polynesian people took 2,500 years or more to sail across the Pacific Ocean and settle its islands. People are still on the move today.

Why are some lands richer than others?
Some lands have good soil, where crops can grow. Some have oil, which is worth a lot of money. But other countries have poor soil, little rain and no minerals. However hard people work there, they struggle to survive.

Some parts of the world are too harsh, too hot or cold for people to settle.

Frozen Arctic wastes

Where do people live?

H UMANS LIVE WHEREVER THEY CAN FIND FOOD AND WATER, which they need to stay alive. Nobody at all lives in Antarctica, the icy wilderness at the bottom of the world. Scientists do visit bases there, so that they can study rocks and icebergs and penguins. The Sahara desert in Africa is a land of burning hot sand and rocks. It has just a few places, called oases, where people can get the water they need to survive.

Have humans changed our planet ?
Over the ages, humans have changed the face of the world we live in. They have chopped down forests and dammed rivers. They have grown new plants and killed wild animals. They have built big cities and roads.

Clothes from round the world

Is there room for everybody?

Just about! But sometime in the future people may have to live in towns under the ocean or even on other planets. In those places they would need a special supply of air to stay alive.

Which country has the most people?

More people live in China than anywhere else in the world. They number about 1,237,000,000 and most of them live in the big cities of the east and the south. In the far west of China there are empty deserts and lonely mountains.

New York City, USA

Places where many people have chosen to settle have become big cities.

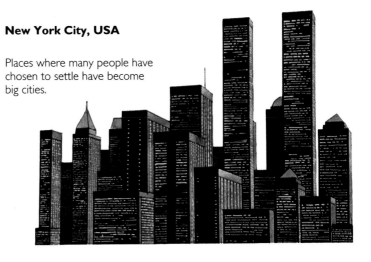

How different are we from one another?

ALL HUMAN BEINGS ARE BASICALLY THE SAME, WHEREVER THEY LIVE. We may speak different languages and have different ideas. We may wear different clothes and eat different foods. Our parents may give us dark or pale skin, blue eyes or brown, or various colours of hair. But in the end we share the same needs, pleasures, hopes and fears. We should not waste our time quarrelling, for we are all members of the same big family.

What is a continent?

The big masses of land that make up the Earth's surface are called continents. The biggest continent of all is Asia, which is home to over 3.5 billion people.

Where are the most crowded places in the world?

Tiny countries and large cities may house many millions of people. The most crowded of the bigger countries is Bangladesh, with over 800 people for every square kilometre of land.

Who are the world's peoples?

Human beings who share the same history or language make up 'a people' or 'ethnic group'. Sometimes many different peoples live in just one country. Over a hundred peoples live in Tanzania, each with its own way of life.

Colourful flags from around the world

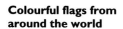

Crossing the world's biggest country, 50 years ago

Which is the biggest country in the world?
The gigantic Russian Federation takes up over 17 million square kilometres of the Earth's surface. It covers two continents, Europe and Asia, and its clocks are set at 11 different times.

Russia is so huge that when the Sun is setting over Moscow, it is rising over Vladivostock, on the Pacific coast.

How long does it take to cross Russia?
It depends how you travel! These days, trains on the famous Trans-Siberian railway take eight days from Moscow to the Pacific coast.

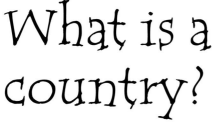

What is a country?

The Trans-Siberian Railway was built over a hundred years ago and opened in 1905.

A COUNTRY IS AN AREA OF LAND UNDER THE RULE OF A SINGLE GOVERNMENT.

A country may be vast, or very small. Its borders have to be agreed with neighbouring countries, although this does sometimes lead to arguments. Countries that rule themselves are called independent. Countries that are ruled by other countries are called dependencies. Sometimes several countries join up to form a single new nation, but countries may also break up into smaller nations, too.

How many dependencies are there in the world ?
Sixty-five of the world's nations are still ruled by other countries. They include many tiny islands in the Caribbean Sea and in the Atlantic and Pacific Oceans.

How many independent countries are there?
There are 192 independent countries in the world today. The number may change from one year to the next.

Swiss Guard, Vatican City

Which country fits inside a town?

The world's smallest nation is an area within the city of Rome, in Italy. It is called Vatican City and is headquarters of the Roman Catholic Church. Only a thousand or so people live there.

Where can you see all the flags of the world?

Rows and rows of flags fly outside the headquarters of the United Nations in New York City, USA. Most of the world's countries belong to this organization, which tries to solve all kinds of problems around the world.

Do all peoples have a land they can call their own?

No, the ancient homelands of some peoples are divided up between other countries. The lands of the Kurdish people are split between Turkey, Iran and Iraq.

What are counties and states?

If you look at the map of a country, you will see that it is divided up into smaller regions. These often have their own local laws and are known as states, provinces, counties or departments.

Refugees are people who have fled their country because of war or hunger.

Kurdish refugees

Why do countries have flags?

FLAGS CAN BE SEEN FLYING FROM BUILDINGS AND FROM BOATS. They show bold patterns and bright colours as they flutter in the wind. Many flags are badges or symbols of a nation, or of its regions. The designs on flags sometimes tell us about a country or its history. The flag of Kenya includes a traditional shield and spears, while the flag of Lebanon includes the cedar tree, which brought wealth to the region in ancient times.

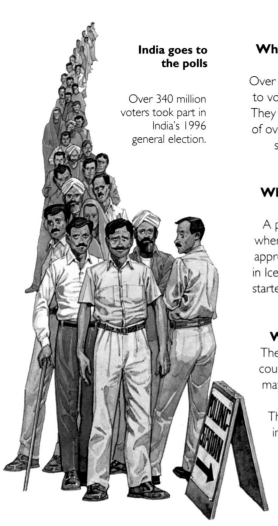

India goes to the polls

Over 340 million voters took part in India's 1996 general election.

Where is the biggest general election?

Over 590 million people are allowed to vote in general elections in India. They can cast their votes at any one of over half a million polling stations set up all over the country.

Which is the world's oldest parliament?

A parliament is a meeting place where new laws are discussed and approved. The oldest parliament is in Iceland. Called the Althing, it was started by Viking settlers in AD930.

What is a head of state?

The most important person in a country is the head of state. This may be a king or a queen or an elected president. The head of state often rides in a big car with a flag on it.

What is a republic?

It's a country that has no king or queen. France is a republic. Over 200 years ago the French king had his head chopped off, during a revolution.

Who invented democracy?

The people of ancient Athens, in Greece, started the first democratic assembly nearly 2,500 years ago. It wasn't completely fair, as women and slaves weren't given the right to vote.

Where do judges wear big wigs?

In Great Britain judges wear wigs, which were in fashion 250 years ago. This old costume is meant to show that the judge is not in court as a private person, but as someone who stands for the law of the land.

An English judge

Governments make the law, but it is up to judges to decide who has broken it.

What are 'Jana-gana-mana' and 'The Star-spangled Banner'?

Both of them are national anthems or songs. The first tune is played to show respect to India, the second to the United States of America. National anthems are played at important occasions, such as the Olympic Games.

Who rules the birds?

Traditionally the king or queen of England owns all the swans on the River Thames, except for those marked in a special ceremony that takes place each summer.

What is a government?

THE MEMBERS OF THE GOVERNMENT ARE THE PEOPLE WHO RUN THE COUNTRY. They pass new laws controlling everything from schools to hospitals and businesses. Countries where the people can choose their government are called democracies. At a general election each person puts a cross on a piece of paper to make their choice known. Then their votes are counted up to see who has won. Some countries do not hold elections or have a choice of political parties. The people who rule these countries are called dictators.

Which is the world's oldest royal family?

The Japanese royal family has produced a long line of 125 reigning emperors over a period of thousands of years.

How do you recognize kings and queens?

For special ceremonies rulers wear glittering crowns and carry symbols of royal power, such as golden sticks called sceptres. The beaded crown and robes shown here were worn by traditional rulers of the Yoruba people, who live in Nigeria.

Traditional robes worn by the Oba (king) of Akure, Nigeria

How does anyone get to be a king or a queen?

NORMALLY YOU HAVE TO BE A PRINCE OR PRINCESS, BORN INTO A ROYAL FAMILY with a king and queen for your mum and dad. About 800 years ago kings were very powerful people. They could have their enemies thrown into some horrible dungeon and then throw away the key. Today kings and queens have to be much nicer to people. They visit hospitals and open new bridges. They travel to meet other heads of state, as a representative of their own country.

How many languages are spoken today?

SOMEWHERE BETWEEN 5,000 AND 10,000 LANGUAGES ARE SPOKEN IN THE WORLD. Some are spoken by very few people. About 200 people in Latvia speak a language called Liv. One African language, Bikya, has only one surviving speaker. The world's most spoken language is Standard Chinese, which is used every day by 1,123 million people. English is the world's most widespread language, spoken by 470 million people.

What has made the world shrink?
Of course the planet hasn't really got smaller, it just seems that way. Today, telephones and faxes make it possible to send messages around the world instantly. Once, letters were sent by ship and took many months to arrive.

Instant communication

Telephones use satellite links to flash messages around the world.

Could we invent one language for all the world?
It's already been done! A language called Esperanto was invented over 100 years ago. Many people have learned how to speak it.

Do we all read left to right?
The Arabic language is read right-to-left, and traditional Japanese top-to-bottom.

Different cities, different signs

Many languages are related to each other and have words that sound similar.

What was that you whistled?
In some parts of Central America, Turkey and the Canary Islands, people worked out a way of communicating using whistles instead of words.

Can we talk without words?
People who are unable to hear or speak can sign with their hands. Various sign languages have been developed around the world, from China to the USA.

How do we talk through space?
Satellites are machines sent into space to circle the Earth. They can pick up telephone, radio or television signals from one part of the world and beam them down to another.

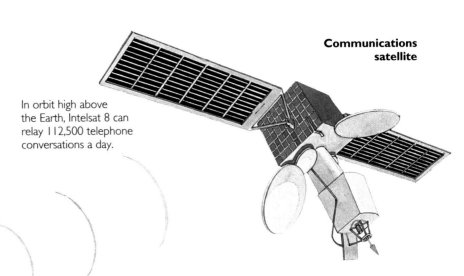

Communications satellite

In orbit high above the Earth, Intelsat 8 can relay 112,500 telephone conversations a day.

Should I stay or should I go?
Movements of the head and hands can be a kind of language. Be careful! In some countries wagging the hand palm down means 'come here', but in others it means 'go away'. Shaking the head can mean 'yes' in some countries and 'no' in others.

Each language has its own culture and traditions.

What's in a name?
In Scandinavia there's a village called Å. In New Zealand there's a place called Taumatawhakatangihangakoa-uauotamateaturipukakapikim-aungahoronukupokaiwhenuaki-tanatahu.

Methods of writing, such as alphabets, are called scripts.

Does everybody in one country speak the same language?
Not often. For example, families from all over the world have made their homes in London, the capital city of England. Their children mostly speak English at school, but at home may speak one of 275 other languages, from Turkish to Urdu.

Different scripts are used in many parts of the world.

Do we use different ways of writing?

MANY DIFFERENT KINDS OF WRITING HAVE GROWN UP around the world over the ages, using all sorts of lines and squiggles and little pictures. This book is printed in the Roman alphabet, which has 26 letters and is used for many of the world's languages. Chinese writers normally use around 5,000 different symbols, or characters, although ten times as many can be used. The Khmer alphabet, used in Cambodia, has 74 letters, while the Rotokas alphabet, used on the island of Bougainville, has only 11 letters.

What are houses made from?

Mud, stone, slate, boulders, bricks, branches, reeds, steel girders sheets of iron, concrete, glass, timber planks, straw, scrap metal, turf, frozen snow, bamboo, animal hides, packing cases, cardboard boxes – you name it! All over the world people make use of whatever materials they can find or produce in order to build shelters and homes. Today many modern buildings look much the same wherever they have been built, from Brasília to Singapore. However, all sorts of local types of houses can still be seen as well.

Why were skyscrapers invented?
So that more people could fit into a small area of city. High-rise flats and offices were first built in Chicago, USA, about 120 years ago. By 1887 new high-speed lifts were saving people a very long climb upstairs!

A Dogon village, Mali

Mud huts and grain stores are built around a yard, or compound.

Where do they build mud huts?
Thatched huts with walls of dried mud can still be seen in parts of Africa, such as Mali. They are cheap to build, cool to live in and they often look beautiful too.

What are houses like in the Arctic?
Today the Inuit people of Canada mostly live in modern houses and cabins made of wood. Traditionally, their houses were made of stone and turf. They also made overnight shelters out of blocks of snow.

Which people live in caravans?
Many of Europe's Gypsies live in caravans, moving from one campsite to another. The Gypsies, who are properly known as Roma, Sinti or Manush, arrived in Europe from India about 1,000 years ago.

Why do people live underground?
To stay cool! At Coober Pedy in Australia it is so hot that miners digging for opals built houses and even a church underground.

Bedouin nomads use camels to move from one part of the desert to another.

Houses must shelter people from cold and heat, rain and snow, storms and floods.

Where do people live in caves?

The first human beings often took shelter in caves. Even today, some people in Turkey and in China still make their homes in caves. These are not cold and dripping, like Stone Age dwellings. They can be snug and very comfortable.

Why do chalets have big roofs?

In the mountains of Switzerland, the wooden houses have broad roofs, designed for heavy falls of snow each winter.

Reeds are used for building from South America to Southwest Asia. They are also used to thatch cottages in parts of England.

Why do people live in tents?

IN MANY PARTS OF THE WORLD PEOPLE DO NOT LIVE IN THE SAME PLACE all year round. They are nomads, following their herds of sheep and goats from one desert oasis to another, or from lowland to mountain pastures. The Bedouin are nomads who live in the dry lands of North Africa and the Near East. Their tents are woven from camel hair. Today some Bedouin have settled in towns.

Why build houses with reeds?

It makes sense to use the nearest building material to hand. Tall reeds grow in the marshes and wetlands of southern Iraq – so the Marsh Arabs who live there use them to build beautiful houses.

A tent can be packed up easily and moved from one place to another.

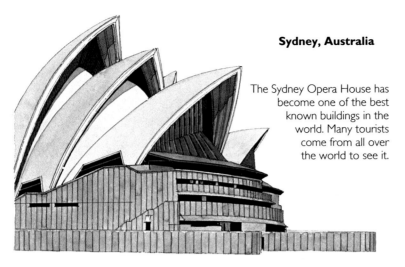

Sydney, Australia

The Sydney Opera House has become one of the best known buildings in the world. Many tourists come from all over the world to see it.

Which famous building looks like a sailing boat?

Sydney Opera House is in Australia. Its roofs rise from the blue waters of the harbour like the sails of a big yacht.

Why are landmarks useful in a city?

Each city has eye-catching buildings and monuments, which help you find your way around. Paris, in France, has the Eiffel Tower. Berlin, in Germany, has the Brandenburg Gate.

Which country has three capitals?

The most important city in a country is called the capital. South Africa has three of them! Cape Town is the home of the National Assembly. Pretoria is where the government offices are. Bloemfontein is the centre for the law.

Where are the biggest cities in the world?

IN JAPAN, WHERE BIG CITIES HAVE SPREAD AND JOINED UP TO MAKE GIANT CITIES! Japan is made up of islands that have high mountains, so most people live on the flat strips of land around the coast. In order to grow, large cities have had to stretch out like ribbons until they merge into each other. Over 27 million people live in and around the capital, Tokyo. It's still growing today. On the other side of the world, Mexico City is catching up fast.

Ancient Çatal Hüyük, Turkey

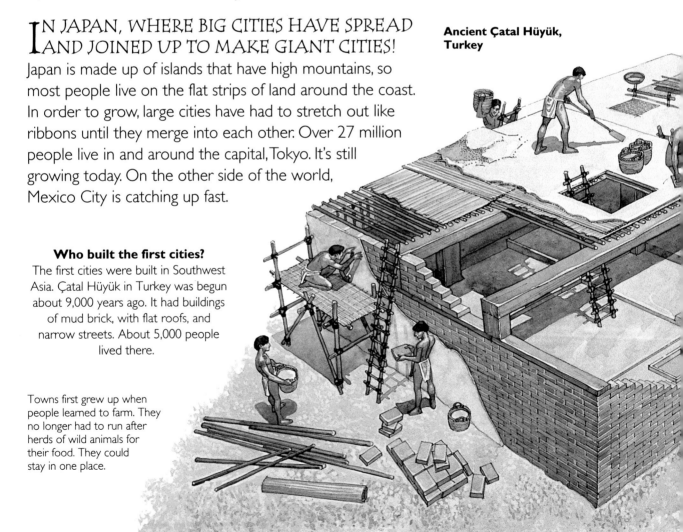

Who built the first cities?

The first cities were built in Southwest Asia. Çatal Hüyük in Turkey was begun about 9,000 years ago. It had buildings of mud brick, with flat roofs, and narrow streets. About 5,000 people lived there.

Towns first grew up when people learned to farm. They no longer had to run after herds of wild animals for their food. They could stay in one place.

What problems do cities cause?

CITIES CAN BE EXCITING PLACES TO LIVE IN. THEY ARE FULL OF HUSTLE AND BUSTLE. But they often have big problems, too. So many people in one place need a lot of looking after. They need water and electricity and proper drains, fire engines and ambulances and police cars. Too much traffic often blocks up the roads and fills the air with fumes. In some countries people pour into the cities from the countryside. They cannot find work and have to live in poor conditions.

Where is the world's tallest building?
The Petronas Towers in Kuala Lumpur, Malaysia, look like two gigantic space rockets. They soar to nearly 452 metres (1,483 ft), making up the tallest building in the world.

Which is the world's oldest capital?
Damascus, capital of Syria, has been lived in for about 4,500 years.

How does this ancient town differ from a modern one?

Cities became centres of trade, where people made pottery, baskets, food, tools and clothes.

Where is the Big Apple?
This is a nickname for New York City, in the eastern United States. Take a bite!

Who lives at the ends of the Earth?
One of the world's most northerly settlements is Ny-Alesund, in the Arctic territory of Svalbard. The southernmost is Puerto Williams in Tierra del Fuego, Chile.

Why was London Bridge falling down?
Children today still sing a rhyme that says 'London Bridge is falling down.' It's a very old song. The ancient bridge over the River Thames was pulled down by a Viking called Olaf the Stout – nearly a thousand years ago!

Which is the highest city?
Lhasa stands 3,684 metres (12,086 ft) above sea level. It is the capital city of Tibet, a region in the Himalaya Mountains that is governed by China. Tibet is sometimes called the 'roof of the world' .

Which city is named after a goddess?
Athens, the capital of Greece, shares its name with an ancient goddess called Athene. Her beautiful temple, the Parthenon, still towers over the modern city. It was built in 438BC.

How do you cross the Arctic snow?

You could always ride on a sled pulled by a team of dogs, as in the old days. But most people today ride snowmobiles, which are a bit like motorcycles with runners instead of wheels.

In Siberia, snowmobiles can use solid frozen rivers as roads during the winter months.

Crossing the Russian Arctic

Where can you catch a train into the sky?

In the Andes mountains of South America. One track in Peru climbs to 4,818 metres (15,807 ft) above sea level. In Salta, Argentina. you can catch another high-rise locomotive, known as the 'Train to the Clouds'.

Where was a hot-air balloon first flown?

The place was Paris, the capital of France, and the year was 1783. The passengers were, believe it or not, a sheep, a dog and a duck! Later, people tried out the balloon for themselves.

Chinese junk

What is the world's longest road?

THE PAN-AMERICAN HIGHWAY. IT STARTS AT THE TOP OF THE WORLD, IN THE CHILLY AMERICAN state of Alaska. It then heads on through Canada and the USA to the steamy forests of Central America. There is still a bit missing in the middle, but the road starts up again and carries on all the way down through South America to Chile, looping round to Argentina and Brazil. The total distance ? Well over 24,000 kilometres (14,914 miles)!

Where is the world's biggest airport?
Riyadh airport in Saudi Arabia is bigger than some countries. It covers 225 square kilometres (87 square miles) of the Arabian desert.

Where are boats used as buses?
In the beautiful Italian city of Venice, there are canals instead of roads. People travel from one part of the city to another by boat.

Who rides in a caravan?
No, not one pulled by a car! This kind of caravan is a group of traders who cross the desert by camel. Camels can carry people across the Sahara for six days without needing a drink of water.

Where are the longest trucks?
In the outback, the dusty back country of Australia, the roads are long and straight and pretty empty. Trucks can hitch on three or four giant trailers to form a 'road train'.

Australian road train

A road train speeds across the Nullarbor Desert in southern Australia.

Traditional wooden boats still sail along the Hong Kong waterfront.

How can you travel underneath the Alps?

THE ALPS ARE SNOWY MOUNTAINS THAT RUN ACROSS FRANCE, ITALY, Switzerland and Austria. They soar to 4,810 metres (15,800 ft) above sea level at Mont Blanc. In the days of ancient Rome a general called Hannibal tried to cross the Alps with 34 war elephants! Today, tunnels carry trains and cars through the heart of the mountains. The St Gotthard tunnel in Switzerland is the world's longest road tunnel, over 16 kilometres (10 miles) long.

Many countries still use wooden boats. Dhows sail off Arabia and East Africa, and feluccas are used on the River Nile.

What is a junk?
It is a big wooden ship, traditionally built in China. Its big sails are strengthened by strips of wood. Junks aren't as common as they used to be, but they can still be seen on the South China Sea.

African mask

This mask is worn at special ceremonies in Baluba, Africa.

Where is the capital of fashion?
Milan, London, New York and many other cities stage fantastic fashion shows each year. But Paris, in France, has been the centre of world fashion for hundreds of years.

What is batik?
This is a way of making pretty patterns on cloth. Wax is put on the fibre so that the dye sinks in only in certain places. This method was invented in Java, Indonesia.

Do people still wear national costume?
Most people in the world today wear T-shirts and jeans, skirts or suits. Only on special occasions do they still put on traditional costumes of their region. In some countries, however, people still wear their local style of dress every day.

How do people dress in hot countries?

IN HOT COUNTRIES PEOPLE PROTECT THEIR HEADS FROM THE SUN WITH all kinds of broad-brimmed hats, from the Mexican sombrero to the cone-shaped straw hats worn by farm workers in southern China and Vietnam. They may wear robes like the Arabs, or loose fitting cotton trousers. In desert lands people may cover their heads with cloths, to keep out the sand. The Tuareg of the Sahara wrap scarves around the face until only the eyes can be seen. Their name means 'the veiled people'.

Clothes today may be made from natural fibres such as wool, silk or cotton, or from artificial fibres such as nylon and plastic.

Which ladies wear tall lace hats?
The Breton people of northwest Europe are proud of their costume, which they wear for special occasions. The men wear waistcoats and big black hats. The women wear lace caps, some of which are high and shaped like chimneys.

18

Actually, Panama hats were first made in Ecuador, where they were plaited from the leaves of the jipijapa palm. They were first exported, or shipped abroad, from Panama, which is why they are now called Panama hats.

Today it is not always easy to tell where people come from by the clothes they wear.

How do we keep warm and dry?

SINCE PREHISTORIC TIMES, PEOPLE HAVE USED FUR AND ANIMAL SKINS TO KEEP out the cold. In the Arctic today, the Inuit people still often wear traditional clothes made from fur, sealskin or caribou (reindeer) hide. The Saami people of northern Finland also use their reindeer herds to provide leather goods. Wool, woven into textiles or pressed into felt, is used wherever the weather is cold. It is a good warm fibre, and the natural oils in it keep out the rain – that's why sheep don't shrink!

Who invented silk?

The Chinese were the first people to make silk, from the cocoons of silkworms, thousands of years ago. Today silk may be used to make beautiful Indian wraps called saris and Japanese robes called kimonos.

Where do soldiers wear skirts?

Guards of honour in the Greek army are called Evzónes. Their uniform is based on the old-fashioned costume of the mountain peoples – a white kilt, woollen leggings and a cap with a tassel.

Who are the true cloggies?

A hundred years ago wooden shoes, or clogs, were worn in many parts of Europe. The most famous clogs were the Dutch ones, which are still often worn today by farmers and market traders in the Netherlands.

Who wears feathers to a singsing?

A singsing is a big festival, Papua New Guinea style. Men paint their faces and wear ornaments of bone and shell and bird-of-paradise feathers. Traditional dress may include skirts made of leaves and grass.

Who are the Gauchos?

The cowboys of the Pampas, which are the grasslands of Argentina. Once the Gauchos were famous for their wild way of life. Today they still round up the cattle on big ranches called estancias.

Where are the world's biggest ranches?

The world's biggest sheep and cattle stations are in the Australian outback. The best way to cross these lands is in a light aircraft.

How can barren deserts be turned green?

Water can be piped into desert areas so that crops will grow there. But this irrigation can be very expensive and the water can also wash salts from the soil, making it difficult to grow plants.

Where do farmers grow coconuts?

Coconut fruits are big and green – the bit we buy in shops is just the brown seed inside. The white flesh inside the nut may be dried and sold as copra. Coconut palms grow best on the shores of the Indian and Pacific Oceans.

Which were the first all-American crops?

Six hundred years ago, nobody in Europe had ever seen potatoes, maize or tomatoes. These important food crops were first developed by the peoples who lived in the Americas before European settlers arrived there.

What grows best in floods and soggy wet mud?

RICE KEEPS THE WORLD ALIVE. BILLIONS OF PEOPLE EAT IT EVERY DAY, ESPECIALLY in Asia. Grains of rice are the seeds of a kind of grass that grows wild in wet river valleys. To cultivate it, farmers plant out the seedlings in flooded fields called paddies. In hilly lands, terraces are cut in the hillsides and the water flows down channels in the muddy soil.

Terraced rice fields

Some rice terraces, like these in the Philippines, are thousands of years old.

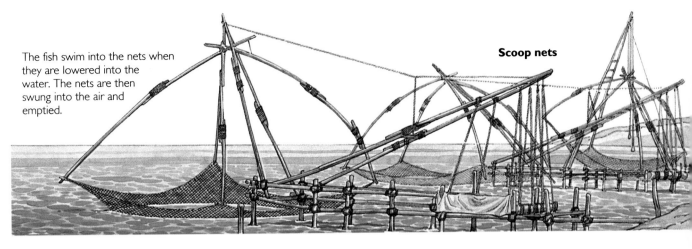

The fish swim into the nets when they are lowered into the water. The nets are then swung into the air and emptied.

Scoop nets

What is a cash crop?
It is any crop that is sold for money. Many small farmers around the world can only grow enough food to feed themselves and their families, without having any to spare.

Where do fishermen use hoops and scoops?
Giant fishing nets like these can be lowered from the shore into lakes and seas. They are often used in China and India.

Are there enough fish in the sea?
Modern boats catch so many fish that in many places fish have become scarce. Some of the richest fishing grounds were off Newfoundland, in the North Atlantic Ocean. Fishing there has now been banned until the numbers recover.

Combine harvester

What is the sweetest crop of all?
Sugar cane is grown on many islands in the Caribbean region. In Barbados, the end of the cane harvest is marked by Cropover, a grand celebration with music, dancing and parades.

Basic foods such as wheat (above) and rice are called staple crops.

Modern types of rice can produce several harvests a year. They can be planted by machines, but these are too expensive for many farmers.

Where are the world's bread baskets?

IMPORTANT WHEAT-PRODUCING AREAS OF THE WORLD ARE CALLED 'BREAD BASKETS' because they provide us with the bread we eat each day. Wheat is a kind of grass, and so it grows best in areas which were once natural grasslands. These include the prairies of Canada and the United States and the steppes of Ukraine and southern Russia. Huge combine harvesters move across the prairies for days and weeks on end, cutting the wheat and separating out the grain.

How do we keep food fresh?

TODAY, BUTTER CAN BE SENT TO EUROPE ALL THE WAY FROM NEW ZEALAND – kept cool by refrigeration. The first ever refrigerator ship was invented in 1877 to carry beef from Argentina. But how did people keep food fresh before that? The old methods were simpler – pickling, smoking or drying. The Native Americans dried meat in the sun and mixed it with fruit to make pemmican for their travels. Traditional methods are still used today to produce some of the world's tastiest foods – Indian pickles and chutneys, Irish smoked salmon, or Italian sun-dried tomatoes.

How much seaweed can you eat?

Various seaweeds are eaten in Japan, and in South Wales seaweed makes up a dish called laverbread. A seaweed called carrageen moss is often used to thicken ice cream and milk puddings. Seaweed is also found in toothpaste!

How do you eat with chopsticks?

Chopsticks are popular in China and Japan. Hold one stick between the thumb and the bottom of the first two fingers. Hold the other stick further along the first two fingers and support it with the third. It's easy!

The food people eat depends not just on the crops they can grow, the animals they can raise or the fish they can catch, but also on their traditional customs and religious beliefs.

Who invented noodles?

Which noodles came first – Italian spaghetti or Chinese chow mein? Some people say that the traveller Marco Polo brought the secret of noodle-making back to Italy from China in the Middle Ages. No! say others – the Romans were making pasta in Italy long before that. Maybe it was invented in both places.

Fresh foods from around the world

What is caviare?

One of the most expensive foods in the world. It is made of eggs from a fish called the sturgeon, which lives in lakes and rivers in Russia and other northern lands.

What is yerba maté?

It is a bitter but refreshing hot drink, made from the leaves of the Paraguay holly. It is sipped from a gourd (a kind of pumpkin shell) through a silver straw, and is very popular in Argentina.

Many southern Indian dishes are vegetarian. Some people in other parts of the world also prefer not to eat meat.

What is jambalaya?

Rice for a start, then prawns and peppers, all in an amazing hot spicy sauce. Where is this served up? New Orleans, in the steamy southern United States.

Who wrote a poem to his haggis?

Robert Burns, Scotland's greatest poet, who lived in the 1700s. The haggis is a traditional dish from Scotland. It is made up of lamb's heart, liver and lungs, suet, onions and oatmeal cooked inside – guess what – a sheep's stomach!

Where do you buy milk by the kilo?

In the Russian Arctic it is so cold in winter that milk is sold in frozen chunks rather than by the litre.

What is the most delicious food?

HAUTE CUISINE IS FRENCH, AND IT MEANS HIGH-QUALITY COOKING. People all over the world love French food. But is it really the most delicious food in the world? Chinese cooking is also thought to be a fine art. But really, which food we like or dislike is just a question of personal taste. Sheeps' eyeballs, insect grubs, snakes and pigs' ears can all be found on menus in one part of the world or another – and many people find them absolutely mouthwatering.

Preparing an African meal

African dishes are often based on cornmeal, and served with spicy vegetables, fish or meat.

Who makes the world's hottest curries?

The people of southern India. A mouthwatering recipe might include fiery spices such as red chilli pepper and fresh hot green chillies, ginger, garlic, turmeric and curry leaves.

Where were banknotes invented?

Paper money was first used in China, a thousand years ago.

More and more people around the world use plastic cards to pay for goods.

What are currencies?

A currency is a money system, such as the Japanese yen, the US dollar, the Mongolian tugrik or the Bhutan ngultrum. The exchange rate is what it costs to buy or sell one currency for another.

Where is the Silk Road?

This is an ancient trading route stretching all the way from China through Central Asia to the Mediterranean Sea. Hundreds of years ago, silk, tea and spices were transported along this road to the West by camel and pony trains.

Plastic, a new form of money

Who catches smugglers?

If you wish to take some goods from one country to another, you might have to pay a tax to the government. Customs officers may check your luggage to see that you are not sneaking in – or smuggling – illegal goods.

Who makes the most money?

The mint – that's the place where coins and banknotes are made. The United States treasury in Philadelphia produces billions of new coins each year.

Why sell stamps on Pitcairn?

Only 50 or so people live on remote Pitcairn Island, in the Pacific Ocean. So why do the islanders print so many postage stamps? Well, they sell them to stamp collectors and this make them a lot of money.

Where do people do business?

IN NIGERIA, MONEY CHANGES HANDS EVERY DAY IN THE BUSY TOWN MARKET. Laid out on the ground are batteries, watches, embroidered hats, peanuts, yams and cans of fish. The customers haggle with the women selling the goods, arguing about the price. In England trading might take in a big supermarket, packed with Saturday morning shoppers. In Switzerland bankers watch their computer screens to check their profits. In the New York stock exchange, traders grab their telephones as they buy and sell shares in companies. It's all in a day's work.

Where do you buy your food? At a city store or in a traditional street market?

All kinds of objects have been used as money

What can people use as money?

TODAY EVERY COUNTRY IN THE WORLD USES COINS AND PAPER BANK NOTES, although goods may still be swapped rather than bought in many regions. Over the ages all kinds of other things have been used as money around the world – shells, large stones, beads, salt, tobacco, blocks of tea, sharks' teeth or cocoa beans. These had no value in themselves, but then neither do the metal, paper or plastic we use today. They are just tokens of exchange.

Where in the world are there floating markets?

In Thailand and other parts of Southeast Asia, traders often sell vegetables, fruit, flowers and spices from small boats called sampans, which are moored along river banks and jetties.

Street market, India

An Indian trader waits for customers to buy her fresh produce. Among her wares are okra, tomatoes, beans, cauliflower, mooli, peppers and lemons.

What are the five 'K's'?

Sikh men honour five religious traditions. Kesh is uncut hair, worn in a turban. They carry a Kangha, or comb, a Kkara or metal bangle, and a Kirpan or dagger. They wear an under-garment called a Kaccha.

Stained glass window

This round window – called a rose window – in Lincoln Cathedral, England, is made of beautiful stained glass.

Which city is holy to three faiths?

Jerusalem is a holy place for Jews, Moslems and Christians. Sacred sites include the Western Wall, the Dome of the Rock and the Church of the Holy Sepulchre.

Where do young boys become monks?

In Myanmar a four year-old boy learns about the life of Buddha at a special ceremony. He is dressed as a rich prince and is then made to wear the simple robes of a Buddhist monk.

Where do pilgrims go?

PILGRIMS ARE RELIGIOUS PEOPLE WHO TRAVEL TO HOLY PLACES AND SHRINES around the world. Moslems try to travel to the sacred city of Mecca, in Saudi Arabia, at least once in their lifetime. Hindus may travel to the city of Varanasi, in India, to wash in the holy waters of the River Ganges. Christians travel to Bethlehem, the birthplace of Jesus Christ, or to the great cathedrals built in Europe during the Middle Ages, such as Santiago de Compostela in Spain.

What is Diwali?

This is the time in the autumn when Hindus celebrate their new year and honour Lakshmi, goddess of good fortune. Candles are lit in windows and people give each other cards and presents.

The lamps of Diwali

Lighted candles mark the feast of Diwali. The Hindu religion grew up in India many thousands of years ago.

Why do people fast?

IN MANY RELIGIONS PEOPLE FAST, OR GO WITHOUT FOOD, AS PART OF THEIR WORSHIP.
If you visit a Moslem city sich as Cairo or Algiers during Ramadan, the ninth month of the Islamic year, you will find that no food is served during daylight hours. Many Christians also give up eating certain foods during Lent, the days leading up to Holy Week, when they think about the death of Jesus. In Spain, during Holy Week, Christians carry crosses and religious statues in street processions.

What is Shinto?
This is the ancient religion of Japan. At its holy shrines people pray for happiness and to honour their ancestors. Many Japanese people also follow Buddhist beliefs.

What is Hanukkah?
This Jewish festival of light lasts eight days. Families light a new candle each day on a special candlestick called a menorah. Hanukkah celebrates the recapture of the temple in Jerusalem in ancient times.

Why is Mount Athos important?
This rocky headland in northern Greece is holy to Christians of the Eastern Orthodox faith. Monks have worshipped here since the Middle Ages. They wear beards, tall black hats and robes.

Which country has the most Moslems?
Indonesia is the largest Islamic country in the world, although some parts of it, such as the island of Bali, are mostly Hindu.

Moslem prayers

Moslems pray to God (Allah) five times a day. The most important worship is at noon on Friday.

Light and fire are important symbols of the holy spirit in many religions.

What is the Tao?
It is said 'dow' and it means 'the way'. It is the name given to the beliefs of the Chinese thinker Lao Zi, who lived about 2,600 years ago. Taoists believe in the harmony of the universe.

Who was Confucius?
This is the English name given to the Chinese thinker Kong Fuzi, who lived at the same time as Lao Zi. His beliefs in an ordered society and respect for ancestors became very popular in China.

Which priests cover their mouths?
Some priests of the Jain religion, in India, wear masks over their mouths. This is because they respect all living things and do not wish to harm or swallow even the tiniest insect that might fly into their mouths.

What are Parsis?
The Parsi religion began long ago in ancient Persia, now Iran. Many of its followers fled to India over 1,000 years ago and are now found in many countries around the world.

Aboriginal art, Australia

Like dance and theatre, art often has its origins in religious and magical rituals.

Who paints pictures of the dreamtime?

Australia's Aborigines look back to the dreamtime, a magical age when the world was being formed, along with its animals and peoples. They paint wonderful pictures of it.

Where do they dance like the gods?

Kathakali is a kind of dance drama performed in Kerala, southern India. Dancers in masks and gorgeous costumes act out ancient tales of gods and demons.

Why do people love to dance?

DANCING IS A VERY DRAMATIC WAY OF EXPRESSING FEELINGS OF EVERY KIND.
In Spain, passionate flamenco dancers stamp and click their fingers to guitar music. In England, morris dancers happily jingle bells tied to their legs and wave sticks. In Africa there are important dances for growing up and for funerals. The first dances of all were probably designed to bring good fortune to prehistoric hunters, where a priest put on the skins and horns of the animal his people wanted to kill.

Who sings in Beijing?

Beijing opera is quite a performance! Musicians bang cymbals together and actors sing in high voices. They take the part of heroes and villains in ancient Chinese tales. Their faces are painted and they wear beautiful costumes with long pheasant feathers.

Where is the world's biggest art gallery?

At St Petersburg in Russia. It is made up of two great buildings, the Hermitage and the Winter Palace, and these hold millions of exhibits.

Mbuti dancers

Young Mbuti people from Zaire decorate their bodies with white make-up for a dance to celebrate the beginning of adulthood.

Where do drums talk?

The tama is nicknamed the 'talking drum'. Its tightness can be varied while it is being played, to make a strange throbbing sound. It is played in Senegal and the Gambia, in Africa.

Where is the world's very oldest theatre?

THE OLDEST THEATRE STILL IN USE TODAY IS CALLED THE TEATRO OLIMPICO and it is at Vicenza, in Italy. It opened over 400 years ago. But people were going to see plays long, long before that. In ancient Greece people went to see masked actors appear in some of the funniest and saddest plays ever written, at open-air theatres made of stone. These can still be seen today all over Greece.

What is kabuki?
Kabuki is an exciting type of drama that became popular in Japan in the 1600s and may still be seen today. The actors wear splendid make-up and costumes.

Kabuki – Japanese theatre

In kabuki, all the parts are played by male actors, some dressed up as beautiful women.

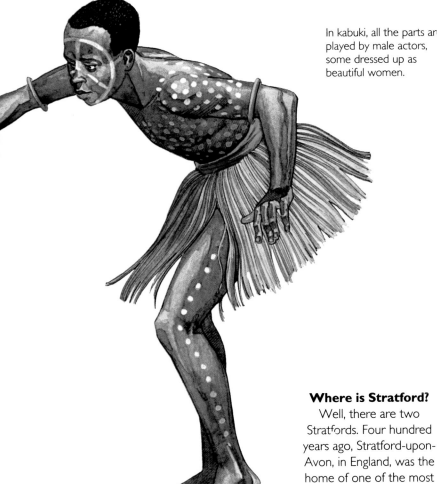

Who dances a hakka?
In New Zealand young Maori people have kept alive many of their traditional dances. The hakka was a dance for warriors, to bring them strength to face the battles ahead.

Where is Stratford?
Well, there are two Stratfords. Four hundred years ago, Stratford-upon-Avon, in England, was the home of one of the most famous playwrights who ever lived, William Shakespeare. The other Stratford in Ontario, Canada, holds a drama festival every year in his honour.

Who plays the 'pans'?
People in the Caribbean, at carnival time. The 'pans' are the steel drums, which can produce beautiful dance rhythms and melodies.

Who makes pictures from sand?
The Navaho people of the southwestern United States make beautiful patterns using many different coloured sands.

29

Fireworks were invented long ago in China.

What is a pow-wow?
It means 'get-together' in Algonkian. The Native American peoples of the United States and the First Nations of Canada meet up at pow-wows each year to celebrate their traditions with dance and music.

Where is the bun festival?
On the Chinese island of Cheung Chau, near Hong Kong, there is a big festival each May, with parades and religious ceremonies. During the celebrations people climb up huge towers made of buns.

What is carnival?

IN ANCIENT ROME THERE WAS A ROWDY WINTER FESTIVAL CALLED SATURNALIA. People copied this idea in the Middle Ages. They feasted and had fun before the dark, cold days of Lent began, when Christians had to give up eating meat. People still celebrate carnival today. In Germany there are wild parties and in Venice, Italy, people wear elegant masks and cloaks. In New Orleans, in the United States, jazz bands parade in the streets. In Trinidad and in Rio de Janeiro, Brazil, people dance wearing sparkling fancy dress and let off spectacular fireworks.

Who rides to the Feria?
Each April the people of Seville, in Spain, ride on horseback to a grand fair on the banks of the River Guadalquivir. They wear traditional finery and dance all night.

Who gets to sit in the leader's chair?
In Turkey, 23 April is Children's Day. A child even gets the chance to sit at the desk of the country's prime minister! There are puppet shows, dances and a kite-flying competition.

Dragon dance

At the Chinese New Year people parade through the streets wearing the skin of a mighty dragon.

Where do dragons dance?

WHEREVER CHINESE PEOPLE GET TOGETHER TO CELEBRATE their New Year or Spring Festival. The lucky dragon weaves in and out of the streets, held up by the people crouching underneath its long body. Firecrackers go bang, to scare away evil spirits. The festival is a chance for families to get together, give each other presents and wish each other good fortune for the year ahead.

The festival of Holi

Hindu children throw coloured powder over each other at the spring festival.

Who wears green on St Patrick's Day?

St Patrick's Day, on 17 March, is the national day of Ireland. It is celebrated wherever Irish people have settled over the ages, from the United States to Australia. People wear green clothes or put green shamrock leaves in their buttonholes.

Who remembers the fifth of November?

People in Great Britain. The date recalls the capture of Guy Fawkes, who plotted to blow up the Houses of Parliament in London nearly 400 years ago. The night is marked by blazing bonfires, fireworks and home-made toffee.

Where is New Year's Day always wet?

In Myanmar people celebrate the Buddhist New Year by splashing and spraying water over their friends!

Index

LAURENCE OLIVIER
Theater and Cinema

LAURENCE OLIVIER,
Theater and Cinema

Robert L. Daniels

SAN DIEGO • NEW YORK
A. S. BARNES & COMPANY, INC.
IN LONDON:
THE TANTIVY PRESS

Laurence Olivier Theater and Cinema text copyright ©1980 by
A. S. Barnes and Co., Inc.

The Tantivy Press
Magdalen House
136-148 Tooley Street
London, SE1 2TT, England

First Edition
Manufactured in the United States of America
For information write to A. S. Barnes and Company, Inc.,
P.O. Box 3051, San Diego, CA 92038
Library of Congress Cataloging In Publication Data

Daniels, Robert L
    Laurence Olivier, theater and cinema.

    Filmography: p.
    Bibliography: p.
    Includes index.
    1. Olivier, Laurence Kerr, Barton Olivier, 1907-
2. Actors—Great Britain—Biography. I. Title.
PN2598.O55D28   ·   791'.092'4 [B]   78-75346
ISBN 0-498-02287-0

1 2 3 4 5 6 7 8 9   84 83 82 81 80

To Mother—
who could always find me at the Oxford Theater

Contents

LAURENCE OLIVIER
Theater and Cinema

The Dane (1948)

Foreword

He Made People Laugh

When I was a youngster in Boston, my buddies and I would steal away to a local museum which generously revived films of the twenties, thirties, and forties. It was there that I first "met" Laurence Olivier. He was unusual; not at all like Jimmy Stewart or James Cagney or John Wayne who always seemed to be themselves. He rolled his eyes like Barrymore; he swooned like Colman; he moved like Fairbanks; he twinkled like Chaplin. Our eyes would inevitably move to his side of the screen. He had enormous appeal. We decided he was very special.

My next encounter with Olivier (now Sir Laurence) was during school when many of us were getting acquainted with Shakespeare's plays. Olivier's film work at that time made the most demanding Shakespearean texts not only credible to us but also terribly exciting. His *Henry V* was a compelling warrior-king-lover, grounded in the fields of Agincourt; his *Hamlet* was complex and electrifying; his *Richard III* was the most attractive monster ever conceived. These were images which held us transfixed and spellbound on the edge of our movie house seats.

When I actually met Olivier (now Lord Olivier) following a performance of *Ah! Wilderness* in which I appeared, I felt compelled to share my excitement about playing Henry V for Joe Papp in Central Park. "You'll be fine," he assured me. "You look just like him."

And now I have worked with "Larry" in a film—*The Betsy*. He performs with such an amazing subtlety of choices in his recent film and television work, that those watching are often taken by surprise and the light dawns at some point—"Oh! For God's sake! That's Laurence Olivier!" His disguise is not merely clever, but rather a signal of his own particular genius, his deep empathy for every nuance of a character. Most impressive of all, he is a hard worker. As I watched him build his role in *The Betsy,* I realized that I was watching the same man who built the National Theatre of Great Britain. The total impact his career and life has made on the profession is simply staggering! His acting style has profoundly influenced generations of actors; his stewardship of the English theater has affected the world. The variety of his role playing has been massive in scope. He has done everything!

Few are aware of his wonderfully wry sense of the absurd. "I really shouldn't be here, you know," he told me as we awaited a lighting shift while on film location. "The day after *Henry V* opened as a film in New York—it was a wonderful night—we were on our way back to England in a four-engine Constellation when suddenly one of the engines caught fire. Having been a pilot in the war I knew we all had seconds before the fuel lines would ignite and blow us all to pieces. Well, that flaming engine dropped into the Connecticut woods leaving an empty housing to create a terrible drag on that side of the plane. The pilot did an amazing thing. He kept favoring that bad side, making circles in the sky, until we landed safely

The Moor (1965)

12

in the field. If I were that pilot I think I might have taken the coward's way and dashed the plane into the ground as quickly as possible to end it all!''

Ironically, courage has been the hallmark of a great part of his career: leaping, flying, screaming, laughing—all the most incredible peak moments of performance. His physical courage in the face of illness is, like so much of him, inspiring. There are few things more exhausting than a twelve hour daily film schedule and to watch him ''stiffen his sinews'' and ''summon up the blood'' for his work in *The Betsy* was nothing less than extraordinary.

His career has probably been the single most effective force in English-speaking theatrical history, yet he would prefer his tombstone to read: ''He made people laugh.'' This man, who made the theater world tremble with his Oedipus and Richard III and Archie Rice, his Hamlet and Coriolanus and James Tyrone, reminisced, ''I think the most enjoyable night for me as a performer was the *Night of a Hundred Stars,* when

Vivien and Danny Kaye and I got into little schoolgirls' clothes and sang 'Triplets'.''*

We shall never see him in a theater role again. Luckily we have an impressive wealth of films. On the screen he becomes one of us. His sense of fun, his strength and courage, his vulnerability and self-mockery, bind him to us all. His prodigious achievements do not place him ''on high.'' He simply stands a little taller.

—Paul Rudd
New York, June 1978

*In 1951, Olivier appeared at the London Palladium in an all-star charity program with Vivien Leigh and Danny Kaye in a performance of ''Triplets'' by Howard Dietz and Arthur Schwartz, a song about precocious siblings.

"No other actor, except Chaplin is as deft a master of everything which the entire body can contribute to a role." (James Agee, 1948.)

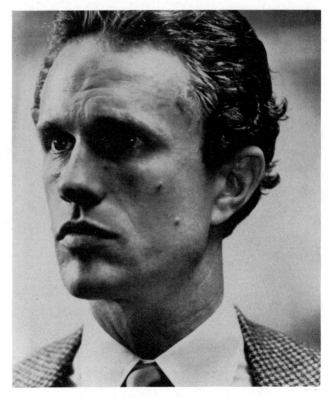

Paul Rudd as Loren Hardeman, Jr. in *The Betsy* (1978)

Acknowledgments

I should like to extend my gratitude to my wife Marilyn, my son Marc, and to Peter Bonanno for their valuable assistance. Sincere thanks is extended to Catherine Hopkins, who provided me with cuttings from Great Britain, and to those who watched the newspapers and magazines for me and offered encouragement and advice: Chet Child, Frank Osmers, Andy McNerney, William Pratt, Bob Bryan, Ronald Rosenkopf, Robert Conaway, Len Kessler, Edward Daniels, Jim Kelly, Jim Danas, Ron Nelson, Joseph Calderone, Ed Gries, Beth Iogha, and Gerald Hazell.

The scenes and advertisements for motion pictures and television presentations reproduced within this book were originally distributed for publicity purposes by: Allied Artists, ABC-TV, Arthur Cantor Productions, British Home Entertainment, British Lion, Columbia Pictures, Continental Films, Granada Television, I.T.C. Entertainment Ltd., J. Arthur Rank Enterprises, Lion International, London Film Productions, Metro-Goldwyn-Mayer, National Theatre, NBC-TV, Lopert Films, Orion Pictures Company, Palomar Pictures International, Paramount Pictures, RKO Radio Pictures, Selznick International, Twentieth Century Fox, Two-Cities Films, United Artists, Universal-International, Universal Pictures, Warner Bros.

Grateful appreciation is also extended to The Museum of Modern Art, Film Stills Archive (Carol Carey, Charles Silver); The National Film Archive, London; British Film Institute (Linda Wood); Cinemabelia; Movie Star News; Norma Nannini of Variety; Royal Shakespeare Theatre, Stratford-upon-Avon, RCA Records (Marguerite Renz), and to Dr. Vernon Schonert of Fairleigh Dickinson University for the use of his *Hamlet* notes.

Grateful acknowledgement is extended to the many critics, reporters, columnists and authors, and to their publishers, who have been quoted in the text. Newspapers and magazines consulted include:

"Olivier, the Director, Speaks of His Career," by Howard Taubman, *New York Times,* May 20, 1969.

"With Olivier in the Cast, Can You Fail?," by Thomas Lask, *New York Times,* December 11, 1966.

"Do You Think You Can Kill Me Easy?," by Jim Watters, *New York Times,* October 3, 1976.

"Olivier, Prince of Players, Recalls His Slings and Arrows," by Mel Gussow, *New York Times,* December 10, 1975.

"Talking with Olivier," by Curtis Bill Pepper, *New York Times,* March 25, 1979.

"Olivier Rewrites Doctors Script," by Thomas Quinn Curtiss, *New York Times,* "n.d."

"The Olivier Method," by Maurice Zolotow, *New York Times,* February 7, 1960.

"London Music Rave Ready for Screen Here," by Wanda Hale, New York *Daily News,* September 28, 1969.

"Laurence Olivier, The Lion of the Stage," by *Kathleen Correll, New York Daily News,* November 30, 1975.

"All the Stage is His World," by Kenneth Harris for the *London Observer,* reprinted in the *New York Post,* February 22, 1969.

"Olivier Scoffs at Retiring—Building Theatre 'A Joy'," *Los Angeles Times,* reprinted in the New York Post, April 15, 1970.

"The Tributes Rain on Sir Laurence Olivier," by Steven M. Silverman, *New York Post,* April 2, 1979.

"Sir Laurence Talked Despite Himself," by Dan *Lewis, New Jersey Bergen Record,* October 22, 1972.

"Olivier Better Than Ever," by Charles Champlin, *Los Angeles Times,* reprinted in New Jersey *Bergen Record,* January 19, 1976.

"Natalie on a Hot Tin Roof," by Cecil Smith, *Los Angeles Times,* reprinted in *New Jersey Bergen Record,* December 5, 1976.

"Zeffirelli: From Romeo and Juliet to St. Francis," by Robert L. Daniels, *North Jersey Suburbanite,* May 9, 1973, reprinted in *The Week Ahead,* May 19, 1976.

"Sir Laurence Olivier," by Fred Robbins, *Genesis* magazine, January, 1973.

"First Lord of the Stage," by Richard Meryman, *Life Magazine,* December 8, 1972.

"The Great Sir Laurence," by Richard Meryman, *Life* magazine, May 1, 1964.

"Join us Richard, I'm Going to be Interviewed," by Robert Musel, *TV Guide,* October 11, 1969.

"It's the most Beautiful Work I've ever had Anything to do With," by Neil Hickey, *TV Guide,* October 21, 1978.

"How I Escaped from Genteel Poverty," by Ian Cotton, *TV Times,* April 21, 1973.

"Lord of Craft and Valor," *Time* magazine, December 29, 1975.

"Up Front," by Judy Kessler and Robert Windeler, *People* magazine, December 22, 1975.

"Ordeal by Camera," by James Goode, *Show Business Illustrated,* September 19, 1961.

"Lord Laurence Olivier as Nazi Hunter," by Bernard Drew, *American Film,* July - August 1978.

"Olivier: A Precious Talent," *Variety,* April 4, 1979.

"At 75, John Gielgud Looks Back – and to the Future," by R. W. Apple, *New York Times,* April 15, 1979.

The following career articles from *Films in Review:*

"Laurence Olivier," by Henry Hart, December 1967.

"Ann Harding," by Gene Ringold, March 1972.

"Jean Simmons," by Alvin H. Marill, February 1972.

"Ralph Richardson," by Alan A. Coulson, October 1969.

"Vivien Leigh," by Ronald L. Bowers, August-September 1965.

Also consulted were television interviews with Laurence Olivier conducted by Stanley Kauffman, Dick Cavett and Mike Douglas.

Appreciation also to the publishers of the following newspapers and magazines and the critics for the portions of reviews which appear in the text.

New York Times: Bosley Crowther, Frank S. Nugent, Mordaunt Hall, Roger Greenspun, Vincent Canby, Thomas Lask, Jack Gould, A. H. Weiler, Clive Barnes, John J. O'Connor, Frank Marcus; *New York Herald Tribune:* Howard Barnes, Judith Crist; New York *Daily News:* Wanda Hale, Liz Smith, Tom McMorrow, Kay Gardella; New Jersey *Bergen Record:* John Crittenden; *Time* magazine; Jay Cocks; *New York* magazine: Judith Crist; *Newsweek:* Paul D. Zimmerman, Jack Kroll; *Saturday Review:* Arthur Knight, Hollis Alpert; *TV Guide:* Judith Crist; New York *Post:* Archer Winsten; *Films and Filming:* Robin Bean, Gordon Gow; *Hollywood Reporter:* Arthur Knight; *Cue* magazine: William Wolf; *The Picture Goer:* Lionel Collier; *The New Yorker:* Penelope Gilliatt; *The Aquarian:* James Testa; *Women's Wear Daily:* Christopher Sharp; and *Life* magazine, *Variety, Films in Review, Sight and Sound, The Trib, Playboy* magazine, *Memphis Commercial Appeal;* and in London, *Daily Mail, Daily Express, Daily Telegraph, The Guardian, The Herald, Sunday People,* and *Punch.*

Appreciation is extended to the publishers who have granted permission to quote from their books: W. H. Allen and Co., Curtis Brown Ltd., Little Brown and Co., Hamish Hamilton Ltd., Hodder and Stroughton Ltd., Weidenfeld and Nicholson, William Collins and Sons and Co.,

Ltd., Stein and Day, and Dell Publishing Co., Inc. Thanks also to the Englewood Public Library (Joseph Kritch, Edward O'Donnell).

Excerpts from *Shakespeare on Film* by Jack J. Jorgens, copyright (c)1977 by Indiana University Press. Reprinted by permission of the publisher.

"Laurence Olivier was in the office the other day," says Stephanie, a receptionist in a Manhattan talent agency.
"Who's that?" asks Tony Manero, a young Brooklyn paint salesman.
"He's only one of the most famous actors in the. . . Oh, you know, the English actor who did the Polaroid commercials?"

From *Saturday Night Fever*

"No man has graced his profession better than Larry Olivier has graced ours. He represents the ultimate in acting. He's the actor's most admired actor." (Cary Grant, 1979.)

Introduction

Destined for the Top of the Tree

In the trunk room of an English cottage there lies a large wooden packing box, and while it would seem to have no special significance upon a first glance, the crate served as the first stage for a six-year-old boy who would grow up to be generally accepted by his public and colleagues as the greatest living actor in the English-speaking world. Fifty years later Laurence Olivier recalled his debut on the crude platform. "My sister shelters—cherishes with great love that wooden box. It was about the size of the inside of a car, and I used to draw window curtains in front of it. My father used to buy Goldflake cigarettes in circular little tins, and I used to cut them and put a candle in so that I'd have little footlights. I performed my own plays, entirely my own works. Let's pretend—I suppose that's the original impulse of acting. That's perhaps why it does become more difficult as you get on in years. I think acting is a young enthusiasm. The childish excitement of it. The glamour disappears very early. And then comes the effort to improve yourself, to carve yourself into different shapes, to be successful—to be famous."[1]

Laurence Kerr Olivier was born on May 22, 1907, in Dorking, a small town southwest of London, where his father had been appointed his first clerical position as a curate in St. Martin's Church. The splendor of the church ritual was to make a strong impression on the young boy as he and his brother carried the incense and marched down the aisle in procession or sat in the choir loft absorbing Reverend Gerald Kerr Olivier's dramatic change of mood, manner, and rhythm as he delivered his sermons. The actor later attributed his father's prowess in the pulpit and the ritual of the high Anglican church as a strong influence on his life. "It made the services extremely attractive, very romantic."

When the family moved to London, young Laurence was enrolled in the choir school at All Saints Church, Margaret Street near Oxford Circus. It was at All Saints where the prominent actress Ellen Terry seeing Olivier in a performance of *Julius Caesar* later noted in her diary, "The small boy who played Brutus is already a great actor." Further theatrical encouragement was directed by the vicar, H. F. P. Mackay and the precentor, Geoffrey Heald. "At that particular little school they were very highly skilled in training us little infants—there were only fourteen of us—how to act," Olivier later recounted. "We had a very gifted precentor. A very artistic man who could have been a wonderful actor himself. He painted all the scenery, taught us all how to act, had a beautiful voice, and was very handsome. He was an effective theatrical preacher, and he taught me, I suppose, a very great deal of the love of it. I was very young—about ten. My first part was Brutus and then I went on to various girls' parts. I don't know why, but I did. I played Katharine and Maria. After I left this private school, which is mistakenly called a public school in England, I was invited to come back and play Katharine in a special production at Stratford-on-Avon for Shakespeare's birthday on a matinee.

That was Friday, April 23, 1922." Following the death of his mother, shortly before his thirteenth birthday, Olivier was sent to St. Edwards School in Oxford, where parsons' sons often prepared for a career in the ministry. He spent three years at St. Edward's and while he might have entertained some thoughts of a career in the theater, there was a greater likelihood that he would follow his brother to India and find employment on a plantation. His suggestion of becoming a tea planter was met by his father's surprising announcement that he would go on the stage. "My father encouraged me to go into the theatre," Olivier recalled. "He was a broad-minded, high Anglican parson. He loved the theatre, as did my mother. I don't think people's gifts are necessarily inherited gifts. I've got a notion that a talent is the result of an inherited wish. My father

"In the course of my life and career no actor has had a greater influence on my appreciation of acting as an art, my love of going to the theatre and my belief that the profession is important and necessary than Laurence Olivier." (Marian Seldes, 1978.)

was an extremely dramatic preacher and my mother, a very fine mimic. So there was a wish there, and so maybe I'm the lucky recipient of all those wishes. It's only inherited in an oblique way, not directly."

In 1924, Olivier auditioned for Elsie Fogerty, a dynamic elocution and speech teacher who in 1906 founded the Central School of Speech Training and Dramatic Art which she directed until her death in 1945. For the audition the young actor had prepared *The Seven Ages of Man* and inserting a flamboyant parry with an imaginery rapier on the lines "sudden and quick to quarrel," Miss Fogerty interrupted with stern suggestion, "I don't think we need *that!*" "She was a very powerful woman, very powerful," Olivier reflected many years later. "She said I had a little too strong an idea of the importance of action, and then she did a marvellous thing, an unforgetable thing. She said 'You have a weakness here,' and she took her little finger and placed it vertically down the middle of my forehead. Well, *something* made me slap on all that putty on my face for years and years afterwards, and I dare say it was that."[2]

Once accepted in the little school located in the Albert Hall, he came to live in London. Upon completion of his first term at the Central School, Olivier appeared in what he considered to be his first real part. At the Brighton Hippodrome in the summer of 1925, he acted in a curtain-raiser for a touring production of *The Ghost Train*.

In spite of repeated warnings by the stage manager about the wooden bars which ran across at the bases of scenery doors, Olivier managed to trip upon his entrance and tumble into the footlights, causing a local critic to comment, "Mr. Laurence Olivier makes a good deal out of a rather small part."

Following brief work as Flavius in *Julius Caesar* with the Lena Ashwell players, from which he was dismissed for his lack of self-control which caused him to giggle uncontrollably on the stage, and a job as a walk-on and assistant manager in *Henry VIII* with Sybil Thorndike and her husband, Lewis Casson, Olivier, not yet twenty, was hired as the romantic lead for the second half of the 1926–27 season with the Birmingham Repertory Theatre.

Founded in 1913 by Sir Barry Jackson, the Birmingham Rep was a company of keen artistic merit and one of the most significant enterprises in the history of the English theater. Several notable British players served their apprenticeship on its stage, among them Felix Aylmer, Cedric Hardwicke, Melville Cooper, Gwen Ffrangcon-Davies, and Ralph Richardson, whom Olivier found to be "formidably superior." Richardson thought Olivier to be frivolous and immature, but in spite of a frosty beginning they developed a long and lasting friendship.

Olivier often acknowledged the experience gained with the Birmingham Rep. "That was a very sought-after thing if you were a serious actor. Jackson not only had the best repertory theatre, but he also had three theatres in London—the Royal Court, the Kingsway and the Regent. So one had a very good chance, if one got on at all, of getting a showing in London, and that was one of the main reasons for wanting to go there, apart from the experience you could pick up at the Rep."[3]

Olivier appeared in an enormous range of parts while engaged as a Rep actor. He was in modern-dress versions of *Macbeth* and *The Taming of the Shrew*, played a young American in Elmer Rice's *The Adding Machine*, Martellus in Shaw's *Back to Methuselah* and, a month before his twenty-first birthday, and with little over two years professional experience, he appeared in the title role of Tennyson's *Harold*, his first leading part in London.

In 1928, Jackson invited Olivier to replace another actor as a squire's son who wants to marry an innkeeper's daughter in a pot-boiler called *Bird in Hand*. Also in the cast was a young dark-haired girl by the name of Jill Esmond, whom Olivier would fall in love with and marry. In November the Stage Society invited Olivier to appear in a special matinee of a sensitive and provocative war play, *Journey's End* by R. C. Sherriff.

Charles Morgan writing for the *New York Times* remembers his performance as Stanhope as one of "vigor, insight and beauty." Olivier consumed by ambition was eager to appear in a Basil Dean production of *Beau Geste*. "I couldn't pin my ambition down, it was all over the place,"

"I believe in the theatre as the first glamourizer of thought." (Lord Olivier, 1970.)

"In a time of rockets that light up the theatrical sky and vanish in the night, this is a planet." (Arthur Miller, 1969.)

he recalled years later talking to Kenneth Tynan. "Of course I wanted to be a West End actor, of course I wanted money. I wanted violently to get married, I wanted to have all the earmarks of success; they appealed to me as they appealed to everybody else. I think I sort of knew, you know, without wanting to sound too prophetic, that I was going to climb towards something, to reach some heights, and I knew the path to such heights was a stony one. But in the meantime I was very happy and content to be a young West End actor of a leading type, as in *Beau Geste*."[4]

Basil Dean, at the suggestion of Madeline Carroll who wanted Olivier as her leading man, signed him for the title role in a dramatized version of P. C. Wren's Foreign Legion adventure. He relinquished his role as Stanhope in *Journey's End* to Colin Clive, who gained considerable success when the play moved to the West End. *Beau Geste*, on the other hand, lasted only a few weeks. While the novel and subsequent film versions were exciting entertainments, the *New York Times* critic found the stage mounting "as dull as a great machine that makes half a dozen revolutions in four hours." Charles Morgan reported that Olivier was "overwhelmed by the sickliness of his part and by the weight of the stage trappings."

He did not fare much better with his New York stage debut in *Murder on the Second Floor*, nor his brief appearance in *The Last Enemy* upon his return to London. Jack Hawkins, who had appeared in *Beau Geste* recalled this low period in Olivier's budding career in his autobiography, *Anything for a Quiet Life*. "He always remained in good spirits, and as ever he was a splendid companion. He consoled himself with the company of an extraordinary dog that he bought from a man in the street. The animal reminded me of two extremely dirty brown face flannels knotted together, but Larry assured me it was a very rare Portuguese Wolfhound. Sadly, it had to go because it developed an addiction to bathtub gin and was constantly fainting.''

Early in 1929, the year the movies began to talk, he appeared in an unpaid performance with Cathleen Nesbitt and Elissa Landi of a John Van Druten play, *After All*. His great accomplishments in the theater were still some years away, and they will be documented further along with the growth of his film career.

With the advent of sound, there came a growing demand for handsome young actors with exceptionally distinct vocal resources. Olivier, possessing clarity of voice and a Ronald Colman moustache was among those drafted. His first films, made in 1929, required but a few days work. The veteran actress and director Ellen Pollack who had a brief role in *Too Many Crooks,* did not even recall Olivier being in the film.

In his screen debut Olivier appeared as a young playboy and amateur crook. In a film career spanning half a century, he appeared as priests and doctors, counts and kings, murderers and detectives, generals and stableboys. The enormous range of characters and the sheer versatility of his performances on the screen remain unequalled. Olivier's extraordinary portrait gallery offers an awesome example of his resourcefulness and daring as an actor.

As a youthful screen actor Olivier possessed incredibly handsome features. His rugged good looks and subtle acting talents brought him international stardom, first as a romantic actor in *Wuthering Heights* and *Rebecca* and later as the foremost interpreter of Shakespeare on the screen. He might very well have settled for the comfortable life of a Hollywood star in the forties and become one of those perennial British leading men, but he wisely chose to keep returning to the stage and the classics to exercise his valuable gifts and sharpen his theatrical skills.

One seldom thinks of Laurence Olivier when swashbucklers are discussed, yet much of his film work is marked with the striking kind of adventuresome flair usually associated with Errol Flynn

Olivier as Richard III by Salvador Dali.

A Shakespearean swashbuckler still swinging a blade in 1976.

and Tyrone Power. The actor's fascination with screen heroics began as a youngster. "The activity of my parts has been due to a schoolboy fascination for Douglas Fairbanks and I was absolutely swept overboard by John Barrymore in films. Barrymore was tremendously athletic playing Hamlet at the Haymarket in 1925. It was part of their glamour, that. Idiotically skinny as I was, one liked to think of oneself as a sort of Tarzan. I had a poor physique when I was young and spent my life making it better."

The swordsmanship Olivier displays in *Fire Over England* and later in *Hamlet* reveals a keen talent developed through his early training as a classical actor. The climactic and intense duel in *Hamlet* which lasts for ten minutes on the screen, took fourteen days to shoot. Roger Manvell in his *Shakespeare and the Film*, states that the sheer

bravura of his performance reaveals him to be "a theatrical showman as well as a great artist."

His daring feats on the stage and refusal to use stand-ins or stunt men on the screen have brought him a goodly amount of real wounds and narrow escapes. He was very nearly scorched while leaping from a burning deck in *Fire Over England*, tore a calf muscle in an athletic leap in *The Beggar's Opera*, and during the filming of *Richard III* was shot in the leg with an arrow. "I have all sorts of slashes from duels. I was stabbed in *Hamlet*. It felt glorious. It was very romantic to have a real dueling wound."

Olivier confesses to having seized physical opportunity where none really existed. "I must have been the most gymnastic Hamlet anyone has ever seen—not more than Barrymore, I suppose. I emulated him." In *The Royal Family*, a comedy

24

"In films, there is no performance. You just shoot a lot of
rehearsals and pick the best." (Laurence Olivier.)

which satirized a great theatrical family by George S. Kaufman and Edna Ferber and retitled *Theatre Royal* in Great Britain, the actor had the opportunity to essay a character which was modeled after John Barrymore. Olivier emulated his idol with vigorous panache causing him to break an ankle while leaping over a balustrade. Another actor had to substitute for him in the final act. In another dramatic flying leap while filming *Hamlet*, Olivier sails from a high landing to strike Claudius a final vengeful blow. The stand-in for actor Basil Sydney who portrayed the king, was knocked unconscious and lost two front teeth as a result of Olivier's flamboyant attack.

As the leading Shakespearean actor of our time, it is indeed unfortunate that only a half dozen performances have been preserved for posterity on film, and it is even more disconcerting that even less have been recorded. On the stage he has excelled in interpretations of Lear, Macbeth, Romeo, Iago, Mercutio, Coriolanus, Caesar, Antony, Malvolio, Hamlet, Shylock, Othello, Hotspur, Shallow, and Titus Andronicus. Sadly, the necessary financing could not be arranged for a planned film of *Macbeth*.

What does remain on film however spans four decades with extraordinary contrast from the youthful romanticism of his Orlando in *As You Like It* to the dark grandeur of *Othello*. As director and star, his great trilogy filmed between 1945 and 1955 are perhaps, the finest examples of the Bard on screen. In his scholarly and poetic *Hamlet*, the menacing *Richard III* and a *Henry V* rich with heroics and regal splendor, he has imaginatively merged the lyricism of Shakespeare's text with the visual demands of the motion picture camera.

As a screen villain, his studies offer a broad spectrum of cunning and cruelty. Even more monstrous than his crook-back Richard III, is Christian Szell, the heinous Nazi dentist of *Marathon Man*. Variety referred to his performance as "an A-budget version of what George Zucco did in hundreds of formula programmers." "I really don't mind what I play," Olivier told a reporter from *People Magazine*, "but this villain is really horrific." Even Lady Olivier had difficulty finding the courage to see it. "When

Larry told me about the dental torture," she told a *New York Times* writer, "I could hardly bear to listen. I know that contemporary life is violent, and the film, as an art form, should reflect contemporary life. Still, I can't tolerate violence. Perhaps it is because I'm a mother."

Another essay in horror from Olivier is the fearsome Mahdi of *Khartoum*. In the film's opening sequence, Olivier as a desert messiah sworn to destroy the infidel in a Holy War, delivers a prayer to Mohammed which is eloquent with fear and trembling. While he has but a few scenes in the film, from that moment on, the deep and dark danger of his presence is keenly felt with a relentless and unnerving strength.

Among his more civilized villains, Andrew Wyke of *Sleuth* is perhaps the most compelling and amusing. As a mystery writer seeking vengeance for his wife's indiscretions, he plays a game of death with aristocratic grace. Oddly enough, the nemesis of Sherlock Holmes, Professor Moriarty, long regarded by the famous detective as the Napoleon of Crime, is portrayed by Olivier in *The Seven-Per-Cent Solution* as a meek and misunderstood mathematics instructor. The cameo, however, which was filmed in a few days time, does include a sequence in which he appears in the hallucinatory subconscious of Holmes. In this brief, unspoken dream scene, without any change in makeup, Olivier as Moriarty becomes the personification of evil. In an instant he is Conan Doyle's villain incarnate.

"Great romantic actors are rarely great comedians," Pauline Kael commented in an assessment of John Barrymore's performance in the film, *Twentieth Century*, adding, "in our day Laurence Olivier is almost the only example." Of his stage acting, Dame Sybil Thorndike accounted him "a comedian in the best and fullest sense of that word." Olivier's comedy performances on the screen are but a handful, but what exists expresses a wide range of style. In *The Divorce of Lady X*, he plays light romantic comedy with the kind of breezy, sophisticated elan which served Cary Grant so well for many years.

The sharp Shavian wit, delivered with such tidy and crisp authority in *The Devil's Disciple* is the film's major asset. Another delightful comic vignette, providing a broad military contrast to his General Burgoyne, is the blimpish Sir John French in *Oh! What a Lovely War*. The true measure of his comic genius, however, is artfully realized in more tragic roles which have been laced with humor. For all of the devious plotting of *Sleuth's* Andrew Wyke, the character is well seasoned with bizarre buffoonery and acerbic wit.

One of Olivier's proudest hours is *The Entertainer*. The decline of a wilting music hall comic reveals inspired comic timing. The actor attributes the success of the role from having watched and admired the British comedian, Sid Field, "I borrowed from Sid Field freely and unashamedly, but I wouldn't like anybody to think that I was imitating him," the actor told Kenneth Tynan. "Sid Field was a great comic and Archie Rice was a lousy one."

Olivier's great tragic roles are eloquent with a rare dignity and strength and with what Ralph Richardson calls, "a splendid fury."

Othello, Oedipus, James Tyrone and Strindberg's Edgar in *The Dance of Death* have been widely acclaimed as awesome stage portraits, but Olivier confesses to not having enjoyed playing the great tragic roles. "They cost too much. You can't really do them very well without suffering a bit yourself and one gets bored with suffering." The demands of filming a tragic performance may have been somewhat less taxing, but the finished studies are no less thrilling.

In Olivier's sensitive portrayal of Dreiser's crumbling George Hurstwood in *Carrie*, director Tony Richardson saw a film blueprint for Laurence's later performance in *The Dance of Death*. The likeness is revealed in the Captain's solitary estrangement from his own life, separated from home and wife by bitterness and failure. As Edgar in the Strindberg drama, Olivier exhibits an extraordinary range of mood and emphasis, requiring contrasting elements of rage, pain, malice, humiliation, triumph, and defeat. Veteran actor Harry Andrews and Sir John Gielgud consider it his best performance outside of Shakespeare. Director Peter Glenville concurs, calling it "remarkably powerful" and Sir John Clements put it at the top

of his list, "without hesitation," as a "staggering brilliant performance." Filmed in 1968 and screened at the Stratford Film Festival in Ontario three years later, the film did not have a New York premiere until 1979.

Another rarely seen Olivier masterpiece is *The Power and the Glory* which was shown on American television, but filmed in an electronic process for release in Great Britain. Olivier was physically exhausted following a long run in *Becket* when he filmed the work for producer David Susskind during a one week shooting schedule. His role as Graham Greene's persecuted priest is tremendously moving.

Of the contemporary roles, Archie Rice in *The Entertainer* is certainly the most complete and illuminating creation Olivier has offered, and the quality which made it a virtuoso performance on the stage was superbly captured in its transference to the screen. In Richard Findlater's marvelous study of great English actors, *The Player Kings*, the author summed up the qualities which made Archie Rice such a compelling and realistic portrait. "This masterly performance was acting *about* acting, its shams and realities; it was the personification of a dying theatre and a dying society; but it was also the incarnation of one man's suffering and despair, nonetheless overwhelming in its theatrical truth because the man was a third-rate comic rather than a Shakespearean king."[5]

Playwright John Osborne contends that Olivier instinctively, but completely unaware, seized the best moments in his career to reflect the pulse and tempo of Great Britain. In *Wuthering Heights*, the relationship of Cathy and Heathcliff summed up the close personal patterns of relationships before the war, and *Henry V*, a few years later, caught the spirit of patriotism and excitement of wartime England. Archie Rice reflected the cynicism, decay, and moral compromises of the late fifties.

As a romantic actor, Olivier had displayed charismatic charm and sheer magnetism. "He is the only one who can be sexy in the best sense of that word," the late Margaret Leighton told Logan Gourley, author of *Olivier*. "He can convey real passion. So he appeals more to my sex and to my intelligence than any other actor."[6] Paul Rudd, who appeared with Olivier in *The Betsy* credits his romantic hold on an audience to an appealing twinkle and a constant flirtation with the camera.

Rudd, a young American actor who has been gaining considerable attention in Shakespearean roles, such as his New York appearances as Henry V and Romeo, was quite delighted to be making his screen debut in an Olivier film. He told WOR radio personality Jack O'Brian, that the women love Olivier. "He makes them feel terrific!" Lesley-Anne Down, who also appeared in *The Betsy*, cited an example. "We'd just started the film and I ran into him on the lift. He looked at me and started whistling—it was the tune I'd sung in a musical version of *Great Expectations*. He was so kind, and you can't help but learn things when he's on the set."

A constantly inventive and resourceful actor, Olivier is always interesting to watch. One is never quite sure of what he will do next, and it is difficult to watch the other players when he is on the screen. While his perceptive Scotland Yard inspector in *Bunny Lake is Missing* is considered one of his low-key performances, it is not without touches of clever little bits of business. While questioning the staff of a nursery school, where a child has disappeared, he walks back and forth in a small room and with each turn his elbow brushes against a window curtain. A seemingly insignificant move, perhaps, but the gesture at once suggested the confining area in which he was required to conduct his investigation. He literally created the dimensions of the room with one effortless move.

Olivier is an exterior performer, carefully building his character from the outside in. The self-transformation may begin with a cane, a limp, or a new nose. As a master of disguise he has hidden behind an alarming variety of moustaches, wigs, warts, and scars. Sir Tyrone Guthrie said Olivier could suggest good looks, partly with makeup, but "far more to the vitality and intelligence that inform every glance, and the athletic energy and grace of every movement."

When Olivier came to the Old Vic in 1937 to appear in Guthrie's *Hamlet*, he had already achieved considerable success in New York and London and was on the threshold of great fame. Guthrie recalled in his autobiography, *A Life in the Theatre*, that offstage he was not notably handsome or striking, "but with makeup he could achieve a flashing Italiante, rather saturnine, but fascinating appearance. The voice already had a marvelous ringing baritone brilliance at the top; he spoke with a beautiful and aristocratic accent, with keen intelligence and a strong sense of rhythm. He moved with catlike agility. He had, if anything, too strong an instinct for the sort of theatrical effect which is striking and memorable. From that first moment of the first rehearsal it was evident that here was no ordinary actor, not everyone's cup of tea—no strong personality can be that; but inevitably destined for the very top of the tree."

Olivier had reached a certain stage in his career by 1937 and attributed it very largely to luck. A decade later he recalled his first association with the Old Vic. "I had made two films, *I Stand Condemned* and *Fire Over England,* about which I make no comment. I could stay in films, and I had opportunities of being a West End leading man; and it would be quite easy to combine them all. But my eyes kept straying towards the rocky mountain tops. I felt young and strong enough to toughen against them now, and if I waited, getting fat and soft in the valleys, I would undoubtedly risk my neck every time I essayed to scale those heights."

"He preferred to use his extraordinary opportunities that his gifts have presented," Guthrie observed, "to extend his expressive range rather than his fortune or fan mail." While Olivier wisely divided his career between the stage and screen, it is through the latter medium that thousands of people have discovered his great talent. Certainly audiences in the United States have had little opportunity to see him other than in films and a few television appearances. He has acted on the New York stage less than ten times in three decades and not since *Becket* in 1960. Alec Guinness does not see much difference in acting for the stage or screen, but feels that Olivier needed the packed and attentive audience in order to really soar.

Fortunately his greatest roles on the stage— Archie Rice, Othello, Richard III, Astrov, Edgar,

Shylock, Hamlet, James Tyrone—were preserved on film. A great deal of the physical command, energy, and sheer presence of these stage portraits were successfully captured in their transference to the screen. "I've never seen so complete an actor in my life," Sir John Clements told Logan Gourley. "He has complete control over his voice, his movements—everything physical that goes into a performance. He knows exactly what he wants to do and whether one agrees with him or not, he does it to perfection within his own conception. When he played Othello as a Negro he was a Negro in every muscle and sinew. As Shylock at the National he was a Jew in every fiber of his being. As Richard III—which was incidentally one of the most memorable performances of his whole career—you felt that the physical defects were congenital, not assumed. Then in *Henry IV, Part One,* when he played Hotspur, he was virility personified. The following night when he played Shallow in *Part Two* you felt that this frail, white-haired little man would be blown across the stage like a leaf in the autumn wind. You simply could not believe that it was the same actor who had played Hotspur the previous night."[8]

Director Otto Preminger contends that despite Olivier's good looks and many excellent performances, he has never become a popular film star. While it is difficult to ignore the tremendous popularity Olivier enjoyed as a screen idol during the period in which he starred in *Wuthering Heights, Rebecca, Pride and Prejudice*, and *That Hamilton Woman*, it is easy to follow the drastic change in his screen image. During and following the war he plunged into his great Shakespearean trilogy and by the mid-fifties he was already established as the most important actor of the time who chose to appear in interesting character parts. During the sixties he devoted his energies to the National Theatre, with time out to appear in a dozen cameo roles for the screen.

Retiring from his duties at the National Theatre he returned to motion pictures as a full-fledged star in *Sleuth*. Finding the demands of stage acting too exhausting, Olivier in his seventies, has reaffirmed his durability and outwitted Mr. Preminger by becoming a very popular film star once again. His success in *Marathon Man* raised

screen villainy to a new peak, and his witty and lecherous patriach in *The Betsy* has amused audiences in spite of a wave of ungenerous support from the press. (The film grossed over $12 million in its first month of distribution at 486 theaters across the country.)

It is difficult to equate the talent and work of Olivier with any other living actor, or to find a parallel that approaches the enormity of his varied role playing. John Gielgud, Ralph Richardson, and Alec Guinness come to mind immediately as splendid actors capable of great pitch and passion, but missing is the classic handsome appearance, the charismatic presence, and the unique magnetism with which Olivier is entrusted.

Paul Scofield is a beautiful actor who is incapable of giving an uninteresting performance. He is an exquisite and sublime craftsman, who possesses a kind of pastoral grace rare in performers, but his acting is confined to the British stage, infrequent visits to the United States, and with the exception of his well-deserved Academy Award winning performance as Sir Thomas More in *A Man for All Seasons,* a mere handful of mostly undistinguished films.

Richard Burton, who is perfectly capable of unleashing a generous dose of what Richardson would assess as "splendid fury," has with a few notable exceptions, shamelessly blundered his enormous potential and deteriorated in an unforgivable parade of wretched motion pictures.

Who will wear the mantle? Who is the likely successor to the great inheritance Olivier will leave as a stage and screen actor, director, producer, and manager? The English stage continues to groom many fine actors. Albert Finney, Alan Bates, Peter O'Toole, and Anthony Hopkins cautiously continue to balance their work between stage and screen, while maintaining a dedication to the classics, but that particular chemistry, that little secret pocket of information which comes from deep within and which makes Olivier such a towering figure in his profession, is simply not in evidence.

There is to be found at the core of Olivier's genius, an overwhelming knowledge, an intrinsic comedic gift, meticulous attention to detail, a sublimely orchestrated voice, a keen sense of daring, mastered technique, and that awesome

"If we care about the theatre, there is not a single award, honor, medal, ribbon, we should begrudge him." (J. B. Priestley.)

physical presence. In 1965, Tyrone Guthrie expressed a wish to see Olivier less celebrated, less distinguished, less important, and more free. He suggested the actor advertise: Throne vacant—will suit hardworking, honest, methodical monarch. The position, of course, remains open.

The whole tradition of heroic acting which Garrick, Kean, Irving, and Booth have passed on to Olivier is perhaps left without an inheritor, but Olivier leaves a greater legacy than his illustrious predecessors; we have his films.

"His acting style has profoundly influenced generations of actors; his stewardship of the English theatre has affected the world." (Paul Rudd, 1978.)

The Cinema of Laurence Olivier

Too Many Crooks

1930, A Fox Film; Story by Basil Roscoe; Screenplay by Billie Bristow; Directed by George King

CAST

The Man	Laurence Olivier
The Girl	Dorothy Boyd
The Man Upstairs	A. Bromley Davenport
The Burglar	Arthur Stratton
The Maid	Mina Burnett
Rose	Ellen Pollock

THE FILM

A young playboy is dared by his fiancée to burgle a particular mansion. While engaged in opening the safe he is first surprised by the appearance of a beautiful girl and then by a professional crook, who proceeds to claim the contents of the safe. With the arrival of the police and the tenant of the house, the crook is revealed as a spy with stolen plans, the girl as a member of the C.I.D., and the amateur burglar as the actual owner of the house, which he has entered merely to procure his passport.

REVIEW

"If Laurence Olivier's future work is up to the standard he has set here, his appearance in the leading role of a more ambitious film is assured."

An elegant screen debut with Bromley Davenport in *Too Many Crooks. Courtesy, National Film Archive, Stills Library.*

1930, A UFA Production; Produced by Erich Pommer, Screenplay by Karl Hartl, Walter Reish, and Benn W. Levy, from the play *Hokuspokus* by Curt Goetz; Photography, Carl Hoffman; Directed by Gustav Ucicky

CAST

Peter Bille	Laurence Olivier
Kitty Kellermann	Lilian Harvey
Defense	Felix Aylmer
Prosecution	Frederick Lloyd
President Grant	Athole Stewart
Lindberg	Henry Caine
Anny Sedal	Gillian Dean
Hartmann	Fritz Schmuck
Loiret	Rene Hubert
Kuhnen	Norman Williams
John	Stanley Lathburg
Soldier	Adolf Schroder
Master Mailor	Johannes Roth
Old Usher	John Payne
Young Usher	Erich Kestin
Jury Foreman	Danchell E. Hambro
Female Juror	Ida Teater
First Juror	Oswald Skilbeck

Kitty Kellermann is being tried for murdering her husband, an unsuccessful artist. The case for the prosecution is strong, the crime apparently having been committed some months previously by the accused upsetting a boat and leaving her husband to drown. It is proved she is an expert swimmer and had appealed to the deceased to divorce her. His body had not been found. Her maid's evidence is prejudicial, the prisoner having ordered black clothes before her husband's disappearance, and afterwards indulged in singing. Still more damaging is the medical testimony that she is about to become a mother. It is suggested she has a lover, having been heard using endearing expressions on the phone. The defense is weak, the accused stating that her husband committed suicide, that she loved him sincerely, never wished for a divorce, and that black suited her. After many witnesses a man rises in the court and confesses to the murder, but ultimately he proves to be the missing artist himself. It seems the couple tricked the public for the sake of enhancing the value of his many unsold paintings.

As Peter Bille in *The Temporary Widow*, with Felix
Aylmer (left). *Courtesy, National Film Archive, Stills
Library.*

As Straker with Nora Swinburne in *Potiphar's Wife*.
Courtesy, National Film Archive, Stills Library.

Potiphar's Wife
(U.S. title: *Her Strange Desire*)

1931, British International Pictures; Written for the screen by Edgar Middleton and Maurice Elvey, from the play by Edgar Middleton; Scenario by Victor Kendall; Photography, James Wilson; Assistant Director, Clarence Elder; Editor, Leslie Norman; Directed by Maurice Elvey; Distributed by Wardour Films Ltd.

CAST

Straker	Laurence Olivier
Lady Diana Branford	Nora Swinburne
Lord Branford	Norman McKinnell
Hon. Maurice Worthington	Guy Newall
Therese	Elsa Lanchester
Major Tony Barlow	Ronald Frankau
Stevens	Henry Wenman
Rosita Worthington	Betty Schuster
Sylvia Barlow	Marjorie Brooks
Geoffrey Hayes	Walter Armitage
Counsel for Defense	Donald Calthrop

THE FILM

Lady Branford is married to a man who is much her senior and devoted to public affairs. Known to be a woman of many amours by her friends and servants, she is attracted to a refined and good-looking chauffeur. Her interest in him soon develops into infatuation and she lures him to her boudoir in an unsuccessful attempt to seduce him. Mad with rage at his indifference, she rouses the house and asserts that he has assaulted her. He is arrested and an exciting trail ensues. The case against the prisoner breaks down and he is discharged.

REVIEW

"There is one really outstanding sequence when the chauffeur is standing his trial—it is one of the best and most realistic court scenes I have seen. Laurence Olivier is admirable in the role of the unemotional chauffeur."

36

1931, An RKO Radio Production; Adapted by Jane Murfin from the novel, *The Sphinx Has Spoken* by Maurice de Kobra; Directed by Victor Schertzinger

CAST

Lieutenant Nichols	Laurence Olivier
Captain Roberts	Adolphe Menjou
Alva Sangrito	Lily Damita
Victor Sangrito	Erich von Stroheim
McNellis	Hugh Herbert
General Armstrong	Frederick Kerr
Lady Alice	Blanche Friderici
Ivanoff	Vadium Uraneff
Non Com	Lal Chand Mehra
French Maid	Yvonne D'Arcy
French Barmaid	Kay Deslys
English Barmaid	Dorothy Wolbert

Opened November 6, 1931, Roxy Theater, New York

THE FILM

Two English officers, Captain Roberts and Lieutenant Nichols, quarrel over their love for a married woman, Alva Sangrito. The lady's husband, Victor Sangrito, a connoisseur of porcelains, savagely whips his wife and is shot and killed by a secretary. Stationed at the Indian frontier, Roberts discovers through a photograph of Alva in Nichols' quarters that the younger officer and he are infatuated with the same young widow. The men argue and then decide to burn Alva's photographs and letters. Afterward they return to London and encounter the object of their past affections in the home of General Armstrong. The jealousy of the two officers is enraged once again, and Nichols threatens to shoot both Roberts and Alva, firing a bullet through a valuable print and arousing the anger of the old General.

REVIEW

New York Times, November 7, 1931

"With such screen personalities as Erich von Stroheim, Adolphe Menjou, Laurence Olivier, Frederick Kerr and the attractive Lily Damita, *Friends and Lovers*, the current attraction at the Roxy, is bound to have its diverting moments. Frederick Kerr as General Armstrong sounds a true note, and curiously enough his lines are always understandable. The other players give competent performances, but there was at this initial exhibition always a strange incoherence about many of their utterances."

COMMENTS

Olivier made his New York stage debut in September, 1929, at the Eltinge Theater. The play was Frank Vosper's melodrama, *Murder on the Second Floor*, in which Olivier portrayed a young playwright, Hugh Bromilow (created in London by Vosper himself), who pens a thriller inspired by the residents of a Bloomsbury lodging house. Brooks Atkinson reviewing the play for the *New York Times* noted that the actor possessed "an alarming suggestion now and then of Alfred Lunt."

Early in 1931 Olivier returned to Broadway in Noel Coward's *Private Lives*, repeating the role of the priggish Victor Prynne which he had originated in the London production, along with the author as Elyot Chase and Gertrude Lawrence as Amanda Prynne. Jill Esmond, who became Olivier's first wife in July of 1930, appeared in the play as the whining Sybil Chase.

During the three month engagement, the couple made a number of screen tests and subsequently accepted a handsome offer from RKO. "Olivier settled down to make his first Hollywood film, a steaming tropical affair with Adolphe Menjou. The studio, noting his moustache and the slight resemblance that had already caused comment in London, let it be known that they had a new Ronald Colman up their sleeve. *Friends and Lovers* was not a very good film, and Olivier was little happier about *The Yellow Ticket*, for which he was loaned to Fox later in the year."[1]

In later years Olivier recalled the glamour of Hollywood at the advent of the talkies. "It was the desirable thing to do in 1930. California, just before the crash, hadn't realized what was going to hit them. And the oddest architecture you've ever seen—a Spanish farmhouse next to an Arab mosque next to an Olde English cottage, looking at each other without surprise. Terribly exciting. I was 23, 24. My then wife and I both had contracts, and we thought we were the luckiest people in the world. I suppose we were."[2]

The Olivier's settled in a house high in the hills on the Appian Way, noted for its spectacular view. "I should think it must have been the topmost house in Hollywood. Bob Montgomery looked at the view one night and said, 'It all spells Marion Davies.' It was a wild, wild place in those days and Bob and Doug Fairbanks and I were the wildest."[3]

The Yellow Passport
(U.S. title: *The Yellow Ticket*)

1931, Fox Film Corporation; Screenplay by Jules Furthman, Guy Bolton; Adapted from the play by Michael Morton; Photography, James Wong Howe; Editor, Jack Murray; Directed by Raoul Walsh

CAST

Marya Kalish	Elissa Landi
Baron Andrey	Lionel Barrymore
Julian Rolphe	Laurence Olivier
Melchoir	Mischa Auer
Orderly	Boris Karloff
Count Nikolai	Walter Byron
Grandfather Kalish	Arnold Kroff
Mother Kalish	Sarah Padden
Fania	Rita LeRoy

Opened October 30, 1931, Roxy Theater, New York

THE FILM

A social melodrama set in Russia in 1913 concerns the plight of Marya Varenka, a Jewish girl, who secures a yellow ticket—a signed pass given to abandoned women—in order to be able to go to St. Petersburg, where she has reason to believe her father is lying ill. After learning that her father has been imprisoned on a political charge and killed, Marya encounters Julian Rolphe, a young British journalist who is in Russia to write articles for his own country's newspapers and those in America. Marya enlightens him, with the result that the tenor of his contributions changes and this is noticed by the alert secret police. Baron Andrey, the sinister head of the Czarist secret police, after hearing that Marya has been persecuted by his men, offers to save her from further

Lionel Barrymore as the sinister head of the Czarist secret police and Olivier as a British journalist in *The Yellow Passport*. Courtesy, Museum of Modern Art, Film Stills Archive.

trouble. When the Baron attempts to seduce her, Marya shoots him and escapes.

REVIEW

New York Times, October 31, 1931

"Out of Michael Morton's old play, *The Yellow Ticket*, in which John Barrymore appeared here in 1914, Raoul Walsh has produced a rugged, unrestrained but often effective pictorial drama in which Lionel Barrymore and Elissa Landi give clever interpretations of their respective roles. Laurence Olivier portrays Rolphe quite persuasively."

Retitled *The Yellow Ticket* for distribution in the United States, Olivier shared romantic interest with the beautiful Elissa Landi. The actress was a great success on the London and New York stage before beginning a colorful Hollywood career in *The Sign of the Cross* (1932) and *The Count of Monte Cristo* (1943). Miss Landi was also an accomplished writer and poet. She died in 1948 at the age of forty-four. *Courtesy, Museum of Modern Art, Film Stills Archive.*

1932, An RKO Pathe production; Produced by David O. Selznick; Photography, Lucien Andriot; Screenplay by Bradley King from the novel by Margaret Ayer Barnes; Directed by Robert Milton

CAST

Olivia	Ann Harding
Nick Allen	Laurence Olivier
Harry Lanman	Irving Pichel
Henrietta	Juliette Compton
Mrs. Truesdale	Zazu Pitts
Diane Van Tyne	Irene Purcell
Mrs. Ottendorf	Florence Roberts
Ottendorf	Emmett King
Lady Caverly	Ethel Griffies
Little Olivia	Bonita Granville

Opened June 3, 1932, at the Mayfair Theater, New York

THE FILM

Nick Allen is a jealous, temperamental, and hot-tempered writer who falls in love and elopes with Olivia, whose sudden glance can quickly cool his anger. He hopes to do something brilliant in the way of novels, but his publishers urge him to give them happy endings—to show at least a little faith in human nature. Olivia's baby is born, and when the child is about three she becomes mischievous and delights in tying strings and ribbons of the keys of her father's typewriter. Nick announces he is tired of married life, and Olivia sues for divorce and marries an old flame, Harry Lanman.

Years pass and when Olivia and Nick meet in Lucerne, they enjoy each other's company. Nick joins Olivia on the same boat when she returns to America, sharing jolly evenings and the usual differences of opinion. Lanman is prevented by business from meeting his wife upon arrival, and the two happy-go-lucky persons drive to Mrs. Truesdale's little inn, to which they fled when they were first married. They squabble and make up, and it is eventually presumed that with all of Nick's quick temper and jealousy, Olivia will throw her second husband overboard and continue living with the father of her child.

REVIEW

New York Times, June 4, 1932

"In *Westward Passage,* a film adaptation of a novel by Margaret Ayer Barnes, which has the decided advantage of the presence of Ann Harding, there are vague reminders of *Up Pops the Devil* and Noel Coward's *Private Lives.* This picture is concerned with a young couple whose bickering will probably go on for the rest of their lives, even though in the end the woman, Olivia, who has married again, is won over to eloping with her first husband, Nick Allen, impersonated by that excellent player, Laurence Olivier. It is a picture with bright dialogue, and the portrayals of Miss Harding, Mr. Olivier, Irving Pichel and Zazu Pitts are emphatically clever."

COMMENTS

RKO suffering an economic crisis during the Depression, appointed thirty-year-old David O. Selznick, a former associate producer at Paramount, as Vice-President in charge of Production. He set up a new committee to find stories suitable for varied public appeal. Proper-

Olivier discovered his leading lady, Ann Harding, to be the complete antithesis of the usual Hollywood star, generously reversing positions so that his face might be turned towards the camera instead of hers, insisting that his part be fattened, and seeing to it that his close-ups were as numerous and well lighted as her own. In this romantic embrace from *Westward Passage,* **the light-** ing clearly serves Olivier to greater advantage. *Courtesy, Museum of Modern Art, Film Stills Archive.*

ties were sought to please women and young people, and many stage plays were examined to see if they could be adapted to films.

"Into which category *Westward Passage* came is uncertain, but it was a slight improvement on Olivier's previous films. In the part of a temperamental young author he had one very roguish scene with a two year old baby, in which he fell into the child's bath, but despite this piece of slapstick he enjoyed the film more than the other two he made for RKO. One reason was that Ann Harding, whom he found the complete antithesis of the usual Hollywood star, so helped him during the making of the film that 'angelic' was the only adequate description he could find for her in a letter he sent to his family about this time. He told them how, during the shooting of a scene, she would turn slightly so that he would be photographed to greater advantage, and sometimes even insisted on completely reversing positions so that his face should be to the camera instead of hers. 'It is unbelievable for a star of her reputation to be so good,' he wrote enthusiastically."[4]

Perfect Understanding

1933, A Gloria Swanson Production, Screenplay by Michael Powell, Based on a story by Miles Malleson; Directed by Cyril Gardner; Distributed by United Artists

CAST

Judy Rogers	Gloria Swanson
Nicholas Randall	Laurence Olivier
Ivan Ronnson	John Halliday
Lord Portleigh	Nigel Playfair
George Drayton	Michael Farmer
Kitty Drayton	Genevieve Tobin
Lady Stephanie Fitzmaurice	Nora Swinburne
Sir John Fitzmaurice	Charles Cullum
Jackson, the Butler	Peter Gawthorne
Cook	Rosalinde Fuller
Maid	Evelyn Bostock
Dr. Graham	O.B. Clarence
Mrs. Graham	Mary Jerrold

Opened February 22, 1933, at the Mayfair Theater, New York

Judy Rogers marries Nicholas Randall, and it is her theory that jealousy is senseless and that any couple who really love each other can always reach a perfect understanding. In the course of time she discovers this to be a fallacy as Nicholas falls victim to the wiles of an old flame while his wife is away. When Nicholas confesses to Judy, she is jealous and disappointed in her young husband and attempts to get even by dining at the home of Ivan Ronnson, an old friend and explorer. Nicholas refuses to believe his wife when she tells him she has not been unfaithful. The bickering continues to the amicable finale.

REVIEW

New York Times, February 23, 1933
"This picture was made abroad and, sad to relate, all the trouble taken in engaging players and a director from Hollywood, in constructing handsome settings and in photographing a lengthy sequence on the French Riviera, does not prevent this picture from being quite tedious. Laurence Olivier gives a sterling performance in a none too fortunate role."

In *Perfect Understanding*, Olivier co-starred with Gloria Swanson, the durable leading lady of the silent screen who began her career as a Max Sennett bathing beauty in 1915. With the advent of sound she formed her own production company and this film was her first British made talkie. Michael Farmer, Swanson's husband at the time proved to be inadequate in the leading role and relinquished the part of Nicholas to Olivier, appearing instead in the minor role of George Drayton. *Courtesy, Museum of Modern Art, Film Stills Archive.*

With Nora Swinburne as Lady Stephanie Fitzmaurice.
Courtesy, Museum of Modern Art, Film Stills Archive.

During the financial crisis suffered by RKO., Olivier started half a dozen films, each of which was aborted after a day or two of shooting, including one with Irene Dunne. He finally completed his three-picture deal with the studio and disillusioned with Hollywood, returned to London at the invitation of Gloria Swanson to appear in *Perfect Understanding,* which he later referred to as the worst film ever made, and to appear in Keith Winter's play, *The Rats of Norway* with Raymond Massey and Gladys Cooper. Jill Esmond, who had been wasted on insignificant film roles, had been offered a key part in *A Bill of Divorcement* from David Selznick. The film version of Clemence Dane's play was an important property being prepared for John Barrymore. In relinquishing the role to return with her husband to England, she was subsequently replaced by Katharine Hepburn, who catapulted to international success.

M-G-M soon courted Olivier, offering a long-term contract which guaranteed forty weeks of work a year at $1000 per week. He declined in favor of a one-picture deal and was offered the role of Don Antonio, a Spanish emissary, opposite Greta Garbo in *Queen Christina.*

Olivier accepted and returned again to Hollywood, turning over his role in *The Rats of Norway* to Louis Hayward. At M-G-M he was rushed into costume to begin a test. Director Rouben Mamoulian announced that they would begin with an important love scene. Olivier arrived on the set, meeting the great Garbo for the first time, finding her cool, remote, and shy.

"Introductions over, Mamoulian told them what he wanted for the scene they were going to shoot. Don Antonio would take the Queen in his arms and she would slowly respond to what Mamoulian called 'awakening passion.' The very first time that they rehearsed the scene it seemed to Olivier that the response was a good deal slower than the director could have possibly wanted. He was not conscious of any passion awakening at all; in fact, so unresponsive was Garbo that he found it quite impossible to give a good performance. He tried to explain this to himself by saying that perhaps Garbo was purposely making this a difficult test for him. But after they tried it several times and there was still no change in her attitude or improvement in his acting he became a little worried."[5]

Olivier had given everything he had in the scene, but recalled Garbo's frigid reaction at the touch of his hand. Even after attempting a one-sided conversation with the actress during a break, he failed to establish a friendly relationship. Eventually producer Walter Wanger summoned the actor to inform him that he was being replaced as Don Antonio. Mamoulian explained that Olivier's test was negative and that he lacked the maturity, skill and acting weight to balance Garbo's. John Gilbert, Garbo's former leading man was summoned. It was a charitable act on Garbo's part, as Gilbert, who had been a great screen lover in silent films, had suffered a declining career with the advent of talking pictures. *Queen Christina* received great critical acclaim, but Gilbert's career continued to wane and he drank heavily. He completed one more film and died of a heart attack at the age of thirty-eight.

Though genuinely distraught at the time, some forty years later Olivier reviewed the incident with amazement and disappointment, but very respectful of Gabor's talent. "I just didn't measure up. I was twenty-five years old at the time, which in itself is no excuse. One can be quite good at twenty-five. But I wasn't good enough for Garbo. She was an absolute master of her trade. She was a great figure with an enormous image for the public. I was groveling like a puppy dog in front of her. That wasn't the way to play her great lover. It was apparent to me and I wasn't really surprised when I was fired. I simply wasn't up to her and there was nothing else she could do."

Many years later producer Walter Wanger very nearly arranged a Garbo comeback. "In the forties Garbo expressed a definite interest in a screen treatment of the life of George Sand. Salka Viertel was the prospective writer, George Cukor was to direct, and Laurence Olivier to co-star. Unfortunately, combined financing by French, British and American interests grew too complicated and the venture broke down."[6]

Olivier returned to the New York stage in the fall of 1933 to appear as Julian Dulcimer in Mordaunt Shairp's *The Green Bay Tree* at the Cort Theater. "Acting of the highest quality," the *New York Times* reported, calling Olivier's Julian "an extraordinary study in the decomposition of a character. It is acting that has design and movement and tragic emotion." Brooks Atkinson remembered the play in later years as a "baleful, enigmatic drama about a homosexual relationship. Olivier acted a character who was in the process of disintegration—all of it subtle and delicate and some of it at a pitch of emotion that left the audience dazed."[7]

As Clive Dering with his first wife, Jill Esmond as Anne Moore in *No Funny Business*. Olivier would appear in three films with his second wife, Vivien Leigh, and four with his third wife, Joan Plowright, but this comedy marked his only screen appearance with Jill Esmond. She later appeared in *This Above All*, *Random Harvest*, *The White Cliffs of Dover* and *A Man Called Peter*, but never fulfilled the prophecy of a 1934 British film annual which predicted certain stardom for her.

1934, John Stafford Productions; Screenplay by Victory Hanbury and Frank Vosper; Based on a story by Dorothy Hope; Photography, W. Blakeley and D. Langley; Editor, Elmer McGovern; Produced by John Stafford; Directed by John Stafford and Victor Hanbury; Distributed by United Artists

CAST	CAST
Clive Dering	Laurence Olivier
Yvonne Kane	Gertrude Lawrence
Ann Moore	Jill Esmond
Monsieur Florey	Gibb McLaughlin
Mrs. Fothergill	Muriel Aked
Edmund Kane	Edmund Breon

Opened March 8, 1934, at the Cameo Theater, New York

THE FILM

A husband and wife, unknown to each other, engage a young man and a young woman respectively to act as co-respondents at a hotel in Cannes. By mistake the two co-respondents engage in a romantic liaison, each of them being convinced that the other is the object of their professional attentions.

REVIEW

New York Times, March 9, 1934
"*No Funny Business* deserves some sort of booby prize for its success in reaching such a devastating level of mediocrity. One of the less distinguished products of the recently rejuvenated British film studios. The pace is laboriously slow, the camera static, the recording bad and the direction gifted with a supreme talent for telegraphing its intentions several scenes ahead. It is all excessively silly and makes almost no sense at any point."

Moscow Nights
(U.S. title: *I Stand Condemned*)

1935, Denham Productions in association with London Film Productions-Capitol; Executive Producer, Alexander Korda; Produced by Alexis Granowsky and Max Schach; Directed by Anthony Asquith; Assistant director, Teddy Baird; Screenplay, Anthony Asquith and Eric Siepmann from a novel by Pierre Benoit; Photography, Philip Tannura; Art direction, Vincent Korda; Musical direction, Muir Mathieson; Supervising editor, William Hornbeck; Editor, Francis Lyon; Costumes, John Armstrong; Sound, A. W. Watkins

CAST

Captain Ignatoff	Laurence Olivier
Brioukov	Harry Baur
Natasha	Penelope Dudley Ward
Polonsky	Robert Cochran
Kovrin	Morton Selten
Mme. Sabline	Athene Seyler
Doctor	Walter Hudd
Mme. Kovrin	Kate Cutler
President	C. M. Hallard
Prosecution	Edmund Willard
Defense	Charles Carson
Servant	Morland Graham
Spy	Hay Petrie
Second servant	Richard Webster
Soldier in hospital	Anthony Quayle

Opened July 1, 1936, Rivoli Theater, New York

THE FILM

Brioukov is a Russian grain merchant, risen from peasant surroundings to wealth and financial importance during World War I. He is deprived of the love of a war nurse, Natasha, by the handsome Captain Ignatoff. The Captain loses 80,000 rubles to Brioukov at a gambling soirée, and, since he is unable to pay the debt within three days, the code of a gentleman and an officer demands that he commit suicide. Madame Sabline, an aged, ineffectual and chattering spy, offers to lend Ignatoff the money to get him in her power. Natasha, meanwhile, has prevailed upon Brioukov to save Ignatoff from the necessity of taking his life by sending to his rooms a receipt for the amount. Ignatoff, ignorant of Natasha's visit to Brioukov, visits the home of Madame Sabline, receives the money and learns what is expected of him. As he approaches a telephone to inform against her, the espionage squad moves in and arrests them both. Madame Sabline swallows a lethal capsule, and Ignatoff is unable to prove his innocence. He has accepted money from the spy ring and the receipt in his rooms gives the lie in his plea that he borrowed the money to pay a gambling debt. In a climactic court-martial scene, a forlorn Brioukov shuffles to the witness stand, but even at the depth of his desolation, he cannot find the strength to take his revenge by claiming to have received his money.

REVIEWS

New York Times, July 2, 1936
"Laurence Olivier's portrayal of Ignatoff is rather too clipped and flippant, and his voice cracked a couple of times just when folks were expecting great things in the way of diction to complete his resemblance to Ronald Colman."

The Observer, "n.d."
"The surprise of the picture is Laurence Olivier, who plays the young officer with as much wit and feeling as if the tom-fool fellow were really a possible character."

Graham Greene, *The Spectator,* November 15, 1935
"*Moscow Nights,* Mr. Anthony Asquith's new film, is completely bogus. This absurd romantic spy-drama of wartime Russia opens with Volga boatmen and carries on with every worn-out property of a Hollywood Russia, even to the gipsy orchestras. The direction is puerile, no one can drop a tray or a glass without Mr. Asquith cutting to a shell-burst. But he has been well served by his players, by M. Harry Baur as an awkward pathetic war-profiteer, by Miss Athene Seyler as an old genteel spy who haunts the hospitals, and Mr. Laurence Olivier as an embittered front-line officer who loves a young society nurse engaged to the profiteer."

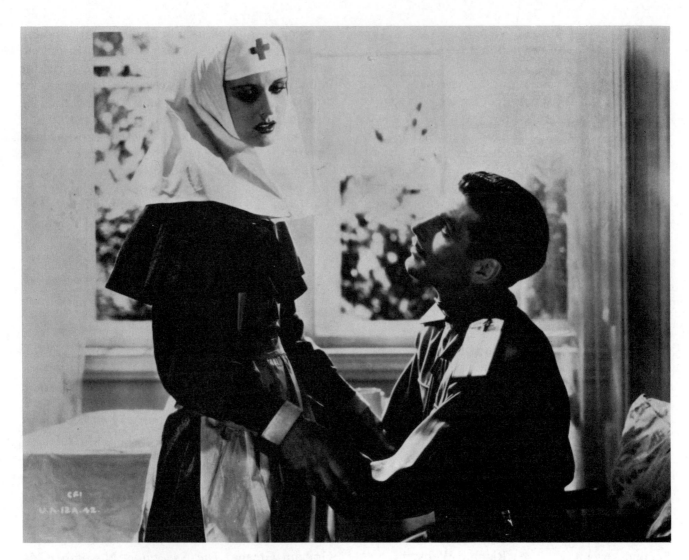

Still sporting a Ronald Colman moustache, Olivier is the dashing Captain Ignatoff in *Moscow Nights,* **with Penelope Dudley Ward as Natasha.**

Olivier returned to England in 1934 and appeared with Ina Claire in S. N. Behrman's *Biography,* followed by an appearance as Bothwell in Gordon Daviot's* *Queen of Scots* with Gwen Ffrangcon-Davies. His next role was as the flamboyant ham, Tony Cavendish, a character patterned after John Barrymore, in the George S. Kaufman-Edna Ferber comedy, *Theatre Royal* (known in America as *The Royal Family*). Early in 1935, Olivier appeared as a semi-paralyzed proprietor of a guest house in Keith Winter's *The Ringmaster* which featured an impressive cast including Dame May Whitty, Nigel Patrick, Jill Esmond, Colin Keith-Johnston, and Cathleen Nesbitt. Raymond Massey directed the drama which premiered at the Shaftesbury Theater. "The honors of the evening went to a brilliant actor, Laurence Olivier," reported the *New York Times,* "who gave a remarkable performance as the personable, crippled manager of a small and exclusive seaside guest house."

Moscow Nights marked the beginning of a new film contract with Alexander Korda, the Hungarian producer-director who settled in London in 1930 and became the beacon of the British film industry. Korda formed London Films and sealed its success with *The Private Life of Henry VIII* in 1932, built Denham Studios, and produced such screen milestones as *The Scarlet Pimpernel, Things to Come,* and *The Four Feathers.*

Olivier recalled his extraordinary friendship with Anthony Asquith, which began with the filming of *Moscow Nights,* with the director's biographer, R. J. Minney. "Puffin (nicknamed so by his doting mother) was a very polite, extremely gentle creature. He spoke very quickly but not more quickly than he was thinking. He was witty. He made you laugh and he laughed at your jokes. But you felt there was a strong layer of nervousness there. He seemed to be very much in awe of Alexander Korda, who produced the film."[8]

*Also known as the celebrated mystery writer, Josephine Tey

1936, Inter-Allied Film Producers Ltd.; Produced and Directed by Dr. Paul Czinner; adapted by Robert J. Cullen from the play by William Shakespeare; Treatment suggested by J. M. Barrie; Music composed by William Walton, played by members of the London Philharmonic Orchestra, conducted by Efrem Kurtz; Costumes, John Armstrong; Photography, Hal Rosson; Editor, David Lean; Released by Twentieth Century Fox (Reissued 1949 by United Artists)

CAST

Rosalind	Elisabeth Bergner
Orlando	Laurence Olivier
Banished Duke	Henry Ainley
Celia	Sophie Stewart
Jaques	Leon Quartermaine
Duke Frederick	Felix Aylmer
Touchstone	Mackenzie Ward
Silvius	Richard Ainley
Corin	Aubrey Mather
Adam	Fisher White
Dennis	George Moore Marriott
Oliver	John Laurie
Charles	Lionel Braham
Le Beau	Austin Trevor
Amiens	Cavin Gordon
First Lord	Cyril Horrocks
Second Lord	Ellis Irving
Third Lord	Lawrence Hanray
Phebe	Joan White
Audrey	Dorice Fordred
OWilliam	Peter Bull
Hisperia	Muriel Johnson

Pages—W. H. Clark, G. Hall, A. H. Scott, G. Lawrence

Opened November 5, 1936, at the Radio City Music Hall, New York

In Shakespeare's romantic comedy, an exiled Duke finds refuge in the lovely Forest of Arden, where a new court is established under the laws of nature. At the court of the wicked Duke Frederick, Orlando, the youngest son of a noble family, is dissuaded from a match with the King's wrestler by Rosalind, who fears the two are ill-matched. Orlando wins the fight, falling hopelessly in love with Rosalind, the daughter of the banished Duke. Disguised as a boy, Rosalind flees with her friend Celia to join her father in the forest. Escaping the malice of his cruel brother, Orlando too enters the forest where he proceeds to hang verses on the trees in praise of his beloved Rosalind. Maintaining her disguise, Rosalind mocks and teases her heart's desire to cure him of his foolish lovesickness. Frederick begs forgiveness and restores to his brother the dukedom and all lands to their rightful owners. With pleasant memories of the carefree days in the Forest of Arden, the story concludes with a joyful wedding celebration.

REVIEWS

New York Times, November 6, 1936
"Shakespeare has come to the screen again, but this time the echoing tread is absent. A genial English company, led by the incomparable Elisabeth Bergner, has accorded his *As You Like It* as friendly a production as a friendly play merits. There is nothing tremendous about the new picture except its simplicity. In sum, we have a gay and congenial production of Shakespeare."

Graham Greene, *The Spectator,* September 11, 1936
"*As You Like It* is a respectful film: that is to say there is far more Shakespeare in it than there was in Reinhardt's *Dream*, and I dare say it is a better production than you will often see on the stage. In Miss Bergner's Rosalind freedom may have become elvishness and poetry sometimes whimsicality, her tear-smudged, bewildered features may be more easily associated with a constant nymph than with the reckless-tongued Rosalind, but certainly in her private version, she is, like white witches, 'mischievously good'; while Mr.

Rosalind: "Are you so much in love as your rhymes speak?" Orlando: "Neither rhyme nor reason can express how much." Olivier's first encounter with Shakespeare on the screen as the lovesick Orlando opposite Elisabeth Bergner as the fair Rosalind.

When *As You Like It* was reissued in 1949, a new promotional campaign capitalized on Olivier's knighthood, raising his name above the title and marking one of the few times he was billed as *Sir* Laurence Olivier. Bergner's career has faded considerably since the war and her name was reduced to featured billing following the title. Olivier is seen here with Austin Trevor as Le Beau.

Laurence Olivier's Orlando, sullen, brooding, a little oafish, is even more satisfying."

Variety, November 11, 1936
"Olivier as Orlando is well cast, intelligent and a fine reader of lines."

Daily Telegraph, September 3, 1936
"Laurence Olivier seems to me to be one of the most brilliant actors in the world. In *As You Like It* his triumph as Orlando is all the more striking for its contrast to his glamorous Romeo and his fiery Mercutio in John Gielgud's recent production of *Romeo and Juliet*."

COMMENTS

When Walter Wanger suggested to Olivier that he might be considered as Romeo opposite Norma Shearer's Juliet, the actor replied that he did not believe in Shakespeare on the screen. In 1935, Warner Bros. released a lavish blend of farce, ballet, and visual splendor with Max Reinhardt and William Dieterle's delightful production of *A Midsummer Night's Dream*. M-G-M followed a year later with George Cukor's *Romeo and Juliet* starring Shearer, Leslie Howard as Romeo, John Barrymore as Mercutio, and Basil Rathbone as Tybalt.

Nineteen hundred thirty-five was the year of Olivier's first Shakespearean success, when he alternated the roles of Romeo and Mercutio with John Gielgud in the now legendary presentation at Lon-don's New Theatre. The production, which featured Peggy Ashcroft as Juliet and Edith Evans as Nurse, was cited in the *New York Times* as London's outstanding event of the season, noting Olivier's "fresh, impetuous Romeo" and a "brilliant sparkling Mercutio" with "flashing, romantic energy."

Ralph Richardson later recalled the "animal magnetism and vitality and passion" which dominated as Olivier stood against the balcony "with such an extraordinary pose," and Gielgud, who had no romantic rival on the English stage at that time, was impressed by "his extraordinary power and originality."

Forty-four years later, on the occasion of John Gielgud's seventy-fifth birthday, the actor assessed the complex relationsihp which existed when he and Olivier were portrayed as career rivals. "I had a certain success in Shakespeare at a time when he (Olivier) couldn't do it. But eventually he beat me. He took chances; he did the *Hamlet* film when I would not. He worked like a demon to get rid of his weaknesses—something I could never have done."

While Olivier was appearing in the dual roles he agreed to act in a film version of *As You Like It*, which would star the celebrated German actress, Elisabeth Bergner. The film was to be produced and directed by Bergner's husband, Paul Czinner. As a curly-haired Orlando, Olivier soon regretted his decision, feeling foolish because the stage convention allowing Orlando to mistake Rosalind for a boy is simply not believable on the screen. He tried to correct the situation by adding a touch of madness to his character, but it didn't help. He was also disturbed by the habit of shooting scenes out of order.

In spite of his reservations, the film today is treasured by students and film buffs as a modest and airy delight, and Olivier's early charismatic grasp of classic role playing is clearly evident. *As You Like It* is an admirable beginning for Olivier's relationship with and legacy of cinematic Bard.

Fire Over England

1937, Pendennis, for London Film Productions; Presented by Alexander Korda; Produced by Erich Pommer; Directed by William K. Howard; Assistant director, W. O'Kelly; Screenplay by Clemence Dane and Sergei Nolbandov, from the novel by A. E. W. Mason; Photography, James Wong Howe; Camera, Paul Barralet; Special effects, Ned Mann, Lawrence Butler, Edward Cohen; Art decoration, Lazare Meerson; Music composed by Richard Addinsell, conducted by Muir Mathieson; Editor, Jack Dennis; Costumes, Rene Hubert; Sound, A. W. Watkins and Jack Rogerson; Production manager, Roland Gillett; Distributed by United Artists

Queen Elizabeth I	Flora Robson
Michael Ingolby	Laurence Olivier
Cynthia	Vivien Leigh
Earl of Leicester	Leslie Banks
Philip of Spain	Raymond Massey
Burleigh	Morton Selten
Elena	Tamara Desni
Hillary Vane	James Mason
Richard Ingolby	Herbert Lomas
Don Pedro	Robert Newton
Don Miguel	Robert Rendell
Admiral Valdez	Charles Carson
Spanish Ambassador	Henry Oscar
Cooper	Roy Russel
French Ambassador	Lawrence Hanray

Olivier as loyal Englishman, Michael Ingolby, poses as a spy in the Spanish court. Raymond Massey is the scheming Philip of Spain.

Lord Amberley	Howard Douglas
Illingworth	Cecil Mainwaring
Tarleton	Francis de Wolfe
Maddison	Graham Cheswright
Gregory	George Thirlwell
Hatton	A. Corney Grain
Don Escobal	Donald Calthrop
Sir Richard	Lyn Harding

Opened March 4, 1937, at the Radio City Music Hall, New York

THE FILM

Michael Ingolby, a young British naval lieutenant, is protected and nursed back to health from battle wounds by his father's old friend Don Miguel and the Spaniard's daughter, Elena, following a fight in which Michael's ship was overtaken and his father and crew captured by the enemy. Michael returns to his native England following the death of his father by the Spanish Inquisition and offers his allegiance to Queen Elizabeth. At court, Michael proclaims his love for Cynthia, the Queen's lady-in-waiting, and thwarts an assassination attempt upon his sovereign. Hillary Vane, an Englishman in the employ of Spain, is revealed to be a spy and is killed in his attempt to flee England. Michael is enlisted to replace Vane as an envoy to Spain and to uncover a group of Englishmen who have been hired by Philip II to assassinate the Queen. In Lisbon his charade is successful until he is recognized by Elena, now married to Don Pedro, one of Philip's loyal officers. Reluctant to reveal his true identity because of the friendship which had existed between their fathers, Elena confides in her husband. Michael is eventually discovered to be a spy by Philip himself, when the British emissary fails to name his contact in England properly. Ordered to the dungeon, Michael escapes with the assistance of Don Pedro whose surprising aid is a gallant gesture to his wife and the memory of her late father. Michael returns once more to England with the names of the traitors and to the arms of his beloved Cynthia. A merciful Queen awards the traitors clemency if they pledge their loyalty to England against the Spanish Armada, and for his gallantry and daring, honors Michael Ingolby with a knighthood.

REVIEWS

New York Times, March 5, 1937
"Erich Pommer's rich production has all the solid virtues of the better English pictures. It is dignified, sound, carefully filmed, extremely well played, and reasonably faithful to the events it sought to reenact. It has, too, a curious lack of vitality for all its wealth of vibrant material. What life it has may be attributed to Flora Robson for her portrait of Queen Elizabeth and to Raymond Massey for his sketch of Philip of Spain. Mr. Olivier is properly impetuous, Vivien Leigh and Tamara Desni are lovely as the fortunate chap's two leading ladies. The materials, in brief, were there; only the vital spark to fuse them into a stirring historical drama, was missing."

Graham Greene, *The Spectator,* March 5, 1937
"The acting is far better than we are accustomed to in English films. Mr. Laurence Olivier can do the hysterical type of young romantic hero with ease."

Lionel Collier, *The Picturegoer,* September 25, 1937
"This picture stands head and shoulders above any historical drama yet made in this country and it has few rivals from other countries. As the young lovers Vivien Leigh and Laurence Olivier are exceedingly good. Their love scenes have a naturalness and tenderness that is particularly attractive."

COMMENTS

Fire Over England was made to arouse British patriotism in the days prior to the Second World War. Ever since his successful historical document, *The Private Life of Henry VIII* starring Charles Laughton, Alexander Korda had been anxious to make a film about Queen Elizabeth I for Flora Robson. Korda waited four years before deciding upon A. E. W. Mason's novel. Olivier's

zealous endeavors as a fictional swashbuckler are related in Janet Dunbar's biography of Flora Robson.

"Olivier sent up the producer's blood pressure by insisting on doing his hair-raising stunts himself. A galleon had been built in a field at Denham, and one night Flora watched the shooting of a scene where Olivier had to perform a dangerous manoeuvre. He lept on board the galleon, threw a firebrand along the petrol-soaked deck, which immediately burst into roaring flames, and dived head first over the side, into a net placed below deck level, out of camera range. After each 'take' the fire was extinguished by hoses, but on one of these occasions the fire did not go out. Instead, water from the hoses rolled along the deck with the burning petrol floating on top, and Flora was appalled to see that the flames were chasing Olivier. He slipped as he lept on to the bulwarks, made a crooked dive, and landed with a crunch into the net below. Everyone expected to find him with a broken neck, but he was fortunately unhurt. Erich Pommer, the producer, said he wished the actor would have a stand-in for these stunts, but Flora defended Olivier's insistence on doing his own dangerous work, saying, 'He would feel a fraud to be praised for a scene he did not do himself.' 'All acting is a fraud,' replied Pommer."[10] Dame Flora repeated her role as Elizabeth again three years later for Warner Bros., in Michael Curtiz' romantic adventure, *The Sea Hawk* with Errol Flynn.

Alan Dent, who collaborated on the screenplays of *Hamlet, Henry V* and *Richard III,* reflected on the teaming of Olivier and Leigh, who fell in love during the filming of *Fire Over England.* "The plot is of less importance than the fact that this was the first film in which Vivien Leigh played opposite Laurence Olivier. They were to appear together in only two more films. But they were also about to make one of the supreme stage partnerships of modern times, appearing in eleven plays together throughout the next twenty years—plays of Shakespeare and Sheridan, of Anouilh and Rattigan, and no rubbish or mediocrity or catchpenny stuff of any sort. She was also to be directed by him in plays by Anouilh and Thornton Wilder. And together at the St. James's Theater and at the Old Vic, in New York, and in tours of Europe and the Antipodes, they were to make some of the most high and exciting stage history of our times. As 'The Oliviers' they were to grace the stage for two complete decades and a year or two more. They soon became as perfect a complementary pair as any in England since the Bancrofts in the middle of the last century and as perfect almost as the Lunts in America in the middle of our own. They were, moreover—and it is by no means an unimportant consideration—just about the best looking couple anywhere or any time in the history of our stage. This fact was no more than glimmered in this particular film *Fire Over England* where the chief acting honors went very justly to Flora Robson's Queen Elizabeth.''[11]

The film advanced Olivier's career on the screen more than any of his ten preceeding pictures. The actor also received considerable recognition and acclaim during the next two years for his appearances with the Old Vic. London's theatrical new year began with Olivier's first turn at *Hamlet* under the direction of Sir Tyrone Guthrie. The *New York Times* found his Dane vivid and virile, ''without entirely discarding tradition nor yet imitating others, bringing his own natural energy and special sympathy into the part.'' In June he repeated the role with Vivien Leigh added as Ophelia under Kronborg Castle's frowning walls at Elsinore in Denmark. The first performance in Shakespeare's own setting was rained out and had to be moved to a nearby hotel ballroom, but 1800 spectators attended the second night despite the chilly aftermath of the storm.

In November of 1937, Olivier appeared as Macbeth for the Old Vic opposite Judith Anderson. The *New York Times* praised his ''poetry and nervous energy'' but found the fierce strength missing. His other Shakespearean roles for the Old Vic during this period included Sir Toby Belch in *Twelfth Night, Henry V,* and *Coriolanus.*

In February of 1938, Ralph Richardson and Olivier fulfilled an ambition to perform together in *Othello.* Charles Morgan in his report for the *New York Times* found Richardson's Moor rich with authority and power. ''A large and pliant face, which in repose, may appear sometimes too heavy and lifeless, is given vitality by his imagination, and there is no actor who can more completely communicate thought to his audience without the use of words.'' Morgan called Olivier's Iago his complement, adding ''he has an extraordinary quickness and urgency of manner and wins his audience not by Richardson's method of slow approach, but by the dashing attack of a cavalry leader and by the impression he gives of zest and personal enjoyment in the part.''

Robert Rendell as Don Miguel and Tamara Desni as his daughter, Elena, attend to the wounded young naval officer, Michael Ingolby.

CAST

1938, London Film Productions; Produced by Alexander Korda; Directed by Tim Whelan; Assistant director, Philip Brandon; Screenplay by Ian Dalrymple and Arthur Wimperis from Lajos Biro's adaptation of the play *Counsel's Opinion* by Gilbert Wakefield; Technicolor photography by Harry Stradling; Camera operator, Jack Hildyard; Special effects, Ned Mann; Art direction, Lazare Meerson; Musical score by Miklos Rozsa, conducted by Muir Mathieson; Technicolor direction, Natalie Kalmus; Technicolor photography advisor, William V. Skall; Supervising editor, William Hornbeck; Editor, L. J. W. Stockviss; Costumes, Rene Hubert; Sound, A. W. Watkins; Sound technician, Charles Tasto; Production manager, David Cunynghame; Unit manager, Wilfred O'Kelly

Leslie	Merle Oberon
Logan	Laurence Olivier
Lord Mere	Ralph Richardson
Lady Mere	Binnie Barnes
Lord Steele	Morton Selten
Slade	J. H. Roberts
Waiter	Gus McNaughton
Saunders	Gertrude Musgrove
Mrs. Johnson	Eileen Peel

Opened March 31, 1938, Radio City Music Hall, New York

THE FILM

This remake of an early London Films production, *Counsel's Opinion,* concerns the plight of Logan, a smart young divorce lawyer who, quite innocently, finds himself in compromising cir-

Olivier and Merle Oberon proved to be a captivating coupling in this sparkling Korda comedy.

Their skillful timing at romantic repartee was to offer a marked contrast to their passionate pairing a year later as Heathcliff and Cathy in *Wuthering Heights*.

Ralph Richardson as Lord Mere in the first of many screen appearances with Olivier.

cumstances when a young woman invades his hotel bedroom following a costume ball at London's Park Lane Hotel. The girl, Leslie, spends the night anonymously in his suite, while the barrister aches on the floor outside. The next day he is visited by a good-natured Lord Mere, who engages him to bring divorce action against Lady Mere who was seen in another man's hotel room. Assuming that Leslie and Lady Mere are the same person, Logan imagines that he himself is the alleged co-respondent.

REVIEWS

New York Times, April 1, 1938
"A gay and urbane comedy, jauntily played by a British cast. There is more to the performances than simply a dutiful fulfillment of the script's requirements. Laurence Olivier, last encountered in the adventurous service of Queen Elizabeth when *Fire Over England* was smoldering, has an engaging inability to defend masculine integrity against the feminine foe. Ralph Richardson, whom you may recall as the huffing puffing dictator of *Things to Come*, makes the sort of beef-eating, slow-burning clubman it is always a pleasure to meet across the protective barrier of the screen."

Film Weekly, "n.d."
"Laurence Olivier is in unusually good form and gives what is his best screen performance yet."

COMMENTS

The Divorce of Lady X was a remake of Alexander Korda's 1933 film, *Counsel's Opinion,* which featured Henry Kendall as Logan and Binnie Barnes as Leslie. The film was the first appearance in technicolor of Merle Oberon, who made her screen debut in Korda's *Service for Ladies* in 1931. Her career was successfully launched the following year when she appeared as the doomed Anne Boleyn to Laughton's gluttonous king in *The Private Life of Henry VIII. The Divorce of Lady X* was her second appearance on the screen since an automobile accident which proved nearly fatal for the actress. Her hospitalization motivated Korda to cease production on the ill-fated epic, *I, Claudius* which was to star Laughton as the crippled emperor and Emlyn Williams as Caligula.

Oberon, who would marry Korda in 1939, worked well with Olivier, and their highly polished duet displayed their keen talent for sophisticated comedy. Binnie Barnes, who played the Oberon role in *Counsel's Opinion,* appeared as Lady Mere, and Ralph Richardson as her husband proved to be an engaging scene stealer.

Merle Oberon was a former dance hostess who called herself Queenie O'Brien, later acting under her real name, Estelle Thompson. She was discovered and groomed for stardom by Alexander Korda, whom she married in 1939. *The Divorce of Lady X* was her first technicolor appearance.

Olivier as Logan, "in unusually good form."

Q Planes
(U.S. title: *Clouds Over Europe*)

1939, Harefield Production; Executive producer, Alexander Korda; Produced by Irving Asher; Directed by Tim Whelan; Screenplay by Ian Dalrymple from a story by Brook Williams, Jack Whittingham, and Arthur Wimperis; Photography, Harry Stradling; Art direction, Vincent Korda; Music direction, Muri Mathieson; Supervising editor, William Hornbeck; Editor, Hugh Stewart; Sound, A. W. Watkins; Distributed by Columbia Pictures

CAST

Tony McVane	Laurence Olivier
Major Hammond	Ralph Richardson
Kay Hammond	Valerie Hobson
Jenkins	George Curzon
Barrett	George Merritt
Blenkinsop	Gus McNaughton
Mackenzie	David Tree
Daphne	Sandra Storme
Stage Door Keeper	Hay Petrie
Editor	John Laurie
Karl	Frank Fox
Air Marshal Gosport	George Butler
The Baron	Gordon McLeod
Peters	John Longden
Pilot	Reginald Purdell
Officer	Pat Aherne

Opened June 15, 1939, at the Radio City Music Hall, New York

THE FILM

Major Hammond, an eccentric Secret Service agent is called in to investigate the disappearance of four bombers, which have been mysteriously vanishing on trial flights to test secret war department apparatus. Tony McVane, a dashing young test pilot, who is in love with Hammond's sister, assists in the investigation of the missing planes, which are being brought down by a radio-beam device being operated at sea.

REVIEW

New York Times, June 16, 1939
"One of the wittiest and pleasantest comedies that have come a capering to the American screen this season. Ian Dalrymple and his writing aides have written chuckles into every fourth line of the script and grins into every second; and what the script has not provided, Ralph Richardson has as the Scotland Yard man. The others in the cast are not quite so good—but Mr. Olivier, Valerie Hobson, George Curzon, and the rest are most acceptable; and the picture is more than that; in these dog days it should be required-reading for every moviegoer."

COMMENTS

The film was inspired by a news item Alexander Korda had spotted about an aircraft which took off and apparently never came down. The story was technically farfetched and the interpretation frivolous. Olivier provided the romantic relief and again Richardson stole the acting honors as the scatterbrain agent.

As Tony McVane with Ralph Richardson as Major Hammond in the comedy spy thriller, *Q Planes*. **Cour-**
tesy, Museum of Modern Art, Film Stills Archive.

Retitled *Clouds Over Europe* **in the United States, Olivier starred as a daring young test pilot with Valerie Hobson in the role of Richardson's sister, Kay Hammond.** *Courtesy, Museum of Modern Art, Film Stills Archive.*

Wuthering Heights

1939, A Samuel Goldwyn Production; Adapted by Ben Hecht and Charles MacArthur from the novel by Emily Brontë; Photography, Gregg Toland; Music composed by Alfred Newman; Editor, Daniel Mandell; Art Director, James Basevi; Set Decoration, Julia Heron; Produced by Samuel Goldwyn; Directed by William Wyler; Released by United Artists

CAST

Cathy	Merle Oberon
Heathcliff	Laurence Olivier
Edgar	David Niven
Ellen Dean	Flora Robson
Dr. Kenneth	Donald Crisp
Hindley	Hugh Williams
Isabella	Geraldine Fitzgerald
Joseph	Leo G. Carroll
Judge Linton	Cecil Humphreys
Lockwood	Miles Mander
Robert	Romaine Callender
Earnshaw	Cecil Kellaway
Heathcliff (as a child)	Rex Downing
Cathy (as a child)	Sarita Wooten
Hindley (as a child)	Douglas Scott

Opened April 13, 1939, Rivoli Theater, New York

Heathcliff (1939)

THE FILM

A violent snowstorm blankets the Yorkshire moors, and the lost Lockwood seeks refuge at Wuthering Heights, whose dour and mysterious owner, Heathcliff, permits him to stay the night. Lockwood's sleep is interrupted by the ghostly voice of a woman calling "Heathcliff" from outside in the raging storm. Heathcliff rushes madly out into blinding snow seeking the spirit of his beloved Cathy. The old housekeeper, Ellen, tells the story of the enigmatic Heathcliff and his lost love, as Lockwood listens. Forty years ago, widower Earnshaw brought a homeless gypsy boy, Heathcliff, home to his farmhouse, much to the distress of his children, Cathy and Hindley. The kindly Earnshaw dies and the children grow up. Cathy falls in love with Heathcliff, but her brother bullies and mistreats him. Heathcliff, reduced to a stableboy, meets Cathy at Penistone

Together again! Olivier and Oberon were teamed for the second time as the turbulent romantics in the film of Emily Brontë's haunting tale of passion on the Yorkshire moors.

Crag on the moors, and she is fearing their love will be discovered and thirsting for the finer things in life, urges him to run away to make his fortune. Drawn by the sounds of a party at Thrushcross Grange, the home of the wealthy Linton family, they are attacked by watchdogs, and Cathy, unable to walk home, remains for several weeks to recover. She soon becomes a refined young lady under the influence of the attractive but weak-willed Edgar Linton, who eventually proposes marriage. Heathcliff leaves Wuthering Heights in despair when he learns of Edgar's proposal and Cathy trying to catch him, collapses on the moors from exhaustion. Recovering again at Thrushcross Grange, Dr. Kenneth suggests a more peaceful life for her, and she eventually marries Linton. Years pass and one day Heathcliff unexpectedly returns, wealthy, arrogant, and vengeful. He has manipulated to purchase Wuthering Heights from the unsuspecting Hindley, who has destroyed his life with drink and gambling. To spite Cathy, Heathcliff marries Edgar's sister, Isabella, who is soon reduced to that of a servant at Wuthering Heights. Hearing that Cathy is gravely ill, Heathcliff rushes to her bedside where she confesses that she has always loved him. Overcome with grief as she dies in his arms, Heathcliff calls on her spirit to haunt him for the rest of his life: "Be with me always—take any form—drive me mad! Only do not leave me in this dark alone where I cannot find you. I cannot live without my life. I cannot die without my soul!" As Ellen finishes her tale the aged Dr. Kenneth rushes in from the storm to explain that he has seen Heathcliff on the snow-tossed moors with a woman, and following after them, found only the body of Heathcliff near Penistone Crag.

With Geraldine Fitzgerald as Isabella, a role which Vivien Leigh firmly refused for her American film debut. Denied the role of Cathy, opposite Olivier, Leigh soon captured the most desired part in film history, that of Scarlett O'Hara.

REVIEWS

New York Times, April 14, 1939
"Out of Emily Brontë's strange tale of a tortured romance Mr. Goldwyn and his troupe have fashioned a strong and somber film, poetically written as the novel not always was, sinister and wild as it was meant to be, far more compact dramatically than Miss Brontë had made it. And it has been brilliantly played. Laurence Olivier's Heathcliff is the man. He has Heathcliff's broad

Traveler: "I'm Mr. Lockwood, your new tenant at the Grange." Heathcliff: "Oh, you are? Well, why aren't you there instead of tramping the moors on a night like this?" With Miles Mander as Lockwood.

Due to a delay in shooting, the California "heather" grew a great deal taller than that which is found on a Yorkshire landscape.

The film was nominated for eight Academy Awards,
including Olivier's first bid for the Best Actor honor.

Heathcliff: "What do they know of Heaven or Hell, Cathy, they who know nothing of life . . ."

lowering brow, his scowl, his churlishness, the wild tenderness, the bearing, speech, and manner of the demon-possessed. Merle Oberon as Cathy, has matched the brilliance of his characterization with hers. William Wyler has directed it magnificently, surcharging even his lighter scenes with an atmosphere of suspense and foreboding, keeping his horror-shadowed narrative moving at a steadily accelerating pace, building absorbingly to its tragic climax. It is, unquestionably, one of the most distinguished pictures of the year, one of the finest ever produced by Mr. Goldwyn, and one you should decide to see."

Kinematograph Weekly, April 27, 1939
"Laurence Olivier puts over a magnificent performance as Heathcliff. The character seldom deserves sympathy, while the transformation from clod to man of wealth and vengeance is, to say the least, fantastic, but he not only brings conviction to his portrayal but translates intelligently its mystical quality."

In the summer of 1938, Olivier and Leigh were enjoying a holiday in the south of France. They rested on the brink of international stardom. While vacationing, an agent's cable arrived inviting them to consider roles in Sam Goldwyn's forthcoming production of *Wuthering Heights,* which would star Merle Oberon as the doomed Cathy. Olivier, discouraged by his previous Hollywood venture, promptly refused the suggestion. A literate script, written by Ben Hecht and Charles MacArthur arrived and while tempted to accept, Vivien was not keen to play the less significant role of Isabella, and they again discarded the offer. Upon his return to England, Olivier was courted by director William Wyler, who made several visits to the actor's home. Having been impressed by Olivier's stage work, he was insistent to have him as the brooding Heathcliff. Robert Newton had been tested for the role, but the result failed to please Goldwyn. Finally convinced, but displeased that he would not be working with Vivien, Olivier reluctantly accepted upon the advice of Ralph Richardson whose brief blessing amounted to, "Bit of fame. Good!"

Back in Hollywood, Olivier soon regretted his decision. First he contracted a severe case of athletes foot from a pair of secondhand clogs issued by the wardrobe department. Disagreements with Wyler on conflicting theories and interpretation, which the director later confessed to have resulted from a lack of communication, were further upsetting. While his association with Merle Oberon had been comfortable enough during the filming of *The Divorce of Lady X,* there was a decided uneasiness this time around. The actress on one occasion stalked off the set, accusing Olivier of having spat in her face during a passionate outburst. Goldwyn himself didn't help matters, calling Olivier, hammy and ugly and threatening to close down the picture. Considering the irritations suffered by all concerned, it's quite remarkable that the result was such a well-crafted masterpiece, bountiful with such romantic fervor.

Wyler reflecting on the experience blamed a lack of articulation on his part and Olivier's unfamiliarity at the time with film acting. "How

"I believe his portrayal of Heathcliff is the most important single contribution to the success of the film." (William Wyler.)

Heathcliff and Cathy at Pennistone Crag—"We'll live here forever—we two against the world!"

gratifying for a director to get from the actor the maximum in performance, often more than is expected, or required, never having to 'coach' him to heighten a scene. I believe his portrayal of Heathcliff is the most important single contribution to the success of the film."[12]

Olivier recalled his snobbish attitude toward films many years later. "Anemic little medium, I used to call it." Wyler told him he had the wrong idea if he thought it was too anemic to take on Shakespeare, advising him, "all you have to do is find out how." "I had good luck—but what hell it seemed at the time—to be directed by Wyler. He was a brute. He was tough. I'd do my damnedest

A lavish technicolor remake, produced in 1970 starring Timothy Dalton and Anna Calder-Marshall failed to recapture the hypnotic spirit and haunting grandeur of its classic predecessor.

in a really exciting and complicated scene. 'That's lousy,' he'd say. 'We'll do it again.' At first we fought. Then when we had hit each other till we were senseless we became friends. Gradually I came to see that film was a different medium, and if one treated it as such, and tried to learn it, humbly, and with an open mind, one could work in it. I saw that it could use the best that was going. It was for me a new medium, a new vernacular. It was Wyler who gave me the simple thought—if you do it right, you can do anything. And if he hadn't said that, I think I wouldn't have done *Henry V* five years later."[13]

Vivien Leigh, who had read Margaret Mitchell's best-selling novel, *Gone with the Wind* early in 1937, had become obsessed with the notion of playing the tempestuous Southern belle, Scarlett O'Hara. At her insistence, agent John Gliddon sent photographs of her to David Selznick who had purchased the film rights, but the producer displayed little enthusiasm for her at the time. The actress began a quiet and constant campaign however, and correspondence continued from London to Hollywood as a publicized search began for the most coveted role in film history.

Soon after Olivier's departure for Hollywood to begin filming *Wuthering Heights*, Leigh began preparations to appear as Titania at the Old Vic in a revival of *A Midsummer Night's Dream* for Tyrone Guthrie. Lonely and despondent and still harboring the desire to portray Scarlett, she made a reckless decision to sail on the Queen Mary to the United States and then flew from New York to Hollywood. The twelve thousand mile journey would only allow her five days with Olivier, before returning to England to resume her role for Guthrie, and there was also a marginal possibility that she might replace Oberon in *Wuthering Heights*.

Meanwhile, Alexander Korda, who had the actress under contract and wanted her to play the Princess in his forthcoming epic, *The Thief of Bagdad*, quietly continued negotiations with Selznick for her release, should she get the role of Scarlett, in exchange for the services of the brilliant art director, William Cameron Menzies. Leigh's arrival in Hollywood activated her competition for the prized role and the somewhat bogus search for Scarlett finally ceased. David Selznick's brother, Myron, arranged a formal introduction between the actress and producer, a screen test was also arranged. Olivier and Leigh were united once more with the release of the films in which they not only embodied two of literature's most colorful and compelling characters but also achieved screen immortality and worldwide fame.

Olivier received his first Academy Award nomination for his performance as Heathcliff. The 1939 Oscar went to Robert Donat for his role as the timid professor in *Goodbye, Mr. Chips*. *Wuthering Heights* was also nominated for Best Film of the year by the Academy of Motion Picture Arts and Sciences, along with Geraldine Fitzgerald's supporting performance as Isabella. Gregg Toland won an Oscar for his photography, but the big winner in 1939 was *Gone with the Wind*, capturing ten Oscars including Best Film and the Best Actress honor for Vivien Leigh. The New York Film Critics singled out *Wuthering Heights* as the Best Motion Picture of the year.

Olivier as Larry Durant in *Twenty-One Days*. Graham Greene, the celebrated novelist and the film's screenwriter, had no good words for the project, recalling "the overpowering flavor of cooked ham."

Twenty-One Days
(U.S. title: *21 Days Together*)

1940, London Film Productions, Denham Productions; Produced by Alexander Korda; Associate Producer and director, Basil Dean; Screenplay by Graham Greene and Basil Dean from the play, *The First and the Last* by John Galsworthy; Photography, Jan Stallich; Art direction, Vincent Korda; Supervising editor, William Hornbeck; Editor, Charles Crichton; Assistant editor, John Guthrie; Music by John Greenwood; Musical direction, Muir Mathieson; South, A. W. Watkins; Distributed by Columbia Pictures

CAST

Larry Durrant	Laurence Olivier
Wanda	Vivien Leigh
Keith Durrant	Leslie Banks
Mander	Francis L. Sullivan
John Aloysius Evans	Hay Petrie
Henry Walenn	Esme Percy
Tolly	Robert Newton
Antonio	Victor Rietti
Alexander Macpherson	Morris Harvey
Carl Grunlich	Meinhart Maur
Solicitor	Lawrence Hanray
Beavis	David Horne

Father	Wallace Lupino
Mother	Muriel George
Lord Chief Justice	William Dewhurst
Swinton	Frederick Lloyd
Frau Grunlich	Elliot Mason
Asher	Arthur Young
Barnes	Fred Groves
Magistrate	Aubrey Mallalieu

Opened May 22, 1940, Rivoli Theater, New York

Larry Durrant accidentally murders the swinish husband of the girl he loves and resolves to surrender himself to the police when an innocent man is accused of the crime. First he spends three troubled weeks with his beloved while the supposed murdered is undergoing trial. The situation is resolved when the accused suddenly dies of heart failure.

Made in 1937, and retitled *Twenty-One Days Together* for U.S. distribution, the film was shelved for two years and finally released after Olivier and Leigh had achieved wide recognition in *Wuthering Heights* and *Gone with the Wind*. Leslie Banks (left), appeared as Olivier's brother.

New York Times, May 23, 1940

"A highly charged 'meller,' rigid throughout with suspense and nicely laced with much tender emotion. Mr. Olivier, who is a great one for tension, never lets you feel for a moment that his isn't a tortured soul—and well it might be, with Miss Leigh and all her tantalizing graces slipping momentarily away from him."

Graham Greene, *The Spectator*, January 12, 1940

"Perhaps I may be forgiven for noticing a picture in which I had some hand, for I have no good word to say of it. The brilliant acting of Mr. Hay Petrie as a decayed and outcast curate cannot conquer the overpowering flavor of cooked ham. Galsworthy's story, *The First and the Last*, was peculiarly unsuited for film adaptation, as its whole point lay in double suicide (forbidden by the censor), a burned confession, and an innocent man's conviction for murder (forbidden by the great public). For the rather dubious merits of the original the adaptors have substituted incredible coincidences and banal situations. Slow, wordy, unbearably sentimental, the picture reels awkwardly towards the only suicide the censorship allowed—and that, I find with some astonishment, has been cut out. I wish I could tell the extraordinary story that lies behind this shelved and resurrected picture, a story involving a theme-song, and a bottle of whisky, and camels in Wales. Meanwhile, let one guilty man, at any rate, stand in the dock, swearing never, never to do it again."

COMMENTS

During the Old Vic season of 1937, Olivier and Vivien Leigh appeared in their second film together for London Films. John Galsworthy's *The First and the Last* was prepared for the screen by Graham Greene and upon its completion was considered so bad that it was not released until its stars had achieved wider recognition two years later. The film was retitled, *Twenty-One Days*. Alan Dent recalled it to be "An inconsiderable film. Vivien was seen in a distinguished company of twelve, all acting, apparently, to very little purpose. The Oliviers forbade me ever to see this film and I never did. They themselves only saw 'about a third of it' at a public showing in New York."[14]

Conquest of the Air

1940, London Film Productions; Produced by Alexander Korda; Associate producer and technical advisor, Nigel Tangye; Directed (all uncredited) by Zoltan Korda, Alexander Esway, Donald Taylor, Alexander Shaw, John Monk Saunders, William Cameron Menzies; Screenplay by Hugh Gray and Peter Bezencenet from stories by John Monk Saunders and St. Exupery; Photography, Wilkie Cooper, Hans Schneeberger, and George Noble; Art direction, Vincent Korda and John Bryan; Editor, Charles Frend and Peter Bezencenet; Assistant editor, Adam Dawson; Music by Arthur Bliss; Musical direction, Muir Mathieson; Sound, A. W. Watkins; Production supervisor, John J. Croydon; Distributed by Key Films and United Artists

CAST

Vincent Lunardi	Laurence Olivier
Jerome de Ascoli	Franklyn Dyall
Otto Lilienthal	Henry Victor
Tiberius Cavallo	Hay Petrie
Von Zeppelin	John Turnbull
Louis Bleriot	Charles Lefaux
Sir George Cayley	Bryan Powley
Roger Bacon	Frederick Culley
Borelli	Alan Wheatley
De Rozier	John Abott
Leonardo da Vinci	Ben Webster
Wilbur Wright	Percy Marmont
Simon the Magician	Dick Vernon
Oliver the Monk	Denville Bond
Orville Wright	Charles Hickman
Isobella d'Este	Margaretta Scott
Narrator	Charles Frend

As Vincent Lunardi in *Conquest of the Air*, a Korda feature about the history of aviation which combined dramatic scenes with documentary footage. The film was first planned in 1934 and periodically shelved during several stages of production. A patchwork product was finally released in 1940. Lunardi (1759–1806) was the first aerial traveller in the English atmosphere. His first attempt at a balloon ascent from the grounds of Chelsea Hospital was interrupted by a riot. On September 15, 1784, from the Honourable Artillery Company's ground at Moorfields, Lunardi after various delays and apprehensions, ascended in the presence of nearly 200,000 spectators. He sailed over London at a great height and descended near Ware. The journey ranks as one of the most courageous flights in the history of ballooning. *Courtesy, National Film Archive, Stills Library.*

From *Alexander Korda* by Karol Kulik:

"*Conquest of the Air* was a feature about the history of aviation which combined documentary footage with numerous dramatic reconstructions. Planned as early as 1934, the project was constantly being shelved, picked up again, and re-shelved. Over a two or three year period at least five directors worked on the film, and most of the staff and players of London Films had a hand in the production. There is some controversy over when the film was actually released; some of the material was assembled and previewed in 1938, although it wasn't until late in 1939 that Charles Frend, an editor and director, compiled all the material into the film which was finally released in 1940. Frend added a narration and more documentary footage (including some shots of early wartime aviation and of Churchill). This seventy-one minute version was trade shown in May, 1940, and then presumably released, although there is no conclusive evidence to substantiate this or any other public screening of the film.

"*Conquest*'s erratic production history is at once apparent in the final result, a scrappy mixture of newsreel footage and reconstructed dramatic scenes which star most of Korda's contract players in the key roles of aviation pioneers. With the exception of one stunning visual sequence—D'Annunzio's leaflet 'bombing' of Vienna—the film lacks imagination and inspiration and pales in comparison with the contemporary work done by British documentary film makers and with present day television documentaries. Its main virtue is the musical score which Arthur Bliss was persuaded to compose during the early stage of production and which, as a concert piece on its own, has since become dissociated from the film. The history of *Conquest of the Air* was further complicated in 1944 when Key Films distributed it in a cut, forty-six minute form which some reviewers found preferable to the 'original.'"

1940, A Selznick International Production, Produced by David O. Selznick; Screenplay by Robert E. Sherwood and Joan Harrison; Adapted by Phillip MacDonald and Michael Hogan from the novel by Daphne du Maurier; Music composed by Franz Waxman; Editor, Hal C. Kern; Photography, George Barnes; Art Director, Lyle Wheeler; Directed by Alfred Hitchcock; Released by United Artists

CAST

Maxim de Winter	Laurence Olivier
Mrs. de Winter	Joan Fontaine
Jack Favell	George Sanders
Mrs. Danvers	Judith Anderson
Major Giles Lacy	Nigel Bruce
Colonel Julyan	C. Aubrey Smith
Frank Crawley	Reginald Denny
Beatrice Lacy	Gladys Cooper
Robert	Philip Winter
Frith	Edward Fielding
Mrs. Van Hopper	Florence Bates
Coroner	Melville Cooper
Dr. Baker	Leo G. Carroll
Chalcroft	Forrester Harvey
Tabbs	Lumsden Hare
Ben	Leonard Carey

Opened March 28, 1940, Radio City Music Hall, New York

THE FILM

The shy, young traveling companion to the wealthy and snobbish Mrs. Van Hopper, falls in love and hastily marries Maxim de Winter, the handsome master of Manderley, whose first wife, Rebecca, has died of mysterious circumstances. The young bride feels inadequate to her new situation as mistress of the awesome mansion, and her increasing lack of self-confidence is not helped by her often brooding husband and a sinister, domineering housekeeper, Mrs. Danvers,

A lobby display card for the 1946 reissue of *Rebecca*.

whose devotion to Rebecca was undaunted. The boat in which Rebecca disappeared is found and Maxim is incriminated by new evidence revealed at an inquest which suggests foul play. Further facts disclosed by Dr. Baker, whom Rebecca consulted before the boating accident, clear de Winter from the shadow of guilt, but the information provokes Mrs. Danvers to destroy Manderley and herself. The flaming destruction of Manderley and the death of her tormentor, relieves the new Mrs. de Winter of her sufferings.

REVIEWS

New York Times, March 29, 1940
"*Rebecca* is an altogether brilliant film, haunting, suspenseful, handsome and handsomely played. Laurence Olivier's brooding Max de Winter is a performance that almost needs not to be commented upon, for Mr. Olivier last year played Heathcliff who was also a study in dark melancholy, broken fitfully by gleams of sunny laughter. Maxim is the Heathcliff kind of man and Mr. Olivier seems that too."

Cinema, May 22, 1940
"Rarely has any writer had a book translated to the medium of the screen with the care and attention obviously lavished on Daphne du Maurier's *Rebecca.* Laurence Olivier is admirably suited to the role of Maxim de Winter, playing it with a moody intensity that is exactly right."

COMMENTS

Olivier followed his success as Heathcliff in a New York engagement at the Ethel Barrymore Theater as Gaylord Easterbrook, opposite Katharine Cornell in *No Time for Comedy* by S. N. Behrman. He had been eager to return to the stage and felt it important to reestablish himself in the theater. He received good notices in the modest theatrical comedy, and his new triumph as a screen star found him being mobbed by legions of adoring fans. In 1975, Olivier remembered wanting fame very much. "I swore to myself, 'When I am popular I shall be so gracious to everybody. I will sit at the steps of the stage door saying, My people, how I love you. There are only 300 here? I can sign all the autographs. Some

Maxim: "I wonder if I did a very selfish thing in marrying you?"

Olivier received his second Oscar nomination as Daphne Du Maurier's brooding master of Manderley.

Joan Fontaine was nominated for an Academy Award for her performance as the timid young bride of Maxim de Winter. She won the Oscar the following year for her role in another Alfred Hitchcock thriller, *Suspicion*.

Joan Fontaine (seated) with Reginald Denny (left), Olivier and Sir C. Aubrey Smith as Colonel Julyan.

of you go off and have a drink, and then come back.' But when I became popular, I wasn't like that at all. I'd take one horrified look at them, turn up my coat collar and run."[15]

Brooks Atkinson recalled "the spectacle of Olivier gaining stature year by year exciting. In *No Time for Comedy* Olivier acted a temptestuous young playwright with a virtuosity that seemed to have one hundred ways of saying what the author had in mind."[16]

David O. Selznick was preparing a film from Daphne du Maurier's best selling novel, *Rebecca*, for the Hollywood debut of British film director, Alfred Hitchcock. Ronald Colman, initially courted for the role of Maxim, feared the murder angle and the possibility that the final result would emerge as a woman-starring vehicle. While Leslie Howard and William Powell were other possible contenders, Olivier was finally chosen. Several actresses were considered for the role of the timid heroine, including Anne Baxter, Margaret Sullavan, Olivia De Havilland, and Loretta Young. Olivier was anxious to have Vivien with him, but Selznick in one of his famous memos confessed that "she could never be right for the girl." The first public showing of Vivien Leigh's screen test for the lead in *Rebecca* was unveiled on March 30, 1979 as part of an Olivier retrospective at the Plitt Century Plaza Theatre in Hollywood. The rare film clip was made available through the courtesy of David O. Selznick's son, Danny. Joan Fontaine was ultimately assigned the part and she along with Olivier were nominated for Academy Awards, but the Oscars went to Ginger Rogers for *Kitty Foyle* and James Steward for *The Philadelphia Story*. The 1940 Best Picture honor, however, did go to *Rebecca*.

Olivier's stage technique troubled Selznick, who wrote to the director: "Larry's silent action and reactions become slower as his dialogue becomes faster, each day. His pauses and spacing on the scene with the girl in which she tells him about the ball are the most ungodly slow and deliberate reactions I have ever seen. It is played as though he were deciding whether or not to run for President instead of whether or not to give a ball. And for God's sake, speed up Larry not merely in these close-ups, but in the rest of the picture on his reactions, which are apparently the

way he plays on the stage, where it could be satisfactory. But while you are at it, you will have to keep your ears open to make sure that we know what the hell he's talking about, because he still has the tendency to speed up his words and to read them in such a way than an American audience can't understand them."[17]

Maxim: "Her shadow has been between us all the time—keeping us from one another. She knew that this would happen."

Rebecca, which marked the American film debut of director Alfred Hitchcock, was nominated for eleven Academy Awards. Losing all acting, writing and directorial honors, the compelling mystery classic was cited as the best picture for 1940.

Pride and Prejudice

1940, Metro-Goldwyn-Mayer, Produced by Hunt Stromberg; Screenplay by Aldous Huxley and Jane Murfin, based on the dramatization of Jane Austin's novel by Helen Jerome; Music by Herbert Stothart; Photography, Karl Freund; Art director, Cedric Gibbons; Set decoration, Edwin B. Willis; Gowns, Adrian; Dance director, Ernst Matray; Editor, Robert J. Kern; Directed by Robert Z. Leonard

CAST

Elizabeth Bennet	Greer Garson
Mr. Darcey	Laurence Olivier
Mrs. Bennet	Mary Boland
Lady Catherine de Bourgh	Edna Mae Oliver
Jane Bennet	Maureen O'Sullivan
Lydia Bennet	Ann Rutherford
Kitty Bennet	Heather Angel
Mary Bennet	Marsha Hunt
Mr. Bennet	Edmund Gwenn
Miss Bingley	Frieda Inescort
Charlotte Lucas	Karen Morley
Mr. Bingley	Bruce Lester
Mr. Wickham	Edward Ashley
Mr. Collins	Melville Cooper
Mr. Denny	Marten Lamont
Sir William Lucas	E. E. Clive
Mrs. Phillips	May Beatty
Lady Lucas	Marjorie Wood

Opened August 8, 1940, at the Radio City Music Hall, New York

THE FILM

Based on Jane Austen's study of the harmless absurdities of her middle-class provincial society at the turn of the nineteenth century, the film relates a captivating story of five sisters in quest of husbands, their frankly scheming mother, their wisely unmettlesome father, and a pair of eligible bachelors. The primary aim of Mrs. Bennet is to see her daughters well married and she is encouraged by the arrival of the wealthy Charles Bingley at nearby Netherfield Hall, who is accompanied by Fitzwilliam Darcy, a handsome young man to whom great wealth was attributed by gossip. Darcy displays a pride in his noble birth which the girls and villagers consider insufferably arrogant. Bingley is immediately attracted to Jane Bennet, but an intense dislike develops between Darcy and the spirited Elizabeth. When Darcy eventually succumbs to her charms he admits it was difficult for him to conquer his pride to the point that he could propose marriage to a girl of such an inferior family as hers. The confession angers Elizabeth and adds to her initial prejudice. Darcy later offers a second proposal, this time as a humble lover and Elizabeth, estimating him more justly, accepts.

REVIEW

New York Times, August 9, 1940

"If your fancy would be for a picture of a charming and mannered little English world which has long since been tucked away in ancient haircloth trunks—a quaint but lively world in which young ladies were mainly concerned with dances and ribboned bonnets and the light in a guardsman's eye, and matrons had the vapors and worried only about marrying off their eligible daughters—then the picture for you is *Pride and Prejudice.* For this, by your leave, we proclaim the most deliciously pert comedy of old manners, the most crisp and crackling satire in costume that we in this corner can remember ever having seen on the screen. It isn't often that a cast of such uniform perfection is assembled. Laurence Olivier is Darcy, that's all there is to it—the arrogant, sardonic Darcy whose pride went before a most felicitous fall. Pictures played in costume often have an artificial air. But for pure charm and romantic diversion, for bubbling and wholesome life, we heartily recommend this exquisite comedy."

COMMENTS

Director George Cukor thought Vivien Leigh would make an admirable Elizabeth Bennet, but studio bosses had other plans and her next role would be as Myra, the tragic dancer who becomes a prostitute when she is wrongly informed that her love has been killed in the war. The film was *Waterloo Bridge* and her co-star was Robert Taylor. While they were filming their respective

"Olivier is Darcy—that's all there is to it!" (Bosley Crowther, 1940.)

pictures, they received word of their divorce decrees and began to lay plans for their marriage and to star together as Shakespeare's ill-fated lovers in a production of *Romeo and Juliet*.

The role of Darcy, which Clark Gable had long before turned down, was one of literature's most notable bachelors and a part perfectly suited to Olivier's talents. Following the enormous popularity of his performances as Heathcliff and Maxim de Winter, the film secured his position as one of Hollywood's most appealing leading romantic actors. Greer Garson, whose screen career had been successfully launched the year before in *Goodbye, Mr. Chips,* had first met Olivier when they appeared on the West End stage in *Golden Arrow,* five years earlier. The Olivier-Garson pairing turned out to be a most attractive combination, but the film which was released in Great Britain during the dark hours before the war did not receive the recognition it deserved. Many years later the film was realized to be a classic of its kind and is still a popular attraction at revival houses. "My admiration and affection for Olivier is boundless," Miss Garson wrote in 1978, adding, "our association has been a most happy one."

That Hamilton Woman
(British title: *Lady Hamilton*)

1941, Alexander Korda Films, Inc.; Produced and Directed by Alexander Korda; Assistant director, Walter Mayo; Screenplay by Walter Reisch and R. C. Sherriff; Photography, Rudolph Mate; Assistant photographer, Edward Linden; Special effects, Lawrence Butler; Art Direction, Vincent Korda; Set design, Julia Heron; Costumes, Rene Hubert; Editor, William Hornbeck; Music composed and conducted by Miklos Rozsa; Sound, William H. Wilmartin; Production assistant, Andre De Toth; Distributed by United Artists

Lord Nelson	Laurence Olivier
Emma Hamilton	Vivien Leigh
Sir William Hamilton	Alan Mowbray
Lady Nelson	Gladys Cooper
Mrs. Cadogan-Lyon	Sara Allgood
Captain Hardy	Henry Wilcoxen
Street girl	Heather Angel
Reverend Nelson	Halliwell Hobbes
Lord Spencer	Gilbert Emery
Lord Keith	Miles Mander
Josiah	Ronald Sinclair
King of Naples	Luis Alberni
Queen of Naples	Norma Drury
Hotel manager	George Renavent
Orderly	Leonard Carey
Gendarme	Alec Craig

Opened April 3, 1941, at the Radio City Music Hall, New York

THE FILM

Because of the deep affection of Horatio Nelson, England's most illustrious naval hero, for the beautiful Emma Hamilton, wife of Sir William Hamilton, the British ambassador in Naples, the far famed victor of the Nile risks his personal reputation and, at one point, perhaps his career. The Admiral is fiercely loyal to his beautiful and bewitching mistress and she to him for many years. The tragic love story follows Emma's marriage to Lord Hamilton, her meeting with Nelson, and her assistance in providing ships for the Nile by interceding with the Queen of Naples. Nursing the wounded hero back to health, Lady Hamilton returns to England with him and faces the scorn of Nelson's wife and lives in retirement with him until he is called back to duty to face Napoleon's fleet. Nelson meets his death at the historic Battle of Trafalgar with the name of his beloved Emma on his lips.

Lord Nelson in *That Hamilton Woman* **(1941)**

REVIEW

New York Times, April 4, 1941
"There is much in the picture which is exciting, and it is absorbing most of the way. The sequence representing the Battle of Trafalgar and the death of Nelson is exceptionally moving, and the manner in which the hero's death is reported to Emma makes the finest scene in the film. And Vivien Leigh's entire performance as Lady Hamilton is delightful to behold. All of the charm and grace and spirit which Miss Leigh contains is beautifully put to use to capture the subtle spell which Emma most assuredly must have weaved. Laurence Olivier's Nelson is more studied and obviously contrived, and his appearance is very impressive, with the famous dead eye and empty sleeve."

COMMENTS

In 1940, Olivier and Vivien Leigh invested their entire savings of $60,000 into a lavish stage production of *Romeo and Juliet.* Olivier staged the drama and assembled an impressive cast including Edmond O'Brien as Mercutio, Alexander Knox as Friar Laurence, and as Tybalt, Cornel Wilde, who would achieve stardom five years later as Fredric Chopin in *A Song to Remember.* Dame May Whitty reluctantly accepted the role of Nurse. Following generally favorable response in San Francisco and Chicago the production arrived in New York on May 9, where it was greeted by disastrous critical reception. While Olivier had already distinguished himself as Romeo in England, Brooks Atkinson in the *New York Times* accused him of throwing his part away. "Although Miss Leigh and Mr. Olivier are handsome young people, they hardly act the parts at all. The superficiality of his acting is difficult to understand. He is mannered and affected, avoiding directness in even simple episodes," Atkinson wrote adding additional displeasure with the staging. "As his own director, Mr. Olivier has never seen or heard himself in the performance. That is just as well. He would be astonished if he did."

During the brief New York engagement in Shakespeare's tragedy, Alexander Korda en route to Hollywood, stopped to see the play and

"They were just about the best looking couple anywhere or any time!" (Alan Dent.)

As Lord Nelson and Lady Hamilton, the handsome combination of Olivier and Leigh suggested a great cinematic future, but the film would mark their final appearance together on the screen.

The Death of Nelson. The recreation of this historical
scene was inspired by the famous A. W. Davis painting
in the National Maritime Museum, London. *That
Hamilton Woman* was issued in Great Britain as *Lady
Hamilton,* and was the favorite film of Prime Minister
Winston Churchill.

Horatio Nelson, Viscount Nelson—by Sir William
Beechey. *National Portrait Gallery, London.*

discuss plans for a film about Lord Nelson, a subject ideal at the time to boost wartime morale. Financially destroyed by the stage venture, the couple returned to the West Coast and passionately intrigued by the colorful historical characters they would be portraying immersed themselves in volumes of research on the subject. The divorce decree became final on August 28, and a few days later Olivier and Leigh were secretly wed at Ronald Colman's ranch in Santa Barbara.

The film was completed in six weeks, and at a modest budget with scriptwriters contributing dialogue each day. It proved to be a popular and successful film, one which Prime Minister Winston Churchill often referred to as his very favorite. "Churchill never tired of it," Olivier recalled many years later. "He even showed it to Stalin!" Because the film was written as the production progressed, Korda did not have a completed script to submit to the censorship office until the picture was finished. "Even though the film was framed by a prologue and epilogue which showed the depths to which Emma Hamilton's adulterous life has led her (a drunken old hag thrown in jail for theft and assault), this was not enough 'retribution' to please the censor."[18]

An additional scene was added with Nelson being reprimanded by his clergyman father. Nelson admit's the error of his passion, but confesses that he cannot give up Emma. The scene satisfied the censor, but Korda disliked it and later had it cut from the British print, titled *Lady Hamilton*. It is likely that it remains in some prints of the film.

With the success of *That Hamilton Woman*, the Olivier-Leigh combination suggested a great cinematic future, but they were not to appear together again on the screen. Olivier cherished the idea that as an acting team they might play on the stage all of the great classical roles together. Neither was this goal achieved, but their stage career together was far more notable than their brief film partnership.

In 1941, Olivier narrated an eight minute short for Crown Films. *Words for Battle* produced by Ian Dalrymple and directed by Humphrey Jennings, was a brief morale booster featuring the inspirational words of Milton, Browning, Churchill, and Lincoln.

Lady Hamilton as "Nature"—by George Romney.
Copyright, The Frick Collection, New York.

The 49th Parallel
(U.S. title: *The Invaders*)

1942, A General Films Ltd. Production, Screenplay by Rodney Ackland and Emeric Pressburger from an original story by Emeric Pressburger; Music composed by Ralph Vaughan Williams; Musical director, Muir Mathieson with the London Symphony Orchestra; Editor, David Lean; Photography, Frederick Young; Art director, David Rawnsley; Produced and Directed by Michael Powell; Distributed by Columbia Pictures

CAST

Johnnie the trapper	Laurence Olivier
The Factor	Finaly Currie
Peter	Anton Walbrook
Anna	Glynis Johns
Philip Armstrong Scott	Leslie Howard
Andy Brock	Raymond Massey
Andreas	Charles Victor
Lieutenant Hirth	Eric Portman
David	David Paper
George the Indian	Tarvera Moana
Art	Eric Clavering
Bob	Charles Rolfe
Commander Bernsdorff	Richard George
Lieutenant Huhnecke	Raymond Lovell
Vogel	Niall MacGinnes
Kranz	Peter Moore
Lohrmann	John Chandos
Jahner	Basil Appleby

Opened March 5, 1942, at the Capitol Theater, New York

THE FILM

A Nazi patrol, led by Lieutenant Hirth, is stranded in Canada, when their U-boat is destroyed in Hudson Bay by Canadian aircraft. The six survivors cut a bloody path across Canada seeking sanctuary in the United States. Their first encounter is at a small trading post where they encounter Johnnie, a French-Canadian trapper who has returned from a long hunting expedition and is not aware of the war. He is brutally shot and his dying words carry a promise that upon allied victory, "we will send missionaries." The Nazi crew continues to a Hutterite colony in Manitoba, finding the former German people happy in their peaceful farming life, living by simple Christian ideals. Sailor Vogel is befriended by a young peasant girl, Anna and is accepted by the community and by Peter, their leader, for his expert baking talents. He chooses to stay behind and is executed by Hirth, who is finally cornered as he attempts to cross into the states in a freight train by an AWOL Canadian soldier.

REVIEWS

New York Times, March 6, 1942
"Among the best of the anti-Nazi pictures which have yet been exhibited hereabouts, you can list the British-made *The Invaders.* For this, indeed, is a picture which not only argues trenchantly but is filmed and played with such intelligence that it gives an illusion of documented fact. It was made in Canada and in England by a group of selfless stars, playing in small but vital roles for the sake of the main idea. The picture is made immeasurably effective by the realistic manner in which it has been put together by Michael Powell. The performances of all of the actors are excellent. *The Invaders* is an absorbing and exciting film."

Cinema, October 10, 1941
"The most appealing of the roles is that of the French Canadian trapper played by Laurence Olivier, for he breaks away from the convention and gives a plain study of a simple soul aghast at the vicious cruelty of the Nazi doctrines and their adherents, incomprehending the politics of the war but ready to die for his faith."

COMMENTS

Olivier applied for active service in the Fleet Air Arm in 1941, was commissioned a sub-lieutenant and assigned to duties. While awaiting to be called he accepted an offer to film a guest appearance as Johnnie, a good natured French-Canadian trapper in the all-star propaganda film, *The 49th Parallel.* Leslie Howard, Anton Walbrook, and

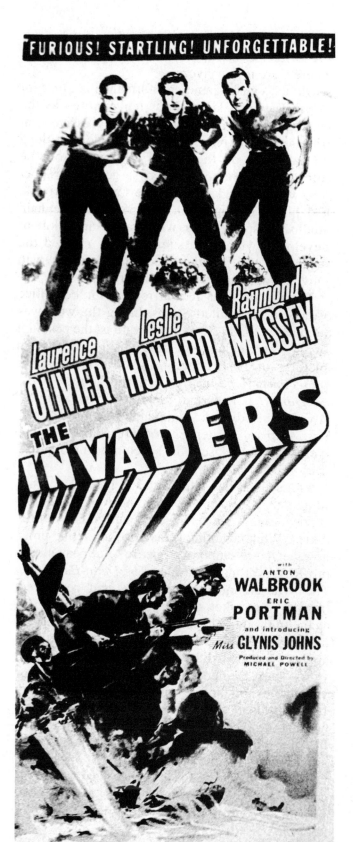

This poster for the Columbia Pictures re-release of *The 49th Parallel* in the United States, suggests a good deal more action than the film actually contained. Retitled *The Invaders*, Olivier appeared as an amiable and innocent French-Canadian trapper victimized by fugitive Nazis. Leslie Howard portrayed a peaceful, nature loving artist. Only Raymond Massey as an AWOL Canadian soldier got a chance to throw a punch at villain Eric Portman in the film's engrossing final moments.

As Johnnie in *The 49th Parallel* (1942). "The best thing he's done in films." (Vivien Leigh.) *Courtesy, Museum of Modern Art, Film Stills Archive.*

Raymond Massey agreed to a salary cut, and Elisabeth Bergner, a German of strong anti-Nazi feelings, was said to have waivered her fee altogether. She withdrew from the production however, when a fundamentalist group of Hutterite's who would appear in the film objected to the actress' excessive use of nail polish, lipstick, and the glamorous makeup befitting a film star. It was also considered unsafe for Miss Bergner to cross the Atlantic for location filming in Canada, for fear she might fall into Nazi hands. She was replaced by a young actress named Glynis Johns, daughter of veteran character actor, Mervyn Johns. Her appealing screen debut as a young peasant girl marked the beginning of a long and successful career on the stage and screen.

Leslie Howard, who had become a screen favorite following his role as Ashley Wilkes with Vivien Leigh in *Gone with the Wind*, appeared in one more film after *The 49th Parallel*. It was *The First of the Few* (retitled *Spitfire* in the United States) in which he portrayed R. J. Mitchell, a scholarly aeronautical engineer who sacrificed his own life in the development of the Spitfire. In 1943, a commercial airliner flying from Lisbon to England was shot down by German fighter planes. Howard, returning from a lecture tour in Portugal and Spain, which he had undertaken for the British Council, was among the passengers. There were no survivors.

Olivier's gusty cameo performance in *The 49th Parallel*, which lasts about ten minutes in the early portion of the film, was an impressive contribution, and Vivien considered it the best thing he had done on the screen. His short tour de force, which was coached by a genuine trapper who was in England with the Canadian troops, and filmed during a ten day period at Denham studios, displayed his wide range and skill at developing vivid character roles. It marked the beginning of a broader spectrum of parts which Olivier would be creating in future films.

The Invaders, as it was retitled for box-office values in the United States during the war, was nominated for an Academy Award as the best film of the year, along with other distinctive motion pictures of 1942; *King's Row, The Magnificent Ambersons, Random Harvest,* and *Yankee Doodle Dandy*. The Oscar for Best Film went to M-G-M's sturdy and sentimental wartime drama, *Mrs. Miniver*. Writer Emeric Pressburger, however, did win an Oscar for his compelling original story for *The Invaders*.

As a second line pilot with the Fleet Air Arm, stationed at Worthy Down, near Winchester, Olivier found himself faced with dull routine duties. While awaiting transfer to an active unit, he received a temporary release to appear in the pro-Russia propaganda film, *The Demi-Paradise*. The Walrus unit, to which he had requested transfer, was taken out of commission and faced again with the bleak prospect of returning to nonoperational duties at Worthy Down, he applied for an extension of his release. Some years later Olivier credited his flying time as valuable experience. "I often think about flying. It taught me an awful lot about coordination. It's not just the eyes and voice which are important to the actor. It's the whole machinery. You can't say what's the most important part of an engine. One can't work without the other very well. You can see weaknesses about the eyes or facial expression, about the stance or coordination. Flying kept me poised."

The Demi-Paradise
(U.S. title: *Adventure for Two*)

1943, a Two-Cities Film production; Produced by Anatole de Grunwald; Music composed by Nicholas Brodszky; Screenplay by Anatole de Grunwald; Editor, Reginald Beck; Photography, Bernard Knowles; Art director, Paul Sheriff, Directed by Anthony Asquith

CAST

Ivan Dimitrievitch Kouznetsoff	Laurence Olivier
Ann Tisdall	Penelope Dudley Ward
Mrs. Tisdall	Marjorie Fielding
Rowena Ventnor	Margaret Rutherford
Mr. Runalow	Felix Aylmer
Herbert Tisdall	George Thorpe
Richard Christie	Guy Middleton
Mr. Walford	Michael Shepley
Aunt Winnie	Edie Martin
Mrs. Tisdall-Stanton	Muriel Aked
Tom Sellars	Jack Watling
Mrs. Flannel	Everley Gregg
Mrs. Pawson	Joyce Grenfell
Waiter	Wilfred Hyde White
Box Office Manager	Miles Malleson
Mrs. Teddy Beckett	Marion Spencer
Sailor	John Laurie
Mr. Jordan	David Keir
George Tisdall	Brian Nissen
Mrs. Tremlow	Josephine Middleton
Toomes	Aubrey Mallalieu
Mr. Bishop	Charles Paton

Opened December 13, 1945, at the Winter Garden Theater, New York

THE FILM

Ivan Kouznetsoff, a young Soviet marine engineer, invents a new type of ice-breaker propeller and is sent to have it manufactured in England. He is invited by Ann Tisdall, granddaughter of an eccentric ship owner, Mr. Runalow, to her country home for the weekend. At first he is gravely disappointed in the evidence of British indifference. He can't understand a people who putter in gardens, drink tea, mix poetry with engineering, and put on boring pageants. He returns to Russia failing to get proper support for his propeller. His notions change considerably when he returns to England again, a few years later. In 1941, he sees a nation at war. The class tensions, the laziness, and indifference are gone. He sees the people "muddling through" in gallant fashion, and his English friends find a new interest in someone they had thought to be a dour and humorless communist. Eventually his propeller is manufactured and tested successfully. Ivan returns to his native land, promising to come back to England, and to Ann, when the war is over.

REVIEW

New York Times, December 14, 1945
"A limp and dampish hand across the sea. Mr. Olivier's melancholy Russian is a ponderous caricature and Penelope Ward's English maiden is a skinny reed."

COMMENTS

Olivier reminisced about the film with Anthony Asquith's biographer, R. J. Minney. "Quite frankly it was a propaganda film. I daresay it was unnecessary propaganda. The purpose of the propaganda was to make the English love the Russians who had just come into the war. We had a marvelous time making the picture. One was conscious of his (Asquith's) strange, seeming mixture of reserve and yet—I wouldn't call it kitten claws, for there was always some admirable strength somewhere—and fondness—and charm—and wit—and delight—delight."[19]

As Ivan Kouznetsoff in The Demi-Paradise, with Wilfred
Hyde-White and Penelope Dudley Ward. *Courtesy, National Film Archive, Stills Library.*

Henry V

1945, A Two-Cities Film, A Screenplay by Laurence Olivier and Alan Dent from the play by William Shakespeare; Produced and Directed by Laurence Olivier in close association with the editor, Reginald Beck; Art director, Paul Sheriff; Assistant art director, Carmen Dillon; Costume designer, Roger Furse; Assistant costume designer, Margaret Furse; Photography, Robert Krasker; Music composed by Sir William Walton, played by the London Symphony Orchestra, conducted by Muir Mathieson; Released by United Artists

CAST

King Henry V of England	Laurence Olivier
Ancient Pistol	Robert Newton
Chorus	Leslie Banks
Princess Katharine	Renee Asherson
Fluellen	Esmond Knight
Constable of France	Leo Genn
Archbishop of Canterbury	Felix Aylmer
Mountjoy, the French Herald	Ralph Truman
King Charles of France	Harcourt Williams
Alice, Lady in Waiting	Ivy St. Helier
Duke of Berri, the French Ambassador	Ernest Thesiger
The Dauphin	Max Adrian
Duke of Orleans	Francis Lister
Duke of Burgundy	Valentine Dyall

95

Henry: "Put off your maiden blushes; avouch the thoughts of your heart with the looks of an empress; take me by the hand, and say 'Harry of England, I am thine'." (Henry V, Act V, Scene II, William Shakespeare.) with Renee Asherson as Princess Katharine

Duke of Bourbon	Russell Thorndyke
Gower, Captain of the English Army	Michael Shepley
Sir Thomas Erpingham	Morland Graham
Earl of Westmoreland	Gerald Case
Queen Isabel of France	Janet Burnell
Duke of Exeter	Nicholas Hannen
Bishop of Ely	Robert Helpmann
Mistress Quickley	Freda Jackson
A Priest	Ernest Hare
French Messenger	Jonathan Field
English Herald	Vernon Greeves
Boy	George Cole
Governor of Harfleur	Frank Tickle
Duke of Glouscester	Michael Warre
Corporal Nym	Frederick Cooper
Bates	Arthur Hambling
Earl of Salisbury	Griffith Jones
Lieutenant Bardolph	Roy Emerton
Sir John Falstaff	George Robey
Captain MacMorris	Niall MacGinnes
Captain Jamie	John Laurie
Williams	Jimmy Hanley

Opened June 17, 1946, at the New York City Center

THE FILM

In the inspired Olivier concept, Shakespeare's play begins as a performance in the Globe Theatre, shifting in broad cinematic terms to an epic narrative of Henry V, who had developed from a dissolute youth to a purposeful monarch. Proving his ability as a soldier and skillful leader, he unites the dissident factions in the English army and goes on to crush the French, against enormous odds, at Agincourt. Arranging a treaty with the French court, he woos Princess Katharine to whom he is formally betrothed as part of the peace agreement.

REVIEWS

New York Times, June 18, 1946
"Out of Will Shakespeare's rather turgid *Chronicle Historie of King Henry the Fifth*—more concisely and conveniently titled for this occasion simply *Henry V*—a fine group of British film craftsmen and actors, headed by Laurence

Olivier, have concocted a stunningly brilliant and intriguing screen spectacle, rich in theatrical invention, in heroic imagery and also gracefully regardful of the conventions of the Elizabethan stage. They have further achieved the full eloquence of Shakespeare's tribute to a conquering English king. Olivier's own performance of Henry sets a standard for excellence. His majestic and heroic bearing, his full and vibrant use of his voice, created a kingly figure around which the other characters rightly spin.''

New York Herald Tribune, June 18, 1946
''England has sent a superlative motion picture to these shores. *Henry V* is a brilliant tour de force. It is an enchanting entertainment. Laurence Olivier has taken one of the least malleable of Shakespeare's chronicle dramas and molded it to a miraculous screen pattern. After his performance during the Old Vic repertory season here, Olivier needs no new laurels. But his staging and production of *Henry V,* added to his portrayal of the title role, enhance his artistic stature tenfold.''

Time magazine, April 8, 1946
''The movies have produced one of their rare great works of art. Almost continually, it invests the art of Shakespeare—and the art of cinema as well—with a new spaciousness, a new mobility, a new radiance. Sometimes, by courageous (but never revolutionary) cuts, rearrangements and interpolations, it improves on the original. Yet its brilliance is graceful, never self-assertive. It simply subserves, extends, illuminates, and liberates Shakespeare's poem. One of the prime joys of the picture is the springwater freshness and immediacy of the lines, the lack of antiquarian culture-clogging. Especially as spoken by Olivier, the lines constantly combine the power and prose and glory of poetry.''

"A little touch of Harry in the night."

William Bayer, *The Great Movies* (New York: Grosset & Dunlop, Inc., 1973), p. 240.

"It is a brilliant transposition of a play to the screen, brilliant in its handling of period reality, and enriched by a brilliant Olivier performance. Even in roles beneath his talent—Max de Winter in *Rebecca* or Archie Rice in *The Entertainer*—he is phenomenal. Playing Shakespeare he has been at his best and deserves the accolades he has received as the world's superlative living actor. In *Henry V* he brings such energy to his heroic role that he makes the swash-buckling of Douglas Fairbanks and Errol Flynn look tame. And as a filmmaker his invention of what the aesthetician Erwin Panofsky called the 'oblique close-up'— when we watch his face in repose listening to his own off-stage voice pronouncing a soliloquy—is one of the few startling visual innovations since the days of D. W. Griffith and Sergei Eisenstein."

Bosley Crowther, *The Great Films* (New York: G.P. Putnam's Sons, 1967), p. 168.

"Olivier's direction has forcefulness and sweep, making a rich and flowing fabric of personalities and pageantry. And his own performance of Henry sets a standard of excellence. His majesty and heroic bearing, his full and vibrant use of his voice, create a kingly figure around which the others rightly whirl."

Jack L. Jorgens, *Shakespeare on Film* (Bloomington, Indiana & London: Indiana University Press, 1977), p. 122.

"*Henry V* is a classic among Shakespeare films, the first to be both an artistic and a popular success. It is a unique blend of realism and artifice, a bold departure from the singleness of style of earlier Shakespeare films. Made in a difficult period in England's fight for survival against Germany, it is brimming over with high spirits, bustling with activity, and full of shifts in mood, fluid motion and changes in color and texture. Olivier was perfectly suited to Henry as he conceived him—a bold adventurer with something of the likeable madcap about him—and the minor parts are graced with a masterful touch of caricature. This *Henry V* is a blend of history and storybook romance, a tribute both to the glories of the English Elizabethan and Medieval past and to Englishmen in 1944. Stylistically, the film is a miracle of lucidity, order and harmony. As an interpretation of the play, it is notable rather for its clear, broad outlines and strokes of bravado than for subtlety or complexity of theme or character."

COMMENTS

Producer Filippo Del Giudice, who guided Noel Coward's courageous account of a destroyer and its crew, *In Which We Serve,* heard Olivier in a full-length radio version of *Henry V* in 1942 and suggested to the actor that it would be an ideal time to film the classic as an example of English triumph in the time of war. Olivier, whose only experience with Shakespeare on the screen had been in *As You Like It,* was hesitant and committed himself only after being promised full control over casting, editing, and producing the project. Lacking technical experience as a film director he approached William Wyler for assistance, but the director of *Wuthering Heights* declined, lacking experience with Shakespeare.

Directors Carol Reed and Terence Young also refused invitations to direct, so Olivier proceeded as director himself and appointed Reginald Beck to assist on technical matters, serve as cutter, and direct those scenes in which he himself would appear in front of the camera. Theater critic and Shakespearean scholar Alan Dent worked with Olivier on the editing of the play and William Walton was assigned to compose the film's heraldic background score.

An impeccable cast was chosen despite the wartime shortage of actors, and temporary release from military duties was obtained for Leo Genn, Robert Newton, and Griffith Jones. Olivier very much wanted Vivien Leigh to appear as Katharine, but David Selznick, to whom the actress will still bound by contract, felt the part was too insignificant for his star of *Gone with the Wind*. Renee Asherson, the wife of actor Robert Donat, played the role.

Henry V was Olivier's first directorial work in the medium, and he later claimed directing films was the most exciting work he had ever done. Directing and writing camera shots was being interpreter of the whole, Olivier recalled, and the nearest you can get to being a creator. "I'm convinced after making *Henry V,* that you can do on the screen almost all the things you can do on the stage—and most of the things you can't do, you shouldn't be doing anyhow. The stage is the actor's medium, because it's the actor who has the contact with the audience and shapes the whole role accordingly. But films are a director's medium and for the same reason. Now I'm convinced that every actor ought to be in films. It isn't until you see yourself acting that you realize how many of the little things you do are foolish and meaningless."[20]

As the first of the great Shakespearean screen trilogy Olivier was to direct and star in, there was a prophetic irony in the opening sequence. The camera swoops over the London of Shakespeare's time, closing in on the Globe Theatre where a performance of *Henry V* is about to begin. A fanfare announces the start of the play, and the audience settles down as the "Prologue" begins. Following the entrance of King Henry the film subtly leaves the confines of the Elizabethan theatre setting and recreates a picturesque fifteenth century England. Olivier's skillful opening statement transformed a stage masterpiece into a film masterpiece. He had discovered an original and successful formula in which to bring Shakespeare to the screen, and it was only the beginning.

Critic John Mason Brown called Olivier's Henry "brilliantly humanized." "His Henry stood out with the bright, bold colors of the English standard. In speech, appearance, posture, thought, and feeling, his Henry was a per-

Henry V **(1945)**

Henry V, 1387–1422 (artist unknown). *National Portrait Gallery, London.*

formance of superlative merit. He shone with spiritual splendor, a quality as rare in actors as it is in other human beings.''

The film was a stunning success. In New York it played for eleven months, longer than any previous British film. Olivier received his third Oscar nomination and the film was nominated for Best Picture. *The Best Years of Our Lives* was the 1946 winner, a timely and powerful document which examined the problems of three ex-servicemen trying to adjust to peacetime living. Its star, Fredric March, won the Best Actor honor for his performance as a disoriented veteran, and William Wyler was cited for his direction. Olivier was awarded a special statuette for his outstanding achievement as actor, producer, and director in bringing *Henry V* to the screen and was recognized as Best Actor of the year by the New York Film Critics Circle.

In 1944, Olivier was invited to join Ralph Richardson and John Burrell in the management of the Old Vic Theatre Company. After a six year absence from the London stage, he returned to gain a new stature as the foremost Shakespearean actor of his day. During the next three years he appeared in a remarkable variety of classic roles, displaying his range and virtuosity to rare effect.

In *Uncle Vanya* he was Astrov, Chekhov's melancholy doctor, opposite Richardson's neurotic Vanya. In Shaw's *Arms and the Man*, he played the romantic Saranoff in perfect contrast to Richardson's casual Bluntschli. ''The best thing I have seen him do,'' wrote *Times* critic W. A. Darlington upon viewing Olivier's *Richard III*.

In *Henry IV* he portrayed Hotspur in the first half of the history and the relatively minor role of Justice Shallow in the conclusion, to Richardson's padded, blustering Falstaff. "His Hotspur is filled with energy, vitality and purpose," commented Lewis Nichols in the *New York Times,* adding "When he comes to Justice Shallow, Mr. Olivier is at the other extreme. The contrast between Shallow's niggardly affairs and Falstaff's grandiose ones makes the Olivier-Richardson scenes pure comedy on a towering level."

In May of 1946, the Old Vic repertory company made its first U.S. appearance in a history-making six week engagement. In addition to Parts One and Two of *Henry IV,* and *Uncle Vanya,* Olivier contrasted a gem of comic acting as Mr. Puff in Sheridan's farce, *The Critic,* with his stirring portrait of King Oedipus in Sophocles' tragedy. "Olivier rises to the highest tragic playing," wrote Nichols. Years later Brooks Atkinson recalled the Old Vic visit as a resounding success. "The company included many of London's finest players. They gave gorgeous performances of five unrelated classics. They performed with grace, ease, resonance, and dexterity."

Later that year Olivier, then thirty-nine, approached another great classic part, that of *King Lear.* Herbert L. Matthews reported in the *Times* that it was a performance of magnificent ease. "No actor we can recall has matched the creative stamina which enables Olivier to equal the demands of every phase."

Olivier at thirty-nine as *King Lear,* Old Vic Company (1946).

"A WORK OF GENIUS!"
—LIFE Magazine

LAURENCE OLIVIER
in
Hamlet
by WILLIAM SHAKESPEARE
with JEAN SIMMONS
A UNIVERSAL-INTERNATIONAL RELEASE

102

Hamlet

1948, J. Arthur Rank Enterprises, A Two-Cities Film Produced and Directed by Laurence Olivier, under the management of Filippo Del Giudice, A Universal-International Release, sponsored by the Theatre Guild; From the play by William Shakespeare; Text editor, Alan Dent; Production design by Roger Furse; Art director, Carmen Dillon; Photography, Desmond Dickenson; Associate producer, Reginald Beck; Production supervisor, Phil C. Samuel; Assistant producer, Anthony Bushell; Production manager, John Gassage; Editor, Helga Cranston; Sound editor, Harry Miller; Assistant director, Peter Bolton; Special effects, Paul Sheriff, Henry Harris, and Jack Whitehead; Music composed by Sir William Walton, Played by the Philharmonia Orchestra, conducted by Muir Mathieson and John Hollingsworth

CAST

Hamlet	Laurence Olivier
Gertrude, the Queen	Eileen Herlie
Claudius, the King	Basil Sydney
Ophelia	Jean Simmons
Polonius	Felix Aylmer
Horatio	Norman Wooland
Laertes	Terence Morgan
First Player	Harcourt Williams
Player King	Patrick Troughton
Player Queen	Tony Tarver
Osric	Peter Cushing
Gravedigger	Stanley Holloway
Priest	Russell Thorndyke
Francisco	John Laurie
Bernardo	Esmond Knight
Marcellus	Anthony Quayle
Sea Captain	Nial MacGinnes

Opened September 29, 1948, Park Avenue Theater, New York

Shakespeare's classic tragedy of murder and revenge in the royal halls of medieval Denmark. Claudius, brother to the King, conniving with the Queen, poisons the monarch and seizes the throne, taking the widowed Gertrude for his bride. Hamlet, son of the murdered King, mournful of his father's death and mother's hasty marriage, is confronted by the ghost of the late King who reveals the manner of his murder. Seeking revenge, Hamlet recreates the monstrous deed in a play with the help of some traveling actors to torment the conscience of the evil Claudius. In a visit with his mother, Hamlet expresses his anger and disappointment concerning her swiftly untimed marriage. Thinking a concealed spy in his mother's chamber to be the lurking Claudius, he mistakenly kills the meddling counselor, Polonius, father of Ophelia and Laertes. Claudius, on the pretext that Hamlet will be endangered by his subjects for the murder of Polonius, sends the Prince to England. Upon his return to Denmark, Hamlet discovers that his beloved Ophelia has gone mad and died. Laertes, seeking revenge for the death of Polonius, consorts with Claudius to kill Hamlet in a fencing match by means of a poisoned foil. Gertrude, by mistake, drinks from a poisoned wine goblet, also intended for Hamlet. Laertes is killed by his own weapon and Hamlet, dying from an arm wound made by the fateful blade, stabs Claudius and succumbs in the arms of Horatio, his trusted friend.

REVIEWS

New York Times, September 30, 1948
"It may come as something of a rude shock to the theater's traditionalists to discover that tragedies of Shakespeare can be eloquently presented on the screen. So bound have these poetic dramas long been to the culture of our stage that the very

Hamlet (1948)

thought of their transference may have staggered a few profound die-hards. But now the matter is settled; the filmed *Hamlet* of Laurence Olivier gives absolute proof that these classics are magnificently suited to the screen. Just as Olivier's ingenious and spectacular *Henry V* set out new visual limits for Shakespeare's historical plays, his *Hamlet* envisions new vistas in the great tragedies of the Bard. Hamlet is nobody's glass-man, and the dark and troubled workings of his mind are difficult even for Freudians. But the openness of which he is played by Mr. Olivier in this picture makes him reasonably comprehensible. His is no cold and sexless Hamlet. He is a solid and virile young man, plainly tormented by the anguish and the horror of a double shock.''

New York News, October 5, 1967
"Anyone who wished to see great acting and to hear the English language spoken with impeccable beauty should have tuned in to the 1948 movie, *Hamlet* last night. With Sir Laurence Olivier in the title role, Shakespeare's tragedy came over with the utmost force. His characterization was a merger of robust action and an appreciation of the subtlest nuances of poetry.''

Jack Jorgens, *Shakespeare on Film,* p. 208.
"*Hamlet* is a collage of styles: lyrical, grotesque, grand. It is a play of grisly humor, oratory, riddles, songs, proverbs and parodies. And, as its stage history attests, the characters have a shimmering, fluid quality. Given the length and complexity of *Hamlet*, it is no surprise that it is seldom performed in its entirety and that actors give us something less than whole characterizations. Even more than most productions, however, Olivier's is a conscious simplification and reduction of the play. Like most recent filmmakers, he has focused upon those areas of life most congenial to modern playwrights and novelists—the family and the individual psyche. Olivier's dreamy, lyrical film, with its misty ramparts, dissolves, and gliding camera, captures the inner *Hamlet* quite well.''

Hamlet: "Alas, poor Yorick! I knew him, Horatio; a fellow of infinite jest, of most excellent fancy; he hath borne me on his back a thousand times; and now, how abhorred in my imagination it is! my gorge rises at it. Here hung those lips that I have kissed I know not how oft. Where be your gibes now? your songs? your gambols? your flashes of merriment, that were wont to set the table on a roar? Not one now to mock your own grinning?'' (Hamlet-Act V, Scene 1, William Shakespeare.)

105

Olivier was impressed as a young actor by John Barrymore's athletic Hamlet at the Haymarket in 1925 and seized the memory to become an equally gymnastic Dane himself. Barrymore made various cuts in his production and crammed handwritten suggestions into the small Temple edition of the play which he used as a promptbook. The volume, now the property of The Players, suggests the shape of Olivier's later film version and the identical cuts seem to indicate that either Olivier saw the little book or that the two actors made the same discoveries when deciding which lines and scenes to eliminate.

Hamlet: "Nymph, in thy orisons, be all my sins rememb'red." With Jean Simmons as Ophelia.

106

Basil Sydney (1894–1967), a veteran character actor of over one hundred plays and several motion pictures, portrayed Claudius in *Hamlet*. He appeared with Olivier again as Lawyer Hawkins in *The Devil's Disciple*.

James Agee, *Agee on Film*, June 28, 1948. (Boston: Beacon Press, 1964), p. 389.

". . . it is worked out with intelligence, sensitivity, thoroughness and beauty; . . . it has everything which high ambition, deep sobriety and exquisite skill can give it. In its subtlety, variety, vividness and control, Olivier's performance is one of the most beautiful ever put on film. There is hardly a line that he speaks, or a gesture he makes, which falls short of shining mastery. Olivier is as sure in his work, and as sure a delight to watch, as any living artist. No other actor, except Chaplin is as deft a master of everything which the entire body can contribute to a role; few actors can equal him in the whole middle register of acting. A man who can do what Laurence Olivier is doing for Shakespeare—and for those who treasure or will yet learn to treasure Shakespeare—is certainly among the more valuable men of his time."

Boston Auditorium
Fairleigh Dickinson University
Teaneck, N.J. March 5–6, 1970

When this production of *Hamlet* was released in 1948, it was hailed by the critics and public alike as an artistic triumph, daring in its concept and brilliant in its execution. To be sure, a few purists and scholars lamented the liberties that Laurence Olivier had taken with the text, but they too found more to praise than to blame. The film went on to reap a number of honors, among them the Academy Award for the best picture in 1958 (the first time a foreign film was so cited). Today the brilliance of the film is still apparent, but in view of modern scholarship and current interpretations of the leading role (notably those by Burton and Williamson), the film seems highly conventional, even hesitant and perhaps altogether too reverent.

Many modern scholars, for example, have, in great number, rejected the notion (which Olivier makes central to his interpretation) that Hamlet so intellectualized every situation that he was paralyzed into a kind of inaction. Indeed, many modern scholars (see Grebanier's *The Heart of Hamlet*) find the young prince a rash even reckless individual who reacts immediately. They cite as evidence his putting "an antic disposition on" immediately after hearing the ghost's story, and they buttress their argument by mentioning his altogether irrational behavior in his mother's bedroom. In Olivier's film we have the more traditional melancholy Dane, dark, brooding, cursing the time for being "out of joint."

Since Olivier produced, directed and starred in the film, the work is a very personal document, similar in that respect to Orson Welles's *Citizen Kane*. Olivier handpicked the cast, he helped with the sets and costumes, and he supervised the photography. Although he uses the camera with great fluidity, moving in and out of arches, employing ceiling shots, the film is in some ways more stagy than cinematic. Perhaps the massive sets with their heavy columns and stone stairways add a stifling or congested effect. Whatever the cause, the mood evoked by the surroundings is (and very properly perhaps) one of confinement and suffocation. Only rarely do we leave the gray chambers of Elsinore and, on those occasions for a tragedy such as the drowning and burial of Ophelia. Furniture is kept at an absolute minimum; in the famous bedroom scene, for example, we have only a bed. There is, in short, a kind stark, austere purity about the sets.

The acting is uniformly high, and the words are delivered with clarity, with precision and, regrettably I think, with entirely too much awe. Olivier, though somewhat old for the role (he was forty-one at the time), makes a handsome Dane, right down to his dyed blond hair. Especially praiseworthy is the performance of Eileen Herlie as the doomed Queen Gertrude; she brings to the role the ideal mixture of womanly passion and maternal concern that are at conflict within her nature. Jean Simmons is a breathtakingly beautiful Ophelia, simple, naive, obedient. The humor, from the low comedy of the gravedigger to the high comedy in the scene with Osric, is delivered with gusto and helps to relieve the almost relentless tragedy of the play.

The most serious reservation I have about the film is the manner in which Olivier edited the original text. Whole scenes have disappeared, others have been moved about, and most critically, certain characters (notably Fortinbras, Guildenstern and Rosencrantz) have been elimi-

Scottish born Shakespearean actor John Laurie, a veteran of fifty years on the English stage, appeared in *Hamlet* as Francisco. He also joined Olivier in *Henry V, Richard III, As You Like It, Q Planes* and *The Demi-Paradise*.

Hamlet: "Mother, you have my father much offended." At twenty-seven Eileen Herlie was already acknowledged as one of the foremost tragediennes of her time. At the age of twenty-two she had already played Queen Gertrude for the Old Vic Company, during its wartime tenancy at The Playhouse, Liverpool. In 1964 she again played the mother of Hamlet opposite Richard Burton in New York. While she was filming *Hamlet* during the day at Denham Studios for Olivier, she was appearing each evening as another tragic queen on the London stage in *The Eagle Has Two Heads*. In 1973 Miss Herlie scored a great triumph as a contemporary queen when she portrayed Queen Mary in Royce Ryton's *Crown Matrimonial* in New York.

Stanley Holloway as the Gravedigger.

nated altogether. By introducing these innovations Olivier has shifted some of the emphasis. For example, the omission of Fortinbras removes from the film what has always been to me an integral part of the play. *Hamlet* is, to be sure, the tragedy of a young prince, but, at another level, it is also the tragedy of a country; indeed "something is rotten in the state of Denmark." And as Hamlet lies dead at the end of the play, so Denmark now lies under a conqueror's heel. All this is now lost. Occasionally, on the other hand, the changes are stunningly creative; the drowning of Ophelia realized visually rather than being merely reported, and the effect is much more moving and poignant. So also improved is the filmed scene where Hamlet actually physically restrains Ophelia and stares deeply into her eyes.

Undeniably Olivier's *Hamlet* is a masterpiece, even though a flawed one. But then aren't also most of Shakespeare's plays? Reviewing the film has been for me, in a very minor way, what writing his famous preface to Shakespeare's plays must have been to Dr. Johnson. After making his comments, sometimes very acid and critical ones, Johnson, recognizing the excellence and worth of the playwright and his plays, dismissed that criticism of men and their works by very narrow principles as "the petty cavils of petty minds."

Dr. Vernon Schonert
Professor of English
Fairleigh Dickinson University

COMMENTS

The artistic success of *Henry V* encouraged Olivier to proceed with the filming of *Hamlet*.

With the blessing of producer Filippo Del Giudice and the J. Arthur Rank organization, he again surrounded himself with those valuable people who had contributed so much to the success of *Henry V.* Among them were Reginald Beck, the associate producer, Roger Furse, designer of the costumes and decoration, art director Carmen Dillon, and composer William Walton. With screenwriter Alan Dent, Olivier collaborated on a concise script which necessitated deft cuts to turn Shakespeare's four hour play into a two and a half hour film. Scenes were cut and transposed and certain phrases and Elizabethan terminology were modernized, and while Shakespearean scholars and purists were likely to be displeased, Olivier wanted the Bard to reach far greater audiences than it had in the past. Unlike *Henry V,* which was filmed in technicolor to accent the glory and pageantry of heraldic England, *Hamlet* he decided, would be filmed in black and white so that it might reflect an engraving rather than an oil painting.

Olivier again assembled a notable group of players, including Basil Sydney, Felix Aylmer (who had appeared with Olivier twelve years before in his Shakespearean screen debut in *As You Like It*), and Stanley Holloway. Twenty-seven year old Eileen Herlie was chosen to play Hamlet's mother, Queen Gertrude. She had played the role five years earlier and would appear as Gertrude sixteen years later in 1964 opposite Richard Burton's Hamlet in New York.

Ninety-four girls were interviewed in the search for an actress to play Ophelia. Of these, thirty were tested. In the end, Olivier returned to his initial choice: an eighteen year old Jean Sim-

Hamlet: "How long hast thou been a gravemaker?"

Polonius: "Do you know me, my lord?" Hamlet: "Excellent well; you are a fishmonger." Polonius: "What do you read, my lord?" Hamlet: "Words, words, words." Polonius, Shakespeare's "wretched, rash and intruding fool," was acted by Felix Aylmer who appeared in Olivier's second film, *The Temporary Widow* and later as Duke Frederick in *As You Like It,* the Archbishop of Canterbury in *Henry V,* and the eccentric Mr. Runalow in *The Demi-Paradise*.

mons. The young actress was one of Rank's most sought after starlets after her appearances in *Great Expectations* and *Black Narcissus*. Her performance as Ophelia brought her an Academy Award nomination, and Olivier offered her an opportunity to work with the Old Vic Company, but she declined, explaining some years later, "I was too busy becoming a movie star."

Hamlet proved again that Shakespeare could sell tickets in movie houses. It became the first English-language picture to appear in the same New York theater for over a year and the first foreign-made film to win the Academy Award for best motion picture. Olivier received the Best Actor Oscar for his performances as the melancholy Dane. It was his fourth acting nomination. He was also nominated as Best Director. Orson Welles, Woody Allen and Warren Beatty, were the only other actor-directors to be nominated as such. Welles did not capture either honor for his 1941 *Citizen Kane*, nor did Beatty for *Heaven Can Wait* in 1978, but Allen won his best film and director in 1977 for *Annie Hall*, losing the actor Oscar to Richard Dreyfuss.

Other Oscars awarded *Hamlet* went to Roger Furse for his art direction and set decoration and to Carmen Dillon for her costume design. During the filming of *Hamlet* Olivier received the news that he was to receive a knighthood. At the age of forty, he became the youngest actor to be so honored.

In January, 1949, Olivier and his wife appeared together on the London stage for the first time in Sheridan's *School for Scandal*. A capacity opening audience gave them a thunderous ovation, after scores of fans stood in line all night to get tickets. Many brought sleeping bags and blankets and depsite a chilly drizzle, stretched out in front of the New Theatre. More than 5,000 ticket orders for the opening night performance had to be rejected.

Carrie

1952, A Paramount Picture, Produced and Directed by William Wyler; Screenplay by Ruth and Augustus Goetz, based on the novel *Sister Carrie* by Theodore Dreiser; Photography, Victor Milne; Editor, Robert Swink; Art directors, Hale Pereira, Roland Anderson

CAST

George Hurstwood	Laurence Olivier
Carrie Meeber	Jennifer Jones
Julia Hurstwood	Miriam Hopkins
Charles Drouet	Eddie Albert
Mr. Fitzgerald	Basil Ruysdael
Allan	Ray Teal
Slawson	Barry Kelley
Mrs. Oransky	Sara Berner
George Hurstwood, Jr.	William Reynolds
Jessica Hurstwood	Mary Murphy
O'Brien	Harry Hayden
Factory Foreman	Charles Halton
Carrie's Father	Walter Baldwin
Carrie's Sister	Jacqueline De Witt
Carrie's Mother	Dorothy Adams
Joe Brant	Harlan Briggs
Little Girl	Melinda Plowman
Slawson's bartender	Donald Kerr
Mr. Blum	Lester Sharpe
Mr. Goodman	Don Beddoe
Stage Manager	John Alvin

Opened July 16, 1952, Capitol Theater, New York

THE FILM

Carrie Meeber, a country girl who has come to Chicago with grand dreams, toils in a shoe factory for five dollars a week, four of which she pays in rent to her brother-in-law. After injuring her finger on a machine and losing her job, she accepts a ten dollar loan from Charles Drouet, a debonair traveling salesman. Drouet takes Carrie to dinner at the fashionable Fitzgerald's Restau-

rant, where she meets the distinguished manager, George Hurstwood. Rather than return to her sister's apartment, where she was reprimanded for accepting a loan from a stranger, Carrie moves into Drouet's lodgings. While the salesman is away on business, Hurstwood and Carrie spend an enchanting week together. Madly in love with Carrie, he tells his coldly, ambitious wife, Julia, that he wants a divorce. Carrie, learning of his marriage is distraught. Hurstwood gets Carrie on a train to New York, taking several thousand dollars of company funds with him. Eventually he is forced to return what is left to the bonding company and is blackballed from working in reputable restaurants. Broke and desperate, he takes a job in a shabby lunchroom. Hurstwood releases any claim to money from the sale of his home, when Julia agrees to a divorce. Carrie gets a job as a chorus girl, leaves Hurstwood and eventually succeeds in the theater. Two years later she learns from Drouet that he had taken the Fitzgerald funds and consequently was not able to secure decent employment. Feeling that she destroyed him, she searches desperately in hopes to make amends. Gaunt, unshaven, a tattered derelict now, Hurstwood waits in the bitter cold outside the stage door, begging for a little money. Relieved and joyful to find him again, Carrie promises to nurse him back to health, but in her temporary absence, Hurstwood takes some small change from her dressing table and leaves.

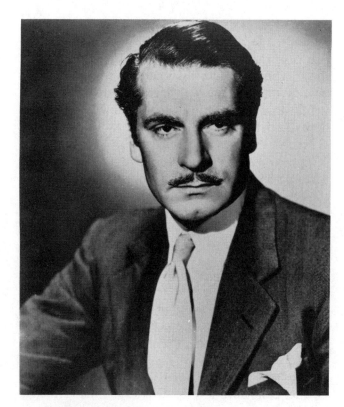

George Hurstwood in *Carrie* **(1952)**
"He can have the spurious elegance." (David Selznick in a memo to William Wyler.)

REVIEW

New York Times, July 17, 1952
"A weak and distorted shadow of the young woman whom Theodore Dreiser drew in his classic novel, *Sister Carrie,* is cast upon the screen by Jennifer Jones in William Wyler's new film drama. And a violently sentimental version of Mr. Dreiser's ironic tale of love and its deterioration is contained in the screenplay by Ruth and Augustus Goetz. But out of this mawkish reworking there does emerge, at least, a haunting reflection of Mr. Dreiser's Hurstwood, whom Laurence Olivier plays. When the word first came

through that Mr. Olivier had been cast in the difficult role of this reckless Chicago gentleman out of America's raw Gilded Age, there were those who regarded this selection as a perilously chancy choice, likely to lead to a distortion that would throw the whole story askew. The emminent British actor was thought too elegant and alien for the role of Mr. Dreiser's middle-aged hero who went to ruin out of love for a pretty girl. Mr. Olivier gives the film its closest contact with the book, while Miss Jones' soft, seraphic portrait of Carrie takes it furthest away.''

COMMENTS

Carrie was filmed in Hollywood in 1950, and not released until two years later. In 1949, David Selznick sent one of his detailed memos to William Wyler, expressing doubts about the commercial prospects of the *Sister Carrie* script, warning the director and his scriptwriters to avoid intellectualism. He voiced enthusiasm, however, in the consideration of Olivier as Hurstwood. ''As to the casting of Hurstwood, I honestly don't know what to say. I still am crazy about the idea of Olivier, and wish you would see it. I think he has every single thing the part requires. He not only looks the exact age, he is the exact age. He can do a brilliant job of aging further before your eyes. He can have the spurious elegance. He would give to the picture the great distinction it should have. He would bring to it extraordinary freshness. If it were my picture, I would be breaking my neck to get him. Saying 'no' to Olivier is in my opinion exactly equivalent to having said 'no' to Jack Barrymore for any role

he could have played. In years to come it's likely to seem incredible to you that you turned down the suggestion.''[21]

Olivier spent a great deal of time with Spencer Tracy during the filming of *Carrie,* who coached him to perfect his American accent for the film. Wyler discovered Olivier to be more serious and respectful as an actor than since their last collaboration in *Wuthering Heights.* Olivier had little faith in the film, feeling that it was too gloomy for popular tastes and the public proved him to be correct.

In 1951, the Oliviers became the toast of two continents with their daring tandem performances of the two Cleopatra dramas, *Caesar and Cleopatra,* Bernard Shaw's comedy of an aging Caesar and his kittenish sixteen-year-old Queen of the Nile, and Shakespeare's *Antony and Cleopatra,* a great tragedy of a fortyish Antony and a mature Cleopatra, who at thirty-one had become a mistress of passions and politics. The plays were presented on alternate evenings in the summer of '51 as a highlight of the Festival of Britain and imported to New York, where they grossed more than a million dollars during the sixteen week engagement. Brooks Atkinson, drama critic for the *New York Times* hailed *Antony and Cleopatra:* ''There has not been an *Antony and Cleopatra* to compare with this in New York in the last quarter of a century; and there have not been many productions of any Shakespearean play that have approached this exalted quality. Mr. Olivier has mastered all the qualities of a full-blooded human being. Everything about the Olivier production is glowing or crackling with vitality.''

Director Tony Richardson saw in Olivier's Hurstwood a film blueprint for his later performance in *The Dance of Death*. Selznick's wife, Jennifer Jones, co-starred in the title role.

Cameo as a Holborn policeman in *The Magic Box*
(1952). "You looked like a sort of celestial Tiger Tim."
(Robert Donat.)

The Magic Box

1952, A J. Arthur Rank and Festival Film presentation, Screenplay by Eric Ambler; Produced by Ronald Neame; Photography, Jack Cardiff; Editor, Richard Best; Costumes, Julia Squire; Production designer, John Bryan; Directed by John Boulting

CAST

William Friese-Greene	Robert Donat
Edith Friese-Greene	Margaret Johnston
Helena Friese-Greene	Maria Schell
Elderly Viscountess	Marjorie Fielding
Maida Vale Doctor	Leo Genn
Broker's Man	Stanley Holloway
Bath Doctor	Barry Jones
Pawnbroker	Mervyn Johns
Orchestra Conductor	Miles Malleson
Sir Arthur Sullivan	Muir Mathieson
Cousin Alfred	Bernard Miles
Second Holborn Policeman	Laurence Olivier
First Platform Man, Connaught Rommes	Cecil Parker
Arthur Collings	Eric Portman
William Fox Talbot	Basil Sydney
Assistant in Labratory	David Tomlinson
Maurice Guttenburg	Frederick Valk
Hotel Receptionist	Kay Walsh
Aristocratic client	Sybil Thorndike
Jack Carter	Richard Attenborough
First company promoter	Ronald Culver
Doctor	Robert Flemyng
House agent	Marius Goring
Official receiver	Michael Hordern
First Holborn Policeman	Jack Hulbert
Sergeant in storeroom	Sidney James
May Jones	Glynis Johns
Warehouse manager	Herbert Lomas
Old gentleman	A. E. Matthews
Assistant in Bond St. Studio	Dennis Price
Mr. Lege	Michael Redgrave
Lady Pond	Margaret Rutherford
Earl, Bond St. Studio	Ernest Thesiger
Industry man	Peter Ustinov
Bank Manager	Emlyn Williams
Sitter in Bath Studio	Googie Withers
Lord Beaverbrook	Robert Beatty
Graham Friese-Greene	John Charlesworth
Marice Friese-Greene	John Howard Davies
Maid	Joan Dowling
Butler	Henry Edwards
Mrs. Collinge	Mary Ellis
Mrs. Clare	Joyce Grenfell
Mother in family group	Kathleen Harrison
Recruiting sergeant	William Hartnell
Mrs. Stukely	Joan Hickson
Doctor's housekeeper	Thora Hird
Kenneth Friese-Greene	James Kenney
Bridegroom's father	Frank Pettingell
Ethel Friese-Greene	Janette Scott
Tom, workman at Lege and Co.	Harcourt Williams

Opened September 23, 1952, Normandie Theater, New York

REVIEWS

New York Times, September 24, 1952
"Eventful and literate. As pretty a period piece as any you'll see, full of the most exquisite little vignettes of Victorian England and Victorian ways and some highly fascinating indications of early experiments with film. An idea of the extravagance may be had in the fact that the distinguished Laurence Olivier plays a policeman 'bit'."

Christian Science Monitor, November 17, 1952
"There is a very fine scene in which a stolid and puzzled policeman (Olivier) is called in by the excited inventor to see his first moving picture."

London Daily Express, September 13, 1951
"The policeman is played by a be-whiskered Laurence Olivier and he and Donat milk the big moment of more tenseness and eye-moistening emotion than you would have thought possible."

Britain Today, September 19, 1951
"Sir Laurence Olivier appears as a bewildered city policeman, dragged off his beat by the inventor in the middle of the night, to form an audience for one of his first public performances of moving pictures. This scene is brilliant in its economy and incisiveness, and in the subdued eloquence of its pantomime. It is also unselfish, with one of the greatest actors of our time deliberately serving as a 'feed' in the interests of the story."

COMMENTS

The Magic Box was made to be shown during the Festival of Britain celebration, as a tribute from the cinema industry to the man who designed and operated the first practicable cinematograph camera. William Friese-Greene was one of the many experimenters with motion pictures back in the pre-Edison Kinetoscope days. "In effect, this was to be the industry's public penance for neglecting Friese-Greene during his life. An inventive genius from Bristol, and a man of personal charm, he was foolish in business, a wayward eccentric, often in penury, once imprisoned for debt, but always creatively energetic and guided by faith."[22] Olivier joined an all-star roster who contributed cameos, including Sybil Thorndike, Renee Asherson, and Michael Redgrave. Olivier was disguised as a policeman to appear in a three minute sequence as the first, wide-eyed spectator of the motion picture. Robert Donat, who starred as the forgotten English inventor, wrote to Olivier, "I don't think I told you how much I adored your make-up. You looked like a sort of celestial Tiger Tim. The kind of Tiger Tim you might find in the desert instead of the Sphinx."[23]

The story of Captain Macheath.

the amorous highwayman

who broke so many laws

and so many hearts!

LAURENCE OLIVIER

"THE BEGGAR'S OPERA"
TECHNICOLOR

The Beggar's Opera

1953, Imperadio Pictures, Ltd., Screenplay by Denis Cannan, adapted by Christopher Fry from the opera by John Gay; Produced by Laurence Olivier and Herbert Wilcox; Music composed and arranged by Sir Arthur Bliss; Photography, Guy Green; Art director, William C. Andrews; Editor, Reginald Beck; Associate producer, Eric Goodhead; Assistant director, Frank Hollands; Special effects, Wally Veevers and George Samuels; Music conducted by Muir Mathieson; Directed by Peter Brook; Distributed by British Lion Film Corporation and Warner Bros.

CAST

Captain Macheath	Laurence Olivier
Lockit	Stanley Holloway
Peachum	George Devine
Mrs. Peachum	Mary Clare
Mrs. Trapes	Athene Seyler
Polly Peachum	Dorothy Tutin
Lucy Lockit	Daphne Anderson
The Beggar	Hugh Griffith
The Actress	Margot Grahame
The Footman	Denis Cannan
Jenny Diver	Yvonne Furneaux
Jack, the Potboy	Kenneth Williams
Innkeeper	Eric Pohlmann
Matt of the Mint	Laurence Naismith
First Turnkey	George Rose
Sukey Tawdrey	Sandra Dorne
Molly Brazen	Jocelyn James
Mrs. Vixen	Isabel George
Betty Doxey	Helen Christie
First Prisoner	Stuart Burge
Second Prisoner	Cyril Conway
Third Prisoner	Gerald Lawson
Female traveler	Eileen Harvey
Filch	Edward Pryor
Mrs. Coaxer	Edith Coates
Drunkard	Max Brent
Dolly Trall	Mercy Haystead
Mrs. Slammekin	Patricia Raine
Second Turnkey	John Kidd
Third Turnkey	H. C. Walton
Fourth Turnkey	Eugene Leahy
Fifth Turnkey	Edgar Norfolk
First Chairman	Oliver Hunter
Second Chairman	John Baker
Gin seller	Madge Brindley
The Governor	Felix Felton
Negro page	Tamba Alleney
Chaplain	Terence Greenidge
Hangman	Billy Wells
The Singers	Jennifer Vyvyan
	Joan Cross
	John Cameron
	Edith Coates
	Bruce Boyce
	Adele Leigh

Opened April 24, 1953, Baronet Theater, New York

THE FILM

The Beggar's Opera was the first successful ballad opera, presented in London in January, 1728. In the ballad opera, the dialogue is often satirical spoken comedy and the songs are separate and distinct pieces, unlike the recitatives of grand opera. The work became the model for all future pieces in this form, setting a tremendous vogue in London in the first half of the eighteenth century. The story concerns a rakish highwayman, Captain Macheath who escapes both the hangman's noose and fetching young wenches with equal ease and dexterity. The musical tale follows his amorous adventures and romances with pretty Polly Peachum and the jailer's comely daughter, Lucy Lockit, his capture and incarceration in the squalid confines of Newgate prison and a last minute reprieve as he is transported to his execution upon his own coffin.

REVIEWS

Saturday Review, August 15, 1953
"Olivier himself plays the dashing Macheath with keen appreciation of the satire implicit in the role. He also sings his own part, revealing a light tenor that is always agreeable if not true. Opera on film requires a bold hand. Sir Laurence has played it to perfection."

121

The Observer, June 7, 1953

"Olivier's Macheath is the most comfortable piece of work he has given us yet in pictures. He romps through the part, whether acting, singing, dancing or riding, without any touch of self-consciousness, and as though all these exercises were a joy, and the player's impression of ease, of relaxation, is irresistably communicated to the audience."

New York Times, August 25, 1953

"Although the ideal marriage between films and opera is not effected in *The Beggar's Opera*, it is a generally happy liason and one that is a credit to both media. Gay's rowdy, lusty, and amorous characters are brought alive again on a variety of sprawling canvasses. Since he is a man who has taken bold liberties with the movie medium before, Sir Laurence is not surprising a moviegoer too greatly by raising his voice in song for the first time. The surprise is that Sir Laurence's baritone is light, audible, but not especially distinguished. Perhaps it is adequate but it strikes a layman's ear as a faint obbligato to his portrayal of the athletic and amorous brigand. Abetted by the racy dialogue supplied by both Gay and Christopher Fry, Sir Laurence is alternately, a reckless daredevil, a wily but manly lover, and a fearless brooding adventurer. It is a characterization that he endows with genuine abandon, stature and feeling."

Pauline Kael, *I Lost It At the Movies*. (Boston: Little Brown & Co., Atlantic Press, 1961), p. 116.
"The star of *The Beggar's Opera* is Laurence Olivier, the champion of the English-speaking theater, the actor who so rarely has an opportunity to demonstrate that he is, in addition to everything else, a great comedian. He has never so freely entertained himself—and us—as in this role of the lecherous Captain Macheath escaping the law and the doxies. Olivier's range is truly astonishing. His Macheath is a brilliant caricature of the romantic bandit; he has a glance that makes a wicked point and a gesture to counterpoint, and his exuberance—his joy in the role—leaps through the whole production."

Producer Herbert Wilcox assembled the cream of the performing arts with playwright Christopher Fry, composer Sir Arthur Bliss, actors Olivier, Dorothy Tutin, Stanley Holloway, and Hugh Griffiths, plus the brilliant young stage director Peter Brook who was making his film debut guiding *The Beggar's Opera* to the screen. The complete harmony expected by Wilcox was shattered by Brook, who was not in agreement with the concept of the film as approached by the producer and Olivier.

Wilcox recalled the clash in his autobiography, *Twenty-Five Thousand Sunsets*. "Larry, with his wide experience of the stage and screen, and I, with nearly thirty-five years of continuous production behind me, endeavored to combine Peter's experimental approach with our experience—and gave him the best of both worlds. But Peter would have none of it. Stage genius though he had undoubtedly proved himself, and as Larry and I freely conceded, we could not get him to accept our practical suggestions—all of which he seemed to regard as criticisms. Larry bent over backwards to cooperate, and how he worked. Not even the usual lunch-hour, of which he spent forty-five minutes with his Italian singing-master. Unlike most stars, Larry refuses to be doubled in any aspect—singing (a tremendous role), riding, swordsmanship, the lot. His riding alone—with cameras mounted on cars doing forty miles an hour—would have made most of the Hollywood western stars have a heart attack. On one occasion, he rode up 'Dead Man's Hill', an incline of one in six, so many times that the horse had a heart attack!

The sad thing was that Peter was frantically keen to turn in the action film of all time, but he lacked the know-how. The climax came when in the film Macheath had to chase his enemy through a gaming saloon, both armed with rapiers. Macheath (Olivier), in an effort to cut off his opponent, vaulted and mounted a gaming table, his rapier at the ready. A dangerous job and one for which any Hollywood artists would, with

One of the theater's most distinguished actresses, Dorothy Tutin, made a rare screen appearance as Polly Peachum opposite Olivier's rollicking Captain Macheath.

justification, have demanded a double. Not Larry. He must do it himself.

The cameras turned, he leapt like a ballet dancer, and let out a yell as he landed on the gaming table. Then he turned on his opponent and said, 'You bloody fool! You struck me as I jumped!' The 'bloody fool' had not struck him, but, as he landed, he tore a calf muscle—and was cut. Larry, the most courteous man I have ever met, couldn't move and the pain was intense. But he sent for his opponent and apologized.''[24]

Olivier was out for three weeks. Upon his return Wilcox advised him to let Brook have his way and the film was completed without further argument. *The Beggar's Opera* marked a rare excursion into the musical art form for Olivier. He spent many hours preparing for the demanding singing role under the special guidance of a vocal coach. The principal players in the film had their singing voices dubbed, but Olivier proved to be an acceptable singing bandit. Except for his musical turns as a song and dance man in *The Entertainer,* the actor has not attempted roles which required singing. In 1970, while serving as artistic director for the National Theatre he planned to appear as Nathan Detroit in Frank Loesser's musical comedy, *Guys and Dolls* with Christopher Plummer, Geraldine McEwan, and Louise Purnell. Plans for the revival were dropped in June 1971 because of Olivier's subsequent illness and the heavy financial burden of mounting the production.

A Queen Is Crowned

1953, A J. Arthur Rank Presentation; Produced by Castleton Knight; Commentary written by Christopher Fry; Musical advisor, Sir Malcolm Sargent; Special music by Guy Warrach; Performed by the London Symphony Orchestra; Narration by Sir Laurence Olivier; Released by Universal-International

Opened June 7, 1953, Guild Theater, New York

THE FILM

An eighty-six minute, eight-reel Technicolor documentation of the Coronation of Queen Elizabeth II, including portions of the colorful procession and the coronation service at Westminster Abbey.

REVIEW

New York Times, June 8, 1953
''In their documentation of the coronation of their Sovereign, the British film makers have made history themselves. A masterful, dignified and cohesive tribute to Queen Elizabeth II and an unsurpassed illustration of this historic event. From the moment that Sir Laurence Olivier, speaking dramatist Christopher Fry's poetic lines, reverently says, ''this royal throne of kings—this England,'' the camera, capturing scenes of the rolling hills of Wales, the mountains of Scotland, and the drowsy hamlets and bustling towns, sets a picturesque and reverential tone for the events to follow. Credit must be given to Mr. Fry and Sir Laurence for not intruding on the camera's precincts. They speak and are heard only as a necessary footnote to the majestic proceedings. With *A Queen Is Crowned* the British have fashioned a historic, beautiful, and living document.''

Richard III

1956, London Films International, Produced by Laurence Olivier in association with Alexander Korda; Screenplay by Alan Dent from the play by

William Shakespeare; Associate director, Anthony Bushell; Assistant director, Gerry O'Hara; Photography (Technicolor and VistaVision), Otto Heller; Production Design, Roger Furse; Editor, Helga Cranston; Music composed by Sir William Walton, conducted by Muir Mathieson; Sound, John Cox; Art Director, Carmen Dillon; Special effects, Wally Veevers; Sword play, Bernard Hepton and John Greenwood; Production manager, Jack Martin; Production supervisor, John Cossage; Directed by Laurence Olivier; Distributed by Lopert Films

CAST

Richard III	Laurence Olivier
Clarence	John Gielgud
Lady Anne	Claire Bloom
Buckingham	Ralph Richardson
Edward IV	Cedric Hardwicke
Henry Tudor	Stanley Baker
Stanley	Laurence Naismith
Catesby	Norman Wooland
Hastings	Alec Clunes
Queen Elizabeth	Mary Kerridge
Jane Shore	Pamela Brown
Duchess of York	Helen Haye
Lovel	John Laurie
Ratcliffe	Esmond Knight
Dighton	Michael Gough
Brakenbury	Andrew Cruickshank
Rivers	Clive Morton
Archbishop	Nicholas Hannen
Priest	Russell Thorndyke
Prince of Wales	Paul Huson
Page	Stewart Allen
Monks	Wally Bascoe
	Norman Fisher
Scrivener	Terence Greenridge
Grey	Dan Cunningham
Dorset	Douglas Wilmer
Second Murderer	Michael Ripper
Young Duke of York	Andy Shine
Abbot	Roy Russell
Lord Mayor of London	George Woodbridge
Messenger to Hastings	Peter Williams
Ostler	Timothy Bateson
Second Priest	Willoughby Gray
Scrubwoman	Anne Wilton
Beadle	Bill Shine
Clergymen	Derek Prentice
	Deering Wells
George Stanley	Richard Bennett
Tyrell	Patrick Troughton
Norfolk	John Phillips
Messengers to Richard	Brian Nissen
	Alexander Davion
	Lane Meddick
	Robert Bishop

Opened March 11, 1956, Bijou Theater, New York

THE FILM

The deformed Richard of Gloucester cuts a bloody path to the throne in Shakespeare's historical tragedy. Determined to seize the French throne from his brother Edward IV, he rouses Edward's hatred for their brother Clarence, who is arrested and murdered while imprisoned. The cunning Richard woos Anne, widow of Henry VI's son whose death he has arranged. Following the death of the king from natural causes, Richard has the little princes murdered in the Tower. The vicious Gloucester removes all who stand between him and the crown. Henry of Richmond raises an army against Richard, drawing supporters from all over England. The two armies meet at Bosworth Field. Richard's horse is killed be-

neath him. Defiant and savagely brave, he cries out, "A horse! A horse! My kingdom for a horse!" and is struck down by the attacking force of Richmond.

REVIEWS

New York Times, March 12, 1956

"The measure of Sir Laurence Olivier's genius for putting Shakespeare's plays on the screen is beautifully and brilliantly exhibited in his production and performance of *Richard III.* The latest of Sir Laurence's films from Shakespeare is done in colors which a Rembrandt might be proud of and projected in the large-screen VistaVision that gives the picture strong clarity and depth. Sir Laurence's Richard is tremendous—a weird poisonous portrait of a super-rogue whose dark designs are candidly acknowledged with lick-lip relish and sardonic wit. Heavily made up with one dead eyelid, a hatchet nose, a withered hand, a humped back, a drooping shoulder and a twisted, limping leg, he is a freakish-looking figure that Sir Laurence so articulates that he has an electric vitality and a fascinatingly grotesque grace. A grating voice, too, is a feature of his physical oddity. More important to the character, however, is the studiousness and subtlety with which Sir Laurence builds up tension within him as his mischiefs and crimes accumulate. Sir Laurence, as director as well as actor, has clearly and artfully contrived to emphasize Richard's isolation and his almost pathetic loneliness."

Saturday Review, March 10, 1956

"For the third time Sir Laurence Olivier had addressed himself to what is, beyond any doubt, the most difficult of all film assignments, the translation of the poetic drama of Shakespeare into the overwhelmingly realistic motion picture medium. And to say that in *Richard III* he has succeeded admirably suggests less the extent of his achievement than the magnitude of the problem itself. Olivier brings to it, above all else, a keen intelligence, an ability to think through the words of Shakespeare to a vivid, visual setting for them, and a deep feeling for the poetry itself, for

Richard III **(1955)**

127

Gloucester: "Now is the winter of our discontent."

the music of the lines, that is reflected not only in his own readings but also in the superb casts he has always gathered around himself. The imagination and interpretive power that Olivier first displayed in his *Henry V* is now coupled with a firm, sure grasp of film technique."

London Evening Standard, December 13, 1955
"It embalms in celluloid one of the greatest Shakespearean performances of our day. Olivier plays his Richard for laughs, and he raises the grisly humor of the horror comic to the level of genius."

Ronald Harwood, *Sir Donald Wolfit*(London: Secker & Warburg, 1971), p. 185.
"With his Richard III, Olivier assaulted the summit of Olympus, and planted his standard there."

COMMENTS

In the fall of 1953, Olivier directed Terence Rattigan's play, *The Sleeping Prince,* appearing as the Grand Duke opposite Vivien Leigh as an American chorus girl. The play marked a triumphant return to the stage for the actress, who had suffered a nervous collapse the previous March while filming *Elephant Walk* in Ceylon. The couple were greeted with a thunderous ovation during an engagement in Manchester. The comedy opened at London's Phoenix Theatre in November, where it ran for eight months. It was Olivier's only stage appearance between 1951 and 1955.

He teamed with his wife again in April, 1955, at the Shakespeare Memorial Theatre, Stratford-upon-Avon in *Twelfth Night, Titus Andronicus,* and *Macbeth.* Brooks Atkinson called his Malvolio a "refreshing item." "He plays the vain steward broadly—larding the lines with comical extravagance, even mocking a little. But he makes his final exit on a note of outraged dignity that gives the comedy a brief startling sense of reality."

His blood-curdling general in *Titus Andronicus* moved Kenneth Tynan to comment, "Sir Laurence's Titus, even with one hand gone, is a five-finger exercise transformed into an unforgettable concerto of grief. This is a perform-

Richard III. (artist unknown.) *National Portrait Gallery, London.*

"With his Richard III, Olivier assaulted the summit of Olympus, and planted his standard there." (Ronald Harwood.)

As *Titus Andronicus*, with Vivien Leigh as Lavinia. Stratford-Upon-Avon, 1955.

Macbeth. Stratford-Upon-Avon, 1955.

ance which ushers us into the presence of one who is, pound for pound, the greatest actor alive.''

Tynan also praised Olivier's *Macbeth* as ''a thing of mounting, not waning excitement.'' Olivier long delayed his plans to film *Macbeth*. Orson Welles had produced a primitive, expressionist version for the screen in 1948, and when Olivier attempted to film it ten years later, he could not get the necessary financial assistance. In 1960, the tragedy was filmed for television with Maurice Evans and Judith Anderson, and subsequently released in Great Britain for commercial theatrical distribution.

Olivier's performance as the blood-thirsty king, described in the *London Times* as ''one of the great things of his career,'' was unfortunately deprived of filmed immortality. A massive portrait by Ruskin Spear of the actor as Macbeth, hangs in the Royal Shakespeare Theatre Portrait Gallery at Stratford, and it conveys the considerable passion and awesome strength of his performance.

''I tried for nine months when I wanted to make a film out of *Macbeth*,'' Olivier later confessed. ''I was never a producer in the accepted sense, only in the more artistic sense. I never had the gift of Mike Todd or, shall I say Alexander Korda. I could never walk around with a script under my arm and get money, any money, out of anybody.''

With the encouragement of Vivien Leigh and Carol Reed, Olivier accepted Korda's invitation to film *Richard III*. Reed again refused to direct the project, and Olivier assembled essentially the same talented team who had made such an enormous contribution to the success of *Hamlet* and *Henry V*. Roger Furse, Carmen Dillon, Alan Dent, and William Walton collaborated with Olivier who as actor and director completed his stunning Shakespearean screen trilogy.

Anthony Bushell, who had acted on the screen in *Disraeli* and *The Scarlet Pimpernell* and co-produced *Hamlet,* served as associate director for *Richard III* assisting Olivier when he was required to appear in front of the camera. The film won three British Academy Awards including best actor and in Hollywood Olivier received his fifth Oscar nomination.

Malvolio in *Twelfth Night*. **Stratford-Upon-Avon, 1955.**

This lobby card illustrates an amorous moment posed for publicity purposes. The provocative embrace did not appear in the film.

1957, Warner Bros. presentation; Marilyn Monroe Production, Inc. and Laurence Olivier Productions Ltd.; Screenplay by Terence Rattigan from his play, *The Sleeping Prince;* Photography, Jack Cardiff; Executive producer, Milton H. Greene; Music by Richard Addinsell, conducted by Muir Mathieson; Editor, Jack Harris; Produced and Directed by Laurence Olivier

CAST

The Regent	Laurence Olivier
Elsie	Marilyn Monroe
Queen Dowager	Sybil Thorndike
Northbrook	Richard Wattis
King Nicholas	Jeremy Spenser
Colonel Hoffman	Esmond Knight
Major Domo	Paul Hardwick
Maud	Rosamund Greenwood
The Ambassador	Aubrey Dexter
Lady Sunningdale	Maxine Audley
Call Boy	Harold Goodwin
Valet with violin	Andrea Malandrinos
Maisie Springfield	Jean Kent
Fanny	Daphne Anderson
Maggie	Gillian Owen
Betty	Vera Day
Lottie	Margot Lister
Theater Manager	Charles Victor
The Foreign Office	David Horne
Head Valet	Dennis Edward
Dresser	Gladys Henson

Opened June 13, 1957, Radio City Music Hall, New York

THE FILM

Grand Duke Charles, Prince Regent of Carpathia is lodged in an ornate royal suite of the Carpathian embassy in London at the time of the coronation of King George V. After viewing a performance, the stuffy Belkan prince invites Elsie Marina, an American showgirl, to dinner at the embassy and proceeds to woo her unsuccessfully. Elsie drinks too much and falls asleep. The angry, rebuked prince leaves her in a bedroom to sleep it

"When she was acting on occasion she showed something that looked remarkably like genius." (Laurence Olivier.)

off. The showgirl awakens with love in her heart, while the prince is eager to dismiss her from his life. Elsie becomes aware of a plot to unseat the Prince Regent by his son and serves as a mediator between them. Young King Nicholas demands an immediate general election which the prince is against. Elsie successfully reconciles them and gains the favor of the prince. He returns to his country but vows to return when his son comes of age and becomes a full-fledged king.

REVIEWS

New York Times, June 14, 1957
"What is perhaps the most diverting piece of casting in many a year—Britain's Sir Laurence Olivier with Hollywood's Marilyn Monroe—turns out to be the most diverting and original thing about their film. The mere thought of Britain's great Shakespearean playing a romantic lead opposite Hollywood's most famous and least pedantic blonde is sufficient to start the mind imagining some highly potential comic scenes. And the mere sight of them together is equally rewarding—for a while. The main trouble with *The Prince and the Showgirl* when you come right down to it, is that both characters are essentially dull. And incidentally, the scene shown in the advertisements of Sir Laurence kissing Miss Monroe's shoulder does not appear in the film."

Pauline Kael, *Kiss Kiss Bang Bang* (Boston: Little Brown & Co., 1968), p. 419.

"Olivier, perhaps with excess gallantry, makes his prince something of a cold cod; but even in an ungratiating role, Olivier has a high gloss—an irony that shines. Miss Monroe's polymorphous perverse nonacting has its special charm that none of her imitators seems able to capture."

New York Herald Tribune, June 14, 1957
"Terence Rattigan is just playing a game, amusing us for two hours, and the actors enjoy the charade immensely. They try to look earnest but a twinkle in the eye betrays them. In the case of Olivier, the twinkle must fight its way through a thick monocle to reach the outside world and it does. This is a performance of rich, subtle humor."

Saturday Review, June 8, 1957
"What gives *The Prince and the Showgirl* its special delight is the stylized work of its costars, and the wit and grace of Olivier's direction."

COMMENTS

Marilyn Monroe's career as Hollywood's great sex symbol of the fifties had peaked in the middle of the decade with her appealing performances in film versions of two successful Broadway comedies. In 1955, she played the sensuous girl upstairs in the screen adaptation of George Axelrod's play, *The Seven Year Itch,* followed a year later by *Bus Stop,* in which she portrayed Cheri, William Inge's dumb little misplaced night club singer.

Playing Elsie in the film of Terence Rattigan's gentle comedy, *The Sleeping Prince* and the prospect of a collaboration with the noted Shakespearean actor appeared to be an appealing concept for the former model, and the announcement early in 1956 intrigued the press and the public. Joshua Logan, who had directed Monroe in *Bus Stop* kept Olivier well informed about the behavior of the actress and extended words of caution. "He must be very careful with Marilyn because she was undisciplined and untamed. If he handled her properly, he could draw a fine performance from her, but if he antagonized her anything could happen—and by that Logan meant anything negative."[25]

Olivier put more effort into his directing than his acting, in an attempt to coax a performance from her. He found her tardiness on the set, her occasional indifference when being explained a scene, and the presence of her drama coach, Paula Strasberg, extremely disconcerting. Monroe often lost her temper, arguing with actors, wardrobe mistresses, and Olivier. The interference of Strasberg was a constant annoyance (she even took the liberty of suggesting to Olivier how to correct his own performance), and he requested that she be sent home.

The three months shooting was an exhausting and disappointing experience for Olivier and his own performance suffered from it. The timing was

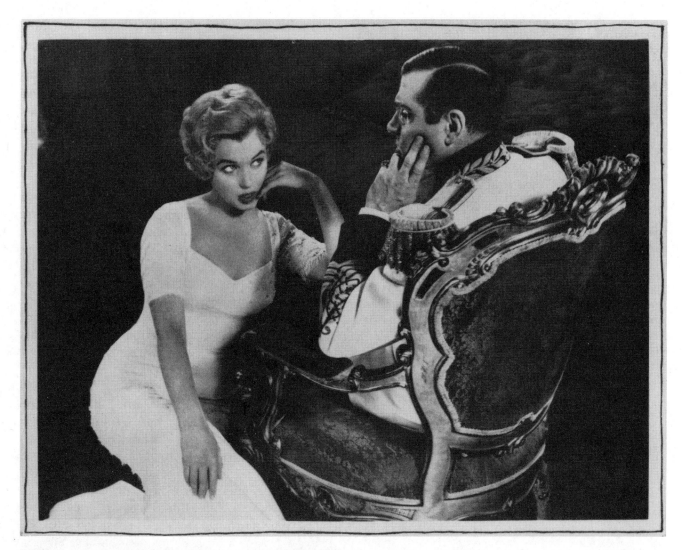

Marilyn Monroe had developed into an appealing comedienne with her performances in *The Seven Year Itch*
and *Bus Stop*. She appeared in three more films following *The Prince and the Showgirl; Some Like It Hot* in
1959 and *Let's Make Love* and *The Misfits* in 1960. In
August, 1962, she was found dead in her home at the age
of thirty-six.

Regent: "Here am I having reached the age of forty and I have never known what it is like to be loved. It is like the legend of the sleeping princess, only here it is the prince that sleeps and awaits the kiss of a beautiful young maiden that will bring him back to life." *The Prince and the Showgirl*, **Terence Rattigan.**

right for a comedy success following the enormous prestige gained by the Shakespeare trilogy, but *The Prince and the Showgirl* despite generally favorable reviews, was not a commercial hit. Alton Cook in the *New York World-Telegram and Sun* praised Olivier for bringing out "qualities none of Monroe's films ever summoned," and William K. Zinsser in the *New York Herald Tribune* called his performance, one of "rich, subtle humor."

Marilyn Monroe, who had developed into a bright and appealing comedienne, followed *The Prince and the Showgirl* with what many regard as her finest performances on the screen in *Some Like It Hot* (1959) and *The Misfits* (1962). The actress was discovered dead in her Hollywood home in August, 1962, at the age of thirty-six.

Olivier, who mellowed with the passing of time, reflected on his association with the actress. "I think everybody has had their say about poor Marilyn. I don't think she was very unhappy with me, working with me. I just don't think I tried terribly hard to get on with her. I think that the job itself wasn't right for her. I think she was a model. I'm not sure she was an actress. Although when she was acting on occasion she showed something that looked remarkably like genius. I think in her inner nature she really didn't want to be an actress. I think that's why she was always late. Some mornings she was three hours late."[26]

"When I was in that film with Larry and Marilyn Monroe, I couldn't hear a word she was saying as I watched her doing her first scenes. I said to myself, 'Is this the great young star from Hollywood? I think she's awful.' I said as much to Larry and he said, 'Come and see the rushes, darling.' Well I did, and everything she'd done that I'd thought was a muck-up came over beautifully on the screen. *I* was the old ham. I'm afraid I've never mastered the movie technique. It always looks underplayed to me—a bit careless. Larry has a flair for acting in any medium." (Dame Sybil Thorndike, from *Olivier* by Logan Gourley.)

The collaboration of the finest actor in the English speaking world and the screen's greatest sex symbol brought Olivier more publicity than he had known since his Hollywood days as a young romantic actor in *Wuthering Heights* and *Rebecca*.

As the Prince Regent, a role Olivier played on the stage in *The Sleeping Prince*, opposite Vivien Leigh.

Bernard Shaw's witty and civilized account of colonial America during the revolution is hardly the action packed adventure depicted in this two-gun advertisement. While a rousing fight sequence was inserted into the screenplay for the brawny talents of Mr. Lancaster who was cast as a mild mannered minister, the film did manage to retain a certain Shavian dignity.

The Devil's Disciple

1959, A Brynaprod, S. A. and Hecht-Hill-Lancaster Films, Limited Production; Screenplay by John Dighton and Roland Kibbee, based on the play by Bernard Shaw by arrangement with the estate of Gabriel Pascal; Photography, Jack Hildyard; Editor, Alan Osbiston; Art direction, Terrence Verity and Edward Carrere; Music composed by Richard Rodney Bennett; Directed by Guy Hamilton; Produced by Harold Hecht; Released through United Artists

CAST

Rev. Anthony Anderson	Burt Lancaster
Richard Dudgeon	Kirk Douglas
General Burgoyne	Laurence Olivier
Judith Anderson	Janette Scott
Mrs. Dudgeon	Eva Le Gallienne
Major Swindon	Harry Andrews
Lawyer Hawkins	Basil Sydney
British Sergeant	George Rose
Christopher Dudgeon	Neil McCallum
Rev. Maindeck Parshotter	Mervyn Johns
William	David Horne
Essie	Jenny Jones

Opened August 20, 1959, at the Astor and Normandie Theaters, New York

THE FILM

Dick Dudgeon, a revolutionary American Puritan is mistaken for a local minister and arrested by the British. Dick discovers himself incapable of causing another human to suffer and continues the masquerade as Reverend Anderson. The minister's wife is moved by Dick's actions and mistakenly interprets them as an expression of love for her. In spite of his protestations she finds herself romantically attracted to him. Brought before British commander General Burgoyne, Dudgeon displays his willingness to die for his principles. At the last minute Dick is saved from the gallows by Anderson who has put aside his ministerial pursuits to become a revolutionary leader.

REVIEWS

New York Times, August 21, 1959
"Its outstanding acting attribute is personified by Sir Laurence Olivier in the relatively minor role of General (Gentlemanly Johnny) Burgoyne. Sir Laurence's portrayal of the polished British commander is a bland, understanding yet taunting and underplayed delineation that most pointedly projects the comic iconoclasm for which Shaw was famed. Sir Laurence's irreverential ribbing of history and historic figures and his compassion for the comparatively roughhewn, embattled provincials are a delight to the eye and ear. He is a suave, funny, practical, and cynical leader who combines a studied but refined contempt for fumblers at the British War Office and his own inept aides with an honest respect for the tough but dedicated Americans who, technically, are his enemies. Moviegoers and students of the drama also are hereby apprised that Sir Laurence's diction and delivery are no small part of his relatively minor, but outstanding, contribution to the picture."

London Evening Standard, September 2, 1959
"The greatest actor in the world . . . Olivier gives the performance of his life, making Lancaster and Douglas look like stupid oafs who have wandered back from a western."

Saturday Review, August 15, 1959
"Olivier as Burgoyne, is in enormously good humor, delivers his speeches with a rare bite and is exactly what Shaw might have asked for, if he had been available to deliver advice on casting and filming."

Olivier as Burgoyne, with George Rose (far left), Janette Scott as Mrs. Anderson and Kirk Douglas as Dick Dudgeon, the devil's disciple. Mr. Rose, who appeared in the film as a British sergeant, was promoted nineteen years later when he portrayed General Burgoyne in a revival of the play presented by the BAM Theater Company at the Brooklyn Academy.

Olivier with Burt Lancaster as Reverend Anthony Anderson.

Commonly referred to as Gentlemanly Johnny, General
John Burgoyne was in command of the English and
German troops in America during the War of Indepen-
dence.

Shaw's Burgoyne is "fifty-five, very well preserved, a man of fashion, gallant, an aristocrat, and a wit." The elegant commanding officer as fashioned by the playwright has been played on the stage by several notable actors, including Roland Young, Dennis King, Cyril Ritchard, Rex Harrison and John Wood.

General John Burgoyne (artist unknown). *National Portrait Gallery, London.*

142

Vivien Leigh (1913–1967). Miss Leigh's deteriorating mental health brought an untimely end to the great Olivier-Leigh partnership. They never fulfilled on the screen the classic stature which they had somewhat attained on the stage. They appeared in eleven plays together over a twenty year period in works by Shakespeare, Anouilh, and Rattigan. A divorce was granted them in December, 1960, and the following March Olivier married Joan Plowright, who appeared as his daughter in *The Entertainer*. Vivien Leigh won a second Academy Award in 1951 for her performance as Blanche du Bois in Tennessee Williams' *A Streetcar Named Desire* and appeared in two more films following her separation from Olivier. In 1961 she starred as an aging screen actress in Williams' *The Roman Spring of Mrs. Stone*. Her last appearance on the screen was in Stanley Kramer's *Ship of Fools* in 1965, in which she portrayed a neurotic divorcee. She died in the summer of 1967 at the age of fifty-three.

143

**As the applause grew fainter...
As the spotlight grew dimmer...
His women were younger!**

LAURENCE OLIVIER

"THE ENTERTAINER"

Co-starring BRENDA   ROGER   and Introducing JOAN
De BANZIE · LIVESEY · PLOWRIGHT

Produced by HARRY SALTZMAN · Directed by TONY RICHARDSON
Screenplay by JOHN OSBORNE and NIGEL KNEALE
A Woodfall Production · A Bryanston Presentation

1960, Bryanston presents a Woodfall Production; Produced by Harry Saltzman; Screenplay by John Osborne and Nigel Kneale, adapted from the play by Mr. Osborne; Photography, Oswald Morris; Music composed by John Addison; Associate producer, John Croydon; Art director, Ralph Brinton; Editor, Alan Osbiston; Assistant director, Peter Yates; Mr. Olivier's musical numbers staged by Honor Blair; Production manager, R. L. M. Davidson; Directed by Tony Richardson; Released by Continental Films Distributing Inc. and Brisith Lion

CAST

Archie Rice	Laurence Olivier
Phoebe Rice	Brenda de Banzie
Jean	Joan Plowright
Billy Rice	Roger Livesey
Frank	Alan Bates
Graham	Daniel Massey
Mick Rice	Albert Finney
Tina	Shirley Ann Field
Mrs. Lapford	Thora Hird
Soubrette	Miriam Karlin
Mr. Lapford	Tony Longridge
Film star	McDonald Hobley
Hubbard	Geoffrey Toone
Cobber Carson	James Culliford
Interviewer	Anthony Oliver
Gloria	Jo Linden
Britannia	Mercia Turner
Other nude	Vicky Travers
Trampoline act	Beryl and Bobo

Opened October 3, 1960, Sutton Theater, New York

THE FILM

John Osborne's sordid story of a glib, cheap unscrupulous actor reflects the demoralization and decay of England's prestige. Archie Rice, a pathetic music hall comic, plagued by debts, manipulates those around him in a defiant and selfish attempt to survive against improbable odds. He drinks, makes crude philosophical jokes about sex and politics, humiliates his lamenting,

144

gin-soaked wife, and is moved only by the death of his son, killed in the 1956 Suez conflict. His father, Billy Rice, a veteran entertainer who has nothing but contempt for England's changing climate, is lured out of retirement for a benefit performance which will ultimately bring financial aid to Archie and his impractical investments. Billy dies of a heart attack destroying Archie's flimsy dreams of success. His shabby pride forces him to continue playing to a handful of uncaring patrons at a rundown amusement pier showplace, pathetically singing, "Why should I care? Why should I let it touch me?"

REVIEWS

New York Post, October 4, 1960
"Great performances all, matched to roles that have been clearly, strongly written! And through it all, Laurence Olivier is simpering, scampering, drinking, preparing to make love, desperately trying to get another show together, dancing, singing like a negro blues singer, bouncing back from defeat time after time, never at a loss for the next line, the next gesture of a performer's pretense!"

Time magazine, October 3, 1960
"A fascinating film. A smashing performance by Olivier . . . a masterpiece."

New York Times, October 4, 1960
"Acting a tinhorn song-and-dance man in second-rate English music halls—a type for which lots of sweet nostalgia has been nicely concocted in recent years—Mr. Olivier, who might be regarded as the first gentleman of the British stage, brings forth a brilliant exposure of a cheap, sentimental theatrical fraud. Mr. Olivier is nothing short of brilliant as he runs the monotonous scale of turns and tricks of his shoddy entertainer, singing banal songs, pumping out endless off-stage wheezes and oozing absurd synthetic charm. Mr. Olivier is terrific in what is not one of his more terrific roles."

Life magazine, October 24, 1960
"As Archie Rice, the cheap and smutty song-and-dance man of England's sleazier seaside resorts, Olivier gives a shattering picture of a corrupt man, revolting, and rapidly disintegrating.

Archie Rice in *The Entertainer* (1960).

145

With Joan Plowright as Jean Rice.

Joan Plowright made her London debut in *The Duenna* in 1954. Three years later she appeared as Olivier's daughter, Jean Rice in *The Entertainer* at the Palace Theatre in London and subsequently at the Royale in New York, also repeating the role for the film version. Her most popular role in the United States was as the girl in *A Taste of Honey*, which won her the 1961 Tony Award for Best Actress in addition to the New York Drama Critics Award. She also appeared with Olivier in the filmed productions of *Uncle Vanya*, *Three Sisters* and as Portia in *The Merchant of Venice*. In 1977 she portrayed Dora Strang in the film of Peter Shaffer's *Equus* with Richard Burton. The actress married Olivier in 1961 and received a C. B. E. in the 1970 Queen's New Years Honours. The couple have three children, Richard, Tasmin and Julie Kate.

He seduces young girls, steals their money, takes strange pleasure in telling his daughter how he betrayed her mother. He is a spiritual bankrupt, 'dead behind the eyes' he says, the precise opposite of Becket, and it is a measure of Olivier's skill that in the end the audience takes pity on him.''

Roger Manvell, *New Cinema in Britain* (New York and London: Studio Vista, Dutton Paperback, 1969), p. 46.

''Laurence Olivier's performance is an impressive tour de force, with his puffy face, glib gestures, flappy restlessness, his sad emptiness of expression in moments of repose. (Tony) Richardson would not let the audience forget that Archie Rice is a melancholy caricature of themselves; only Archie's daughter, touchingly played by Joan Plowright, offers him a slender lifeline to salvation through her sympathy and compassion.''

COMMENTS

Outside the classics, Olivier achieved his greatest performance as Archie Rice, the third-rate vaudevillian in *The Entertainer*. It was the second play by John Osborne, who had come into prominence with *Look Back in Anger* in 1956. Olivier has often claimed to be most proud of this performance. ''It had the advantage of being a complete break from the other sort of work and that made it much more refreshing than tormenting oneself through these punishing roles of Shakespeare. I have an affinity with Archie Rice. It's what I really am. I'm not like Hamlet.''[27] The character provided Olivier with an opportunity to be broadly comic as the pathetic song and dance man in a run-down variety hall. He appeared on the London stage in *The Entertainer* in 1957 and repeated his success the following year in New York.

''I read the first act and knew I had to play that role. It's a marvelous part—so many parts within the part. He *was* an entertainer, and he was a man who acted parts in his real life, his unreal life, perhaps I should say. And he was real, real in his unreality. I know him. I recognize the creature. When I was a young man in rep in Birmingham the Archie Rices used to come into my digs, and I used to go and see them in the music halls. I knew

Archie Rice. I didn't really know if John Osborne recognized the Archie Rice that I did, but he certainly wrote him. And never was heard a discouraging word. It was a wonderful part.''[28]

Olivier received his sixth Academy Award nomination for his performance as Archie Rice, but lost the honor to Burt Lancaster who won the Oscar for his title role as *Elmer Gantry*.

With Shirley Ann Field as Tina.

Olivier's proudest creation: "He was real . . . I recognize the creature."

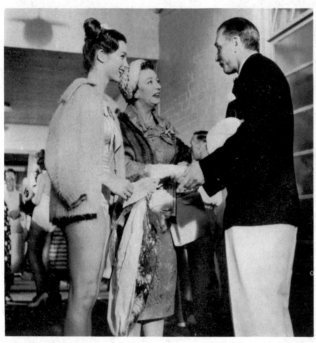

With Shirley Ann Field and Thora Hird as Mrs. Lapford.

1960, A Bryna production; Produced by Edward Lewis; Executive Producer, Kirk Douglas; Screenplay by Dalton Trumbo based on the novel by Howard Fast; Music Composed and Conducted by Alex North; Photography, Russell Metty; Editor, Robert Lawrence; Art director, Eric Orbom; Directed by Stanley Kubrick; Released by Universal-International

CAST

Spartacus	Kirk Douglas
Crassus	Laurence Olivier
Varinia	Jean Simmons
Gracchus	Charles Laughton
Batiatus	Peter Ustinov
Caesar	John Gavin
Antoninus	Tony Curtis
Helena	Nina Foch
Tigranes	Herbert Lom
Crixus	John Ireland
Glabrus	John Dall
Marcellus	Charles McGraw
Claudia	Joanna Barnes
David	Harold J. Stone
Draba	Woody Strode
Ramon	Peter Brocco
Gannicus	Paul Lambert
Guard Captain	Robert J. Wilke
Dionysius	Nicholas Dennis
Roman Officer	John Hoyt
Laelius	Frederic Worlock
Symmachus	Dayton Lummis

Opened, October 6, 1960, at the DeMille Theater, New York

THE FILM

Spartacus, a Thracian slave in pre-Christian Rome is trained at a gladiatorial school to fight to the death in the arena as a public sport for the amusement of the citizenry. As a reward for his victory, Varinia, a slave girl is sent to his cell. Draba, an expert fighter is matched with Spartacus, but cannot bring himself to kill him and attacks his spectators, dying in the attempt. Driven by the cruelty of bondage, his hatred for his

Magnificent Human Drama of a Love so Strong
it Sparked the Revolt that Shook the World!

The General desired her... even more than he wanted to possess Rome!

Spartacus loved her!

The Senator stole her... and used her for a cunning revenge!

The Slaver sold her... for a handful of gold and betrayed an Empire!

The Rebel worshipped her... as fiercely as his dream of freedom!

Caesar used her... in his power drive to become ruler of Rome!

KIRK DOUGLAS · LAURENCE OLIVIER · JEAN SIMMONS
CHARLES LAUGHTON · PETER USTINOV · JOHN GAVIN

SPARTACUS

and TONY CURTIS as Antoninus

WINNER OF 4 ACADEMY AWARDS

A RETURN COLOR · CINEMASCOPE
ENGAGEMENT OF THE EPIC ADVENTURE!

A Universal-International Release

149

Crassus in *Spartacus* (1960). *Courtesy, Museum of Modern Art, Film Stills Archive.*

captors, and his intense love for Varinia, Spartacus resolves to escape. After two years of revolt, Spartacus leads an army of ninety thousand men and triumphs over every encounter with Roman legions. Crassus, the most powerful general in Rome has little success in crushing the rebellion, which causes fierce political rivalry in the Senate. Finally defeated, through sheer force of numbers, Spartacus and six thousand survivors of his army are crucified along the road to Rome. The dying leader of the great slave revolt has a final moment of pride and fulfillment as Varinia cradles their newborn son.

REVIEWS

New York Times, October 7, 1960

"It is bursting with patriotic fervor, bloody tragedy, a lot of romantic fiddle-faddle and historical inaccuracy. It is heroic humbug—a vast, panoramic display of synthetic Rome and Romans, slaves and patricians, men and maids, at the time of the great slave rebellion in the first century B.C. There is a handsome, eye-filling re-enactment of a battle between the slaves and the Roman legions, which matches the Battle of Agincourt in *Henry V.* The performances are uneven. Mr. Douglas sets his blunt, horse-opera style against the toga-clad precision of Mr. Laughton and the Roman-nosed gentility of Mr. Olivier."

Stanley Kauffmann, November 14, 1960

"*Spartacus* is a trap for snobs. They assume that because it is a costume drama three and a half hours long and has seven stars and a cast of many thousands, it must ipso facto be bad. In proof, it is an entertaining show. In direction, acting, writing, editing, use of color, and general whammo, it is one thousand statute miles ahead of its most recent competitor, *Ben-Hur.* Some of the scenes, particularly those played by Laurence Olivier, Charles Laughton, and Peter Ustinov, are incisively written; for example, the scene in which Olivier states obliquely to a slave his sexual predilections is done with subtlety indeed.

Olivier, as the rich Crassus, gives an impeccably patrician performance that fits a certain aloof element in his personality. A lot of first-rate professionals have pooled their abilities to put on a first-rate circus."

COMMENTS

Spartacus, Stanley Kubrick's lavish "thinking-man's" spectacle, was acclaimed for its intelligent screenplay by Dalton Trumbo, who received his first screen credit since suffering political blacklisting as one of the "Hollywood Ten" of the McCarthy investigation. The subtle skill and polish of the British contingent—Olivier, Laughton, and Ustinov added enormous prestige rarely found in screen epics. Olivier gives a superb performance as an effete aristocratic general. The Legion of Decency had a scene removed, which had been seen by some critics at early screenings, in which Olivier as the Roman officer indicates a desire to possess a handsome male slave (Tony Curtis) for sexual gratification. Its removal considerably lessened the impact of the young slave's escape to join the army of Spartacus.

Peter Ustinov, who won an Academy Award for his performance as Batiatus, a corrupt slave dealer, offers an amusing account of the filming of a scene with Olivier in his autobiography, *Dear Me* (Boston: Little Brown and Company, 1977), p. 302. "One of my first scenes with Larry Olivier consisted in my rushing up to the horse as it cavorted among a huge mass of prisoners of war, grabbing its bridle, and gazing up at its immaculate rider: 'If I identify Spartacus for you, Divinity, will you give me the women and the children?' I said, in the character of the sleazy slave dealer. There followed the most enormous pause while Larry let his eyes disappear upwards under his half-open lids, licked his lips, pushed at his cheeks from within with his tongue, let his head drop with a kind of comic irony at the quirks of destiny, hardened once again into the mold of mortal divinity, looked away into the unknown as his profile softened from brutal nobility into subtlety. 'Spartacus!' he suddenly cried, as though

Jean Simmons, chosen at the age of eighteen by Olivier to portray Ophelia in *Hamlet*, appeared with him again, twelve years later, as Varinia, the slave girl in *Spartacus*. Courtesy, Museum of Modern Art, Film Stills Archive.

slashing the sky with a razor, and then hissed, 'You have found him?'

I was so absolutely staggered at the extent of the pause that I expressed precisely the surprise I felt. Now I gazed over the prisoners with a closed expression, giving nothing away. Then I let a furtive smile play on my lips for a moment at some private thought, chasing it away and seemed about to say something, but changed my mind. I ran the gamut of impertinence, of servility, and of insincerity as he had of vanity, power, and menace. At long last, when he least expected it, I let a practically inaudible 'Yes' slip from my mouth. 'Dear boy,' said Larry, in a businesslike voice which ill-concealed a dawning annoyance. 'D'you think you could come in a little quicker with your 'Yes'?'

'No' I said politely. We both looked at one another straight in the eye and smiled at the same moment.''

When he later won the Oscar for best supporting performance, Olivier sent him a humorous cable thanking Ustinov for having supported him so well.

The Power and the Glory

1961, Paramount Talent Associates; Produced by David Susskind; Screenplay by Dale Wasserman from the novel by Graham Greene; Associate producer, Audrey Gellen; Associate director, Robert Hopkins; Photography, Alan Posage, Leo Farrenkopf; Editors, Sidney Meyers, Walter Hess; Art direction, Burr Smidt; Music composed by Laurence Rosenthal; Directed by Marc Daniels; A Paramount Release

CAST

Priest	Laurence Olivier
Marie	Julie Harris
Police Lieutenant	George C. Scott
Peasant	Roddy McDowall
Bootlegger	Keenan Wynn
Dentist	Cyril Cusack
Police Chief	Martin Gabel
Padre Jose	Frank Conroy
Coral	Patty Duke

152

| Woman | Mildred Dunnock |
| Schoolmaster | Fritz Weaver |

Telecast, October 29, 1961; Commercially released in Great Britain

THE FILM

A sadistic and avenging police officer relentlessly pursues the last surviving priest in a Latin American state governed by anti-Christian revolutionaries. Dissipated by drink and exhausted from the chase, the priest is sheltered by villagers. In a last desperate attempt to flee across the frontier, the priest is called upon to attend a dying man. In his final compassionate act of mercy, he is trapped by his undaunted pursuer and sentenced to execution.

REVIEW

New York Times, October 30, 1961
"Graham Greene's specific and uncompromising story of a dissolute priest was a major forward step for a mass medium traditionally skittish over controversial themes, most especially those of a religious nature. Sir Laurence's performance attained a stature and illumination in the concluding jail scene when the priest beseeches God's compassion."

Variety, November 1, 1961
"A fine, frequently moving performance . . . If only for the portrayals of Laurence Olivier and George C. Scott in two extraordinary performances, the one counter pointing the other, it was well worth the viewing. Olivier's 'whiskey-priest' in essence brought to visual fulfillment the agonies and the ecstasies of a haunted, tormented soul seeking peace with himself and with God."

COMMENTS

Olivier's stage career following his widely acclaimed portrayal of Archie Rice in 1958, included the title role in Shakespeare's *Coriolanus* at Stratford-upon-Avon in 1959 followed by Ionesco's *Rhinoceros* the next year in London, in which he appeared as Berenger opposite Maggie Smith. In February of 1960, Olivier directed Benn Levy's play *The Tumbler* in New York, with Charlton Heston, Rosemary Harris, and Martha Scott. The psychological melodrama, written in blank verse, was not well received by the critics, and Olivier was taken to task for his comments in an interview with Maurice Zolotow on American actors. Olivier remarked that American actors had a doleful habit of theorizing. "Instead of doing a scene over again that's giving trouble, they want to discuss, discuss, discuss," he told Zolotow. Brooks Atkinson reviewing the play in the *New York Times* called his direction "heavy and flat," and Walter Kerr in the *New York Herald Tribune* suggested Olivier might better have discussed the play with somebody. Actress Nancy Coleman, disturbed by Olivier's comments, wrote a letter to the drama editor of the *New York Times,* suggesting "his knowledge of the American actor must be quite limited."

In October Olivier was considerably more successful when he appeared at the St. James' Theater in Jean Anouilh's *Becket,* appearing as the martyred Archbishop of Canterbury opposite Anthony Quinn's Henry II. When Quinn withdrew to make a film, the play toured with Arthur Kennedy playing Becket, and Olivier switching to the role of Henry II. It returned to New York in May 1961 for an engagement at the Hudson Theater and won a Tony Award as the most distinguished play of the season. Howard Taubman reporting in the *New York Times* commented on Olivier's Becket: "He plays the part with admirable scope." Lewis Funke reviewed the return engagement for the *Times* praising Olivier for his turn as the King: "A vibrant, throbbing ruler. Olivier is the center of focus when on stage. As soon as the curtain goes up the evidence is there that this is going to be one of those rare performances. There is Henry being drawn full of buoyancy and earthiness, shrewd and lighthearted as the Olivier eyes glisten and sparkle. There is the bravado and the swagger, too. Mr. Olivier makes it an unforgettable experience."

At the conclusion of the *Becket* engagement in May of 1961, Olivier was approached by producer David Susskind to appear in *The Power and the Glory.* A CBS engineer noted that it was possible to make an old-fashioned kinescope recording, with the same frame size as a motion picture film,

The hunted priest in *The Power and the Glory* (1961).

at the same time standard television tapes were being shot. Susskind realized he could make a movie as he taped a TV show with the new electronic process and at a fraction of the time a normal film would take.

The producer searched his properties for a suitable story and chose Graham Greene's novel about a dissolute revolutionary priest on the run in Mexico, who is betrayed by a man who once sheltered him. The novel had been previously filmed by John Ford in 1947 as *The Fugitive* starring Henry Fonda.

Having decided upon the play, Susskind wanted Olivier as the first star for the revolutionary new medium. The actor was anxious to return to London for a much needed rest following his long run in *Becket,* but in view of the brief rehearsal schedule and a one-week shooting period, he agreed to play the "whiskey priest."

Susskind rented two NBC color studios in Brooklyn, the only facility in New York at that time large enough to handle the complex jungle setting and was given a firm taping-availability schedule from May 30 to June 4, allowing one day of grace in the event of complications.

By the end of the week director Marc Daniels was making up for lost time by shooting straight through a twenty-four hour period. Olivier had suffered an eye infection, caused by the irritation of contact lenses to make his hazel eyes darker as the Mexican he was to portray, and the crushing pace of the production had tired him considerably. During the filming of one scene he forgot a line and Patty Duke, who had recently triumphed on Broadway as young Helen Keller in *The Miracle Worker* and was soon to appear in the film version, ad-libbed a line which put him back on the track. Olivier admired her alertness and called her a "brilliant girl" upon completion of the scene.

The role of Graham Greene's tormented priest had appealed to Olivier ever since seeing Paul Scofield in a 1956 stage version.

155

With Roddy McDowell (left) as a traitorous peasant and Keenan Wynn as a bootlegger.

With George C. Scott who appeared as a relentless police pursuer.

On the final day of shooting, Olivier had to be kept awake with cold compresses and coffee and was so near exhaustion that he had to be lifted onto a burro for the final sequences in the jungle. Filming completed, Olivier sailed for home on June 7 as planned, having added another towering achievement to his laurels.

The role of the priest had long appealed to Olivier after seeing Paul Scofield in a London stage production of the work in 1956. He often praised Scofield's priest as the greatest performance he had ever seen. "I was struck dumb by his acting," he told Mel Gussow of the *New York Times* in 1975. Three years earlier talking with Fred Robbins, Olivier described the unique Scofield qualities. "Very beautiful and fascinatingly interesting and very richly intellectual, as well as being highly and colorfully sympathetic, and he has wonderful gifts. Marvelous appearance, wonderful face. An actor has gifts; it is their use of their gifts that counts. And his use is very remarkable. I think it was the best performance I can remember seeing. I was acting at the time in something else in London, and I went to see one matinee, and I went again the next matinee, and I don't often go to see things more than once. I just don't. I was floored by his performance. It was wonderful."

With Mildred Dunnock and prisoners.

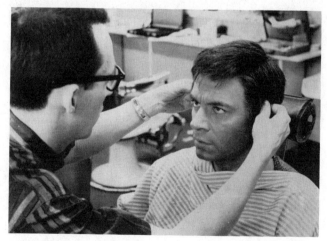

Olivier's make-up as the Mexican priest included dark contact lenses to cover his hazel eyes and a black wig.

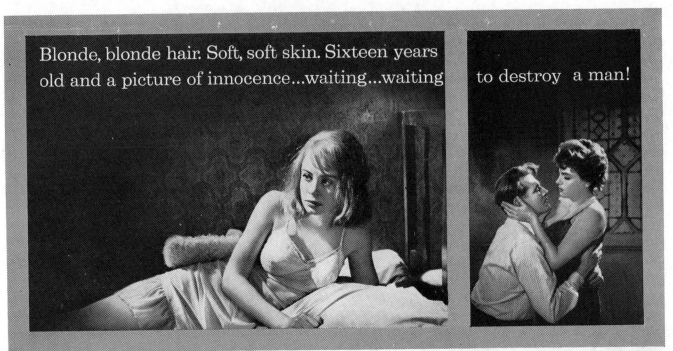

Blonde, blonde hair. Soft, soft skin. Sixteen years old and a picture of innocence...waiting...waiting to destroy a man!

HE IS A MARRIED SCHOOLMASTER. SHE IS ONE OF THE YOUNGEST GIRLS IN HIS CLASS.

Laurence Olivier
Simone Signoret

TERM OF TRIAL Introducing the exciting **Sarah Miles**

WINNER SPECIAL AWARD VENICE FILM FESTIVAL 1962

Co-starring HUGH GRIFFITH · Also starring TERENCE STAMP as Mitchell · Written and Directed by PETER GLENVILLE Based on an original novel by JAMES BARLOW · Produced by JAMES WOOLF · Presented by WARNER BROS.

Term of Trial

1963, A Romulous Production, Presented by Warner Bros., Produced by James Woolf; Based on an original novel by James Barlow; Photography, Oswald Morris; Production designer, Wilfred Shingleton; Art director, Anthony Woolard; Assistant director, Gerry O'Hara; Music composed by Jean-Michel Demaes; Production manager, Charles Blair; Associate producer, James Ware; Editor, James Clark; Written and Directed by Peter Glenville; Released by Warner-Pathe.

CAST

Graham Weir	Laurence Olivier
Anna Weir	Simone Signoret
Shirley	Sarah Miles
O'Hara	Hugh Griffith
Mitchell	Terence Stamp
Trowman	Roland Culver
Ferguson	Frank Pettingell
Mrs. Taylor	Thora Hird
Detective Sgt. Kiernan	Dudley Foster
Mr. Taylor	Norman Bird
Prosecutor	Newton Blick
Sylvan-Jones	Allan Cuthbertson
Magistrate	Nicholas Hannen
Joan	Barbara Ferris
Thompson	Roy Holder

Opened January 30, 1963, Paramount Theater, New York

THE FILM

Graham Weir is a schoolmaster and a man of integrity who teaches in the poorer section of England's industrial north. The dedicated teacher discovers among his often unruly pupils, one or two youngsters with a real desire for knowledge and self-improvement. When a young girl, Shirley, tells Weir that she has the chance of a good position upon leaving school, he agrees to provide her extra tutoring on his own time. Weir's wife, Anna, an attractive French woman, is discontented with her surroundings and the modest financial rewards of Weir's job, but she is genuinely fond of him despite his weaknesses. Shirley makes good progress with her private studies, and it appears obvious to everyone but the schoolmaster that she is falling in love with him. On a return journey from a cultural class trip to Paris, the school group misses a train and is forced to remain overnight in London. The infatuated girl comes to Weir's room and proclaims her love for him. Weir is amazed by the revelation and, with a genuine concern for her feelings, reminds her that he is a happily married man and sends her off with a paternal whack on the bottom. Back home, Weir is booked by police on charges by the girl's parents, who through the girl's twisted story, have believed she was indecently assaulted. Weir's lawyer pleads his case wisely and eloquently but Weir is first found guilty. The case is dismissed upon disclosure of the girl's confession, but the village continues to believe Weir guilty. Anna, who has supported her husband throughout the trial now berates him for "that rubbish about purity and humiliation. Guilty, at least you'd have proved yourself a man, but I know you too well." So Weir lies— "What the girl said in her original accusation was true"—and smiles ruefully as he sees new admiration and light come into his wife's eyes.

REVIEWS

New York Times, June 31, 1963
"A hero more afflicted than Lazarus and more humble and patient than Job is not likely to cut a dynamic or captivating figure in a film, no matter how finely he is acted, even by Laurence Olivier. The meek and shabby high-school teacher that Mr. Olivier plays in this British rehash of *Blackboard Jungle,* with minor *Lolita* overtones, is a wistful and well-meaning fellow for whom your heart bleeds a drop or two as you watch him enduring all sorts of troubles and woes. No matter how patiently and deftly Mr. Olivier plays the role, with all of his skill at portraying discomfort and down-at-heel wistfulness, he cannot quite make this fellow absorbing—or even real."

159

Graham Weir in *Term of Trial* **(1963).**

London Daily Express, August 16, 1962

"It is an excellent story that fails to make its full effect principally because of the miscasting of Sir Laurence, who seems to have a taste for playing insignificant little men, but his noble looks, his commanding personality and his natural authority are against him. He can play a king but he cannot play a mouse."

Roger Manvell, *New Cinema in Britain* (New York and London: Studio Vista Dutton Paperback, 1969), p. 62.

"An altogether darker film about the effects of children on adult relationships; it was slow, loaded, oppressive, and remarkable mainly for Laurence Olivier's quietude and the first appearance of Sarah Miles and Terence Stamp."

With Sarah Miles as Shirley.

COMMENTS

Kenneth Tynan suggests that Olivier has seldom succeeded in his attempts to play "the common man" such as Graham Weir, the seedy schoolmaster in *Term of Trial.* "That outside emotional candor cannot help breaking through," Tynan explains. "The actor impatiently bursts the seams of the role, and the common man becomes extraordinary." The film's director, Peter Glenville, who also staged the Broadway production of *Becket,* prefers Olivier's low-key performances on the screen. "The man is a natural theater actor, rather than a natural cinema actor," he told Logan Gourley, author of *Olivier.* "A great actor wants to act, which he has more freedom to do on the stage. He doesn't want to worry about mechanical things, as he has to do in the film studios."

Tynan notes that while Olivier has acted in many good movies, he has seldom performed at the height of his talent, "mostly because his performances need to be seen as flowing, consecutive wholes, not chopped up into long-shots and close-ups and spread over months of shooting." In *Term of Trial* there is a long courtroom speech in which Weir must defend himself against the lurid accusations of a teenage girl. Glenville chose to disregard camera angles or close-ups and let Olivier play it non-stop without technical interference. The scene was shot twice and the first take was used in the final print.

With Simone Signoret as Anna Weir.

1963*, Chichester Festival Theatre production, Directed by Laurence Olivier; Directed for the screen by Stuart Burge; Written by Anton Chekhov and translated by Constance Garnett; A British Home Entertainment production; Distributed by Arthur Cantor Productions.

CAST

Mihail Lvovitch Astrov	Laurence Olivier
Ivan Petrovitch Voynitsky (Uncle Vanya)	Michael Redgrave
Sofya Alexandrovna (Sonya)	Joan Plowright
Ilyena Andreyevna	Rosemary Harris
Marina Timofeyevna (Nurse)	Sybil Thorndike
Alexandr Vladimirovitch Serebryakov (Professor)	Max Adrian
Ilya Ilyitch Telyegin	Lewis Casson
Marya Vassilyevna Voynitsky (Maman)	Fay Compton
Yefim	Robert Lang

*Filmed for television; commercially released at the Thalia Theater, New York, March 28, 1977. Initially presented on NET Playhouse, February 10, 1967.

THE FILM

Ever since the arrival of old Professor Serebriakoff and his young wife, Elena, everything has been in disorder on the estate. Uncle Vanya, the brother of the professor's first wife, has lost his formerly intense desire to manage the estate and is disillusioned by Serebriakoff's dull, egotistical, nagging ways. He is also confused by his own unreturned love for Elena. Sonia, the retired professor's daughter by his first wife, tries to continue running the estate, but her strength is inadequate, and she is emotionally drained by her deep love for the local doctor, Astrov. The doctor is himself frustrated by life, so much so, that he cannot return her love. Serebriakoff discusses his plan to sell the estate, an act which would leave Vanya, Sonia, and Vanya's aged mother desti-

Simone Signoret, a popular actress of the French stage and screen, made her British film debut in *Room at the Top*, which won her the 1959 Academy Award for Best Actress in addition to top honors at the Cannes Film Festival, the British Academy Award and recognition from the American National Board of Review and the German Film Critics. *Term of Trial* marked her first English speaking role since her award winning performance.

tute. A crisis is averted when Elena, who has remained faithful to the professor, despite her unhappiness, persuades him to leave. She is afraid of the passion Astrov is beginning to arouse in her. With their departure Astrov again becomes concerned in healing the sick and in reclaiming the land, while Vanya and Sonia begin with renewed determination to manage the estate and to bear their suffering.

REVIEWS

New York Times, television review by Jack Gould, February 11, 1967
"A taped testament to the overriding strength of the British Theatre. Every part was filled by a star, yet the total effect was that of an integrated ensemble accomplishment in which Chekhov's relentless account of a purposeless and dark environment was always dominant. The company is the realization of a theatrical dream. The loneliness, frustration, and bitterness were captured in the individual portrayals. Sir Laurence's performance as the country doctor had the ring of vitality."

New York Times, March 29, 1977
"A noteworthy movie curiosity. It's the filmed recording of the production staged in 1963 at the Chichester Festival. Photographed entirely on the Chichester stage in black and white, the production is neither a movie nor a play, but the sort of on-the-spot report that looks best on television. Mr. Redgrave and Mr. Olivier are splendid. One of the best readings of the play you're ever likely to hear."

New Yorker, April 18, 1977
"It is probably the best 'Uncle Vanya' in English that we shall ever see. Dr. Astrov, (is) played by Laurence Olivier with the hesitant rush that he particularly understands."

COMMENTS

In the Spring of 1962, following the completion of filming *Term of Trial* in Paris and Dublin, Olivier returned to London to appear as Fred Midway, the obsessively social-conscious insurance agent in David Turner's *Semi-Detached.* In the summer of 1962, he assumed the directorship of the

Astrov in *Uncle Vanya* (1963). An Olivier favorite: "A part with which Chekhov identified himself."

Chichester Festival Theatre in Chichester, England. He directed and appeared in John Ford's tragedy, *The Broken Heart,* playing the role of Bassanes, a jealous nobleman whose wife was forced into a loveless marriage by her brother. A notable cast included Rosemary Harris, John Neville, Joan Greenwood, Keith Michell, Fay Compton, and Alan Howard. *Variety* called the presentation "bold and imaginative, bolstered by Olivier's fluid direction" and Howard Taubman in the *New York Times* wrote, "As an actor Sir Laurence was in fine fettle and knows how to make richly embellished Elizabethan style sound both dramatic and musical," but of his direction could not be as commendatory. "One has the impression that he has not yet mastered the open stage. His staging often seemed contrived where it should have flowed naturally."

The Broken Heart was followed by the distinguished production *Uncle Vanya* which was subsequently filmed for television and several years later released as a commercial film. *Variety* called Olivier's direction "subtle and sensitive" and praised the impressive cast which included Olivier, Rosemary Harris, Michael Redgrave, and Sybil Thorndyke. Astrov has remained one of Olivier's favorite roles. He told Kenneth Harris, writing in the *London Observer* that it gave him the most satisfaction. "I don't know why. I think because I sense it is a part with which Chekhov identified himself to a certain degree, and because playing a part of that kind brings you the added sense of playing a pivotal role, and because the company was particularly congenial—this is important."

Bunny Lake Is Missing

1965, Columbia Pictures Release of an Otto Preminger production; Screenplay by John and Penelope Mortimer, based on a novel by Evelyn Piper; Music composed by Paul Glass; Photography, Denys Coop; Editor, Peter Thornton; Sound, Jonathan Bates; Filmed in Panavision; Production designer, Don Ashton; Associate producer, Martin C. Schute; Assistant directors, Bryan Coates, Bernie Williams, Ivor Nightingale; Special effects, Charles Staffell; Produced and Directed by Otto Preminger.

CAST

Ann	Carol Lynley
Steven	Keir Dullea
Inspector Newhouse	Laurence Olivier
Wilson	Noel Coward
Ada Ford	Martita Hunt
Elvira	Anna Massey
Andrews	Clive Revill
Doll Maker	Finlay Currie
Clerk in Shipping Office	Richard Wattis
Cook	Lucie Mannheim
Sister	Megs Jenkins
Taxi Driver	Victor Maddern
First Mother	Delphi Lawrence
Second Mother	Suzanne Neve
Dorothy	Adrienne Corri
Nurse	Kika Markham
Teacher	Jill Melford
Daphne	Damaris Hayman
Policeman	Patrick Jordan
Policewoman	Jane Evers
Rogers	Michael Wynne
Barman	Bill Maxam
Newscaster	Tim Brinton
Man in Soho	Fred Emney
Doctor	David Oxley
Attendant	John Forbes-Robertson
The Zombies	Themselves
Fingerprint Man	John Sharp
Police Photographer	Geoffrey Frederick
Policeman at Station	Percy Herbert

Opened October 4, 1965, Victoria, Beekman, and 34th Street East theaters, New York

164

Olivier as Inspector Newhouse, Clive Revill as Andrews and Carol Lynley as Ann in *Bunny Lake is Missing*.

With Carol Lynley.

With Keir Dullea as Steven.

THE FILM

A young American mother, recently arrived in London, leaves her daughter at a day nursery, returning later to discover that there is no trace of the girl, and the nurses deny that she was registered there in the first place. Inspector Newhouse arrives to investigate, looking for a lead to the disappearance of the child only to discover that the young mother cannot even produce any evidence of her daughter's existence. Newhouse begins to believe that the child is a figment of the mother's imagination, emphasized by his discovery that she is unmarried. He also reveals an unnaturally close relationship between the young woman and her brother, who is shielding her from being made to realize that the child is illusory. Caught up in a nightmare world in which reality, illusion, and childhood fantasy are inseparable, the young woman's life is eventually endangered by her neurotic brother.

New York Herald Tribune, October 5, 1965

"*Bunny Lake Is Missing* has surface interest and intermittent fascination, but it ultimately boils down to a routine game of psycho, psycho, who's got the psychosis. Noel Coward's spoof of an ultraesthete given to collecting whips and memorabilia of de Sade and Martita Hunt's fascinating portrait of an aged kindergartner devoting her retirement to a study of children's fantasies hasn't much to do with Bunny Lake, but at least they are given a moment to perform. Laurence Olivier is not so fortunate in his downbeat flat-toned role of investigator—any number of other gifted actors are given even shorter shrift than he, ranging from Clive Revill, wasted as his assistant, to Finlay Currie as a doting doll maker, to Megs Jenkins, a one-line nurse."

Variety, October 6, 1965

"Olivier does give it dignity and purpose and makes it a calm and restful contrast to the highly-strung emoting of Dullea and Miss Lynley."

London Sunday Express, February 10, 1966

"Laurence Olivier with his towering technique of wit and timing makes this inspector one of the most beguiling policemen in the history of criminology."

NOTES

The thriller marked a reunion for Olivier and Noel Coward, who had appeared together thirty-five years earlier in Coward's comedy, *Private Lives*. Coward appeared as a lecherous, perverted, old landlord. The Master's legendary acerbic wit was noted to be in rare form one morning on the set when Coward crept up behind a rather annoyed young actor who portrayed Carol Lynley's neurotic brother, and murmered, "Keir Dullea . . . Gone Tomorrow."

Othello

1965, Warner Bros. release of a B. H. E. Production from the National Theatre of Great Britain; Produced by Anthony Havelock-Allan and John Brabourne; National Theatre production of the play by William Shakespeare, directed by John Dexter; Sets and costumes by Jocelyn Herbert; Director of photography, Geoffrey Unsworth; Editor, Richard Marden; Music by Richard Hampton; Directed by Stuart Burge

CAST

Othello, the Moor of Venice	Laurence Olivier
Iago, Othello's Ancient	Frank Finlay
Desdemona, wife to Othello	Maggie Smith
Cassio, lieutenant to Othello	Derek Jacobi
Brabantio, father to Desdemona	Anthony Nicholls
Roderigo, a guiled gentleman	Robert Lang
Emilia, wife to Iago	Joyce Redman
Clown, servant to Othello	Roy Holder
Gratiano, brother to Brabantio	Michael Turner
Lodovico, kinsman to Brabantio	Kenneth MacIntosh
Montano, retiring governor of Cyprus	Edward Hardwicke
Bianca, a courtesan	Sheila Reid
Senate Officers	David Hargreaves
	Malcolm Terris
Senator	Keith Marsh
Sailor	Tom Kempinski
Messenger	Nicholas Edmett
Cypriot Officers	William Hobbs
	Trevor Martin
	Christopher Timothy
Duke of Venice	Harry Lomax
Duke's Officer	Terence Knapp

Senators, Soldiers, Cypriots—Petronella Barker, Janie Booth, Andrew Bradford, Peter Cellier, Nicholas Edmett, Mike Gambon, Reginald Green, David Hargreaves, William Hobbs, Peter John, Lewis Jones, Tom Kempinski, Terence Knapp, Trevor Martin, John McEn-

Olivier's Moor. "An anthology of everything that has been discovered about acting in the last three centuries." (Franco Zeffirelli.)

ery, Bruce Purchase, Dan Meaden, Malcom Reynolds, Robert Russell, Clive Rust, Malcolm Terris, Christoper Timothy

Opened February 2, 1966, for a two day, four performance engagement at several theaters in the New York metropolitan area

THE FILM

Iago, Venetian army officer and ensign to the Moorish general, Othello, bitterly resents the appointment of Cassio as Othello's lieutenant. Roderigo and Iago maliciously bait Brabantio, an old senator, with the news that his daughter Desdemona is betrothed to Othello. Before Council Chamber, Brabantio accuses Othello of abducting his daughter. The Moor denies this, and Desdemona affirms loyalty to her husband. Othello is ordered to defend Cyprus, of which he is Governor, against the Turks. Iago assures Roderigo, who is secretly in love with Desdemona, that she will not love Othello for long. Iago brings Desdemona to Cyprus to celebrate Othello's victory against the Turks and incites Cassio and Montano into a drunken brawl. Montano is seriously hurt and Iago beckons Othello, blaming Cassio, who is dismissed from duties. Iago then advises Cassio to seek Desdemona's assistance in regaining Othello's favor. Iago arranges Othello to find his wife in earnest conversation with Cassio, and subtly arouses the Moor's jealousy. Iago then

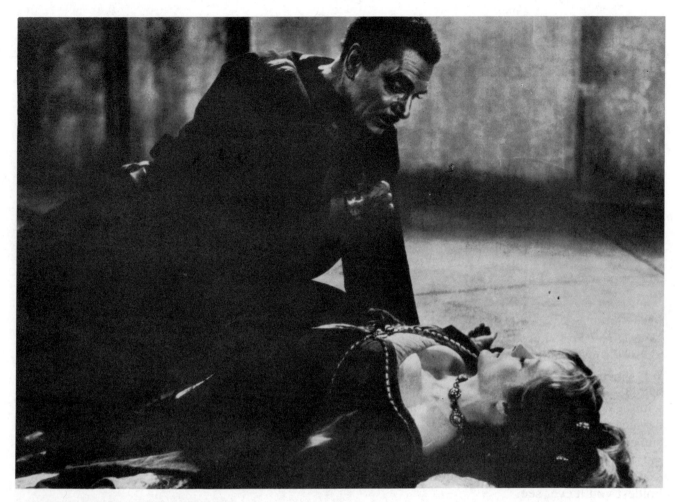

With Maggie Smith as Desdemona.
  Othello: "Excellent wretch! Perdition catch my soul
           But I do love thee! And when I love thee not,
           Chaos is come again." (William Shakes-
           peare.)

creates a slanderous piece of evidence by placing Desdemona's handkerchief in the possession of Cassio. Othello demands proof from Iago of Desdemona's faithlessness and is told about the missing handkerchief seen in the possession of Cassio. Desdemona confesses to have mislaid the handkerchief and denies committing any wrong. Othello enters the sleeping Desdemona's room. In remorse he kisses her and she awakens, realizing his intent as he talks of reconciliation with Heaven and her death. He stifles her cries with a pillow. Iago's wife, Emilia, reveals the truth about the handkerchief to Othello and accuses her husband, who promptly kills her. Othello wounds Iago and then kills himself with a dagger concealed in his bracelet.

REVIEWS

New York Times, February 2, 1966
"There is no question that Sir Laurence's Othello is a spectacular rococo man who becomes more flamboyant and exciting as his mind is inflamed with jealousy. He commands us with graphic devices—his strutting movements, his gleaming smiles, his stormy frowns, his blood-chilling muscular tensions, his howlings of anguish at the sky. In this respect, this Othello is one of the boldest you'll ever see."

New York Herald Tribune, February 2, 1966
"Laurence Olivier's Othello is now on the screen for all to see, and, inevitably, argue about in a beautiful and fascinating film of Britain's National Theatre production of the Shakespeare tragedy. And this Olivier has embodied in almost minstrel show makeup, so that we meet Othello as a pitch black figure, flashing teeth and crimson mouth slashing the shiny ebony of his face—a slightly effete figure in his hour of relaxation, flourishing a scarlet rose as his thoughts linger on love. It is a powerful effect. Here we have, beyond the record of great stage performances, a great film."

Saturday Review, February 5, 1966
"This Othello, thankfully brought to the screen almost whole and pure, is as brilliant and beautifully modeled a version as one would wish to see."

New York Post, February 2, 1966
"The Laurence Olivier Othello, justly famous on the stage, brings a full measure of eloquence to the screen. He rises to heights of his speeches in *Henry V.*"

Variety, December 15, 1965
"As theater, this filmed version of *Othello* should be seen by every lover of fine acting. As proper use of film, however, it is inferior to Laurence Olivier's previous Shakespearean efforts. What, then, makes *Othello* so important? First and foremost to see and hear Olivier play Othello. To see him create the tormented soul who 'loved not wisely, but too well.' To hear, as the ear is regaled by his incredible feat of turning the richly-embroidered lines into understandable conversation. Olivier combines the many-faceted characteristics of Othello into a single, remarkable human being. Need another reason for seeing *Othello?* To stake claim for the future of having witnessed one of the great performances of our time."

Sight and Sound, Summer 1966
"Olivier exposes unsparingly the bestiality of a creature possessed by passion; in its unbuttoned grace the performance is marvelously in tune with the spirit of its age. The anguished progress of his jealous rage has all the cruel excitement of the bull fight."

Films and Filming, May 1966
"The center of interest is Laurence Olivier's performance as the Moor. This is acting of a virtuosity that is rare even in the theater now. Watching it like this, it is important to remember that Olivier knows the difference between stage and cinema as well as any man alive. We have proof elsewhere of his compatibility with the camera, and we need look back no further than his junket-eater in *Bunny Lake Is Missing* for a reminder of his talent for underplaying. Here it is as

if the camera were an interloper. The actor repeats his stage performance, which was already placed in relief and seems more now. What we see is not a performance that works on film, but an X-ray of theatrical technique. As such it is beyond valuation, because the technique in itself is superlative. An uncommonly privileged view of a great actor at work."

Martin Gottfried, September 26, 1966 *Opening Nights* (New York: G. P. Putnam's Sons, 1969), p. 276. "Laurence Olivier's 'Othello' is the definitive one. His is the 'Othello' of a lifetime. His makeup is Negroid and his accent African. More than that, he has actually *become* Negro, assuming the physical characteristics, the bodily structure, and the movement mannerisms of the race. What does 'acting' mean, if not that? In this creation of the basic human animal, Olivier reached a monumental peak. He is the greatest actor alive on the English-speaking stage."

Franco Zeffirelli (of Olivier's performance)
"I was told that this was the last flourish of the romantic tradition of acting. It's nothing of the sort. It's an anthology of everything that has been discovered about acting in the last three centuries. It's grand and majestic, but it's also modern and realistic. I would call it a lesson for us all."[29]

Jack J. Jorgens, *Shakespeare on Film,* p. 194. "Olivier's triumph is that he liberates film audiences from trivial, demeaning images of man and allows us a glimpse of a splendid, more Shakespearean image of an earlier age. Olivier accomplishes something that the director-ridden art of film seldom permits: an unfettered actor-generated performance. Othello is always larger than life, even in his quieter scenes, and in the big scenes Olivier reaches for a grand, breathtaking presence lost to audiences since the nineteenth century. His costumes and gestures are flamboyant, his speeches lyrical and beautifully finished, and despite a West Indian veneer and notes of domestic playfulness and tenderness, the *character's* performance (not merely Olivier's) reeks of the magnificence of the stage."[30]

Pauline Kael, *New Yorker,* February 19, 1966
"*Othello* with Laurence Olivier is a filmed record of the theatrical production; it would be our loss if we waited for posterity to discover it. Olivier's negro Othello—Deep voice with a trace of foreign music in it, happy, thick, self-satisfied laugh; rolling buttocks; grand and barbaric and, yes, a little lewd—almost makes this great impossible play work."

With Frank Finlay as Iago.
  Othello: **"Dost thou hear, Iago?**
            I will be found most cunning in my patience;
            But—dost thou hear—most bloody."
                        (William Shakespeare.)

**Frank Finlay was cited as Best Actor for his perform-
ance as Iago at the San Sebastian International Film
Festival in 1966.**

New York Times, April 22, 1964
"It is Sir Laurence who keeps pressing back into the mind. The Shakespeare anniversary could not have a finer piece of individual homage than this performance."

Daily Mail, London, April 22, 1964
"Olivier played 'Othello' for the first time and scored a resounding triumph. He has scaled the last unconquered Everest and planted his standard firmly, triumphantly on the top."

The Herald, London, April 22, 1964
"He triumphs in a performance that is a combination of great physical and bravura acting and considerable thought."

Daily Express, London, April 22, 1964
"It is a performance of grace, terror and insolence. I shall dream of its mysteries for years to come."

The Guardian, London, April 22, 1964
"Olivier struck deeper chords than I have heard from him. The sheer variety and range of the actor's art made it an experience in the theatre altogether unforgettable."

Thomas Lask, *New York Times,* "n.d.", (Phonograph record supplement)
"A signal for much rejoicing. A performance of great power, with an Elizabethan sweep and with a fascinating portrayal of the character of the Moor. A performance of enormous vitality."

COMMENTS

In 1962, Olivier was named director of the National Theatre. The inaugural production at the historic Old Vic Theatre was *Hamlet,* presented in October, 1963, with Peter O'Toole, Rosemary Harris, Michael Redgrave, Diana Wynyard, and Max Adrian. "That this combination failed to burst into the brightest of flames," wrote London critic T. C. Worsley, "must be accounted one of those unlucky accidents familiar to everyone connected with the theatre." *Hamlet* was performed for only twenty-seven performances and was joined in repertory by the successful Chichester production of *Uncle Vanya,* with Olivier repeating the role of Astrov. He also appeared as Captain Brazen in George Farquhar's restoration comedy, *The Recruiting Officer* and as Halvard Solness in Ibsen's *The Master Builder.*

In 1964, Olivier undertook the title role in Shakespeare's *Othello,* achieving one of his greatest successes. For a long while he had been reluctant to play the part and explained to Kenneth Tynan. "It's very tough on your imagination, it's very tough on your resourcefulness of variations of all kinds, and therefore, it's also a very great strain physically." The actor went through a long period of vocal training to increase the depth of his voice and spent six months of rigorous physical training to prepare his body for the peak fitness required to play the demanding role.

The production became the biggest hit of the theatrical season, with all night queues forming outside the Old Vic in a constant demand for tickets. The press and public praised Olivier's Othello as definitive. George R. Marek, vice-president of RCA Records, commented in the album notes for the recorded version that he had seen every Othello on the New York stage, beginning with Walter Hampden and Paul Robeson, plus on the stages of London and Vienna, "and to me Olivier's interpretation is by far the most satisfactory, by far the greatest."

A gala audience of 1,200 greeted Olivier and members of the National Theatre with a ten minute standing ovation at the Kremlin Theater when the production visited Moscow in September, 1965. The National Theatre was the first Western theatrical company to play in the Kremlin Theater. Replying to the prolonged applause, Olivier said in well-accented Russian, "Comrades, it has been our dream to play for you here in Moscow. We want to thank you for having made our dream so beautiful." An account of the Russian visit was recorded in a short documentary film.

In a three week period in July of 1965, Stuart Burge who had directed the film recording of *Uncle Vanya,* supervised the filming of *Othello.* It was filmed under studio conditions, with no cuts from the stage version, nor the addition of exterior shots. Film critic Pauline Kael citing Olivier's "thirty-five years in movies and master-

With Derek Jacobi (right) as Cassio. Mr. Jacobi received wide acclaim a decade later for his television performances in *I Claudius* and Shakespeare's *Richard II*.

piece upon masterpiece acclaimed in the theatre" finds it surprising he could not raise money to do a real movie version of his Othello. "Olivier's greatness is in his acting; as a movie director, he is merely excellent and intelligent. Yet his Shakespearean performances deserve—at the minimum—the kind of movie he or other talented directors might do, what he brought to *Henry V, Hamlet, Richard III*. It is a scandal, an indictment of Anglo-American civilization and values, that eight million dollars can go into a spy spoof, twelve into a comic chase, twenty-seven into a spectacle, for Olivier in *Othello*, we and history must content ourselves with a quickie recording process. And yet the joke is on the spoofs, chases, and spectacles. *Othello* lives. Olivier's presence on the screen is the pictorial beauty of heroism. Perhaps that is why we may leave the photographed version of *Othello* with a sense of exaltation and the wonder of sheer admiration."[31]

Olivier received his seventh Academy Award nomination for his performance as the Moor. The 1965 Oscar was awarded to Lee Marvin for his portrayal of an alcoholic gunslinger in *Cat Ballou*.

175

THEY SAY THE NILE STILL RUNS RED FROM THE BATTLE FOR KHARTOUM!

CHARLTON HESTON
as GORDON

The City
That Became
A Torch—
The Torch
That Fired
The World!

LAURENCE OLIVIER
as THE MAHDI

RICHARD JOHNSON
RALPH RICHARDSON

A JULIAN BLAUSTEIN
PRODUCTION

"*Khartoum*"

Produced by
JULIAN BLAUSTEIN

Written by
ROBERT ARDREY

Directed by
BASIL DEARDEN

Filmed in
ULTRA PANAVISION®

ORIGINAL MOTION PICTURE SCORE AVAILABLE ON UNITED ARTISTS' RECORDS.
FERRANTE & TEICHER SINGLE OF MAIN THEME AVAILABLE ON UA RECORDS.

TECHNICOLOR® Released thru UNITED ARTISTS

T H E A T R E

Khartoum

1966, United Artists release of a Julian Blaustein production, presented by Cinerama; Produced by Julian Blaustein; Screenplay by Robert Ardrey; Music composed and conducted by Frank Cordell; Photography, Ted Scaife; Editor, Fergus McDonnell; Art director, John Howell; Special effects, Richard Parker; Production supervisor, Charles Orme; Directed by Basil Dearden

CAST

General Charles Gordon	Charlton Heston
The Mahdi	Laurence Olivier
Col. J. D. H. Stewart	Richard Johnson
Prime Minister Gladstone	Ralph Richardson
Sir Evelyn Baring	Alexander Knox
Khaleel	Johnny Sekka
Lord Granville	Michael Hordern
Zobeir Pasha	Zia Mohyeddin
Sheikh Osman	Marne Maitland
Gen. Wolseley	Nigel Green
Lord Hartington	Hugh Williams
The Khalifa Abdullah	Douglas Wilmer
Col. Hicks	Edward Underdown
Bordeini Bey	Alec Mango
Giriagis Bey	George Pastell
Major Kitchener	Peter Arne
Awaan	Alan Tilvern
Herbin	Michael Anthony
Frank Power	Jerome Willis
Dancer	Leila
Lord Northbrook	Ronald Leigh Hunt
Sir Charles Dilke	Ralph Michael

Opened July 13, 1966, Warner Theater, New York

THE FILM

A British general and 10,000 untrained Egyptian troops are massacred by a fanatical Arab religious leader known as the Mahdi. Prime Minister Gladstone sends General Charles "Chinese" Gordon to the Sudan to evacuate 13,000 troops and civilians. Preparing for a siege, Gordon is ambushed by the Mahdi's dervishes and saved by a column of Egyptian cavalry led by Colonel Stewart. Gladstone refuses to believe Gordon's situation is serious and does not send additional troops. Stewart runs the Arab blockade to reason with Gladstone, who finally agrees to dispatch General Wolseley and 7,000 handpicked men to rescue Gordon but not to save Khartoum. Gordon steadfastly refuses to abandon the besieged city. The Mahdi tries to dissuade Gordon from his defense of Khartoum, but the British leader refuses to back down. Hopelessly outnumbered, his starving soldiers heave themselves into position for the last stand and the Mahdi's hordes sweep over them. The unarmed Gordon is impaled on a spear as the hysterical dervishes overrun Khartoum.

REVIEWS

Variety, June 15, 1966
"Olivier, playing the Mahdi, is excellent in creating audience terror of a zealot who sincerely believes that a mass slaughter is Divine Will, while projecting respect and compassion for his equally-religious adversary, Heston. The role calls for Olivier to have a darkened face, relative physical immobility and heavily-garbed body. Thus, through eyes and voice only, his impact is all the more noteworthy."

Time magazine, August 5, 1966
"Olivier's Mahdi is a small masterpiece of single-minded religious insanity—the lambent black eyes never blinking, the measured voice conjuring up holy terrors from his private heart of darkness."

New York Times, July 14, 1966
"The role of the Mahdi is so impressively and eloquently played by a dark-stained Sir Laurence Olivier, wearing a gleaming white burnoose and addressing his seething cohorts and General Gordon in beautifully chiseled words, that it is not surprising that he puts the gold-braided figure of Mr. Heston's Chinese Gordon in the shade."

The Mahdi (1966).
"His skin was dark, almost as dark as that of a Sudani, and it seemed darker against the impeccable white of his robes; there was a mole on his left cheek which he liked to declare was the symbol of his divinity, as was also, he would say, the slight gap between his front teeth; for this man, to his followers at least, was indeed little less than a god." (From *Khartoum* by Alan Caillou.)

The Mahdi: "I shall take Khartoum in blood, and the streets will run in blood, and the Nile will taste of blood for one hundred miles, and every Egyptian will die; every child, woman, man, Sudanese too, who opposes the will of my Lord Mohammed will die. This is how it must be in Khartoum—great and terrible thing."

Playing *Othello* Olivier spent three hours preparing and removing his all-black body makeup. In December, 1965, while filming *Khartoum* he had to black-up for Othello one day and repeat the process all over again the next day for his role as the Mahdi, the fanatical religious leader of desert tribes. Weeks of voice lessons enabled the actor to lower his voice a full octave for his stage performances as the Moor, while his playing of the Mahdi required a singsong voice of considerably higher pitched sounds. His meticulous preparation for the film role found him at Pinewood Studios each morning for a three hour session of makeup, where he endeavored to get every physical detail as accurate as possible, including the v-shaped gap in the Moslem leader's front teeth.

Introducing the epic adventure to television audiences, Judith Crist called the film "another example of a thinking-man's spectacular, thanks to a literate screenplay." On the occasion of the television debut of *Khartoum,* Miss Crist wrote in *TV Guide,* "Charlton Heston gives his best performance to date as the enigmatic General 'Chinese' Gordon and Laurence Olivier is simply stunning as the Mahdi, fanatic leader of the dervishes."

With Charlton Heston as General Gordon. Heston was disturbed by the critical response following his stage appearance in *The Tumbler,* which was directed by Olivier in 1960. "I guess I should learn to dismiss the bad reviews," the actor confided to Olivier, who advised, "Learn to dismiss the good ones."

"'THE SHOES OF THE FISHERMAN' RESTORES FAITH IN FILMS!"

—Look Magazine

A distinguished international cast ignites all the dramatic power... all the magnificent spectacle of Morris L. West's best-selling novel.

Metro-Goldwyn-Mayer presents a George Englund production

THE SHOES OF THE FISHERMAN

starring **Anthony Quinn**
Oskar Werner
David Janssen
Vittorio De Sica
Leo McKern · John Gielgud
Barbara Jefford · Rosemarie Dexter
and **Laurence Olivier**

screenplay by John Patrick and James Kennaway
based on the novel by Morris L West · directed by Michael Anderson · produced by George Englund
Panavision and Metrocolor MGM

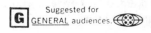

Suggested for GENERAL audiences.

180

The Shoes of the Fisherman

1968, A George Englund Production, presented by Metro-Goldwyn-Mayer; Screenplay by John Patrick and James Kennaway, based on the novel by Morris L. West; Music composed by Alex North; Director of photography, Erwin Hillier; Editor, Ernest Walter; Art director, Edward Carfagno; Production supervisor, Stanley Goldsmith; Costumes, Orietta Nasalli-Rocca; Assistant directors, Tony Brandt, Victor Tourjansky; Produced by George Englund; Directed by Michael Anderson

CAST

Kiril Lakota	Anthony Quinn
Piotr Llyich Kamenev	Laurence Olivier
Fr. David Telemond	Oskar Werner
George Faber	David Janssen
Cardinal Rinaldi	Vittorio De Sica
Cardinal Leone	Leo McKern
The Elder Pope	John Gielgud
Dr. Ruth Faber	Barbara Jefford
Chiara	Rosemarie Dexter
Igor Bounin	Frank Finlay
Peng	Burt Kwouk
Gelasio	Arnoldo Foa
Augustinian	Paul Rogers
Gorshenin	George Pravda
Vucovich	Clive Revill
Capuchin Monk	Niall MacGinnis
Cardinal Rahamani	Marne Maitland
The Marchesa	Isa Miranda
Brian	George Harper
Dying Man's Friend	Leopoldo Trieste
Dominican	Jean Rougeul
English Cardinals	Peter Copley
	Arthur Howard

Opened November 14, 1968, DeMille Theater, New York

THE FILM

Once a prisoner in a Russian labor camp, Kiril Lakota becomes the Pontiff of the Roman church and is singled out to solve crucial political problems where all the world leaders have failed. In a last desperate effort to prevent World War III, a secret meeting is arranged and Pope Kiril I finds himself as the Devil's Advocate between East and West. A secondary plot involves a reconciliation between Dr. Ruth Faber and her husband, a television commentator who explains the traditions of the Vatican and reveals the news of Chinese famine and troop movement on the Russian border which affects the actions of the Pope and other world leaders.

REVIEWS

Variety, November 20, 1968
"A most timely narrative. Quinn's performance is excellent. Olivier, along with Frank Finlay and Clive Revill are superior in projecting not unsympathetic Russian politicians."

New York Post, November 15, 1968
"Among the gems are Olivier's confrontation with Quinn after his twenty year imprisonment. Makes you feel the world would be a safe place if we had Laurence Olivier as the Soviet premier and Anthony Quinn as the Pope to guide the western world."

New York *Daily News,* November 15, 1968
"I was impressed by the actors and acting—Laurence Olivier in almost perfect disguise as the Soviet premier."

COMMENTS

In June of 1967, Olivier, then sixty, was hospitalized for cancer of the prostate gland, aggravated by pneumonia. At the time he had been directing a production of *Three Sisters* for the National Theatre. His role as Tattle in *Love for Love* was assumed by Derek Jacobi and he was succeeded in *The Dance of Death* by Anthony Hopkins.

In October he was well enough to embark upon a Canadian tour, but was forced to withdraw *Othello* from his repertoire due to the strenuous demands the part required. Speaking to Howard Taubman of the *New York Times,* Olivier expressed regret at having to say farewell to the Moor "I hated to give up *Othello,* but I had to. It was a seven hour stint—two to put my makeup on, one to take it off and four for the play. It's

181

Kamenev in *The Shoes of the Fisherman* (1968).

Olivier as the Soviet premier, Anthony Quinn as Pope Kirik and Bert Kwouk as Peng.

quite a part but I doubt that I shall ever play it again.'' On another occasion he referred to Othello as the most demanding role in drama. ''It is merciless. It never stops spurring its interpreter 'Now be good, be very good,' it seems to urge. 'Now better than that, now be your best, yes, once more—and now better than that.' It is absolutely relentless, always calling for more and more and more.''

The Canadian slate included *A Flea in Her Ear* in which Olivier played the indignant butler, Etienne Plucheux, *The Dance of Death,* and William Congreve's *Love for Love.* ''Sir Laurence's own tongue is visibly tucked in his cheek,'' Dan Sullivan wrote of his Tattle in the *New York Times.* ''—when he isn't biting it or sticking it out at somebody—as he dances his way through the part. He slinks, he minces, he rolls his eyes to Heaven, he absorbs insults with long Jack Benny 'takes.' He is a howl. But he is not—a tribute to his tact as an ensemble player and to the skill of this particular ensemble—the whole show.''

When the Restoration comedy was recorded for RCA Victor, Thomas Lask said ''the merits of the play must take second place to this performance. I do not know whether people in the eighteenth century spoke or behaved this way, but they should have. All that the human voice can do to give meaning to words, add shade and nuance to a phrase, or supply a hint through a cool or heightened tone is done on these records. Not a syllable is lost, not an emphasis slighted. Indeed if nothing else, it is a feast just to hear English spoken as it is here. Perhaps the idea is to have someone like Sir Laurence in your corner, for then you can't fail.''[32]

In February 1968, Olivier underwent surgery in London for removal of his appendix. He had suffered pain while performing in the Strindberg play in Edinburgh, Scotland and finished a performance despite the inconvenience and was flown 480 miles to London for the operation. Continued cobalt treatments, meanwhile, successfully retarded the cancer.

Romeo and Juliet

1968, Paramount Release of a British Home Entertainment production, in association with Verona Productions and Dino De Laurentis Cinematografica. Produced by Anthony Havelock-Allan and John Brabourne; Associate Producer, Richard Goodwin; Screenplay by Franco Brusati and Masolino D'Amico from William Shakespeare's play; Photography, Pasquale de Santis; Production designer, Renzo Mongiardino; Art director, Luciano Puccini; Costume designer, Danilo Donati; Set decorator, Christine Edzard; Editor, Reginald Mills; Music by Nino Rota; Directed by Franco Zeffirelli

CAST

Prologue and Epilogue	Laurence Olivier
Juliet	Olivia Hussey
Romeo	Leonard Whiting
Friar Laurence	Milo O'Shea
Tybalt	Michael York
Mercutio	John McEnery
Nurse	Pat Heywood
Prince of Verona	Robert Stephens
Lady Capulet	Natasha Perry
Balthazar	Keith Skinner
Gregory	Richard Warwick
Sampson	Dyson Lovell
Abraham	Ugo Barbone
Benvolio	Bruce Robinson
Lord Capulet	Paul Hardwick
Lord Montague	Antonio Pierfederici
Lady Montague	Esmerelda Ruspoli
Count Paris	Roberto Bisacco
Peter	Roy Holder
Friar John	Aldo Miranda
Page to Tybalt	Dario Tanzini

Opened October 8, 1968, at the Paris Theater, New York

THE FILM

Shakespeare's immortal tragedy of star-crossed lovers in Renaissance Italy. Juliet, daughter of Capulet, meets the masked Romeo, son of her father's archenemy, at a ball and falls in love with him. At her window she soliloquizes on her feelings and Romeo, who overhears her, pledges eternal love with equal passion. They are secretly wed, but Romeo is soon banished for killing Tybalt, Juliet's cousin. When Juliet is informed by her father that she must marry Paris, she accepts a potion from Friar Laurence which puts her into a temporary deathlike trance. Romeo, thinking she is dead, kills himself. When Juliet awakes she finds her lover lying dead beside her and stabs herself.

COMMENTS

Director Franco Zeffirelli revealed the circumstances of Olivier's unbilled contribution as the narrator for his film in an interview with the author. "He had refused to be the narrator of the Laurence Harvey version (John Gielgud narrated the 1954 film). While he was in Rome shooting *The Shoes of the Fisherman* I decided to call him. I wanted an important voice there. The prologue sets a kind of style, so I showed a rough copy of the script to Larry and he loved it. He was in tears! He said, 'Can I do something?', and in five minutes he had done the narration, both the beginning and the end. Then he wanted to do more, so while we were there dubbing, he altered his voice and did the voice of Lord Montague for the Italian actor who played the part. He even dubbed in shouts for the crowd scenes and *still* he said, 'Give me more to do!' He was so lovely."[33]

Jack L. Jorgens in his scholarly volume, *Shakespeare on Film,* calls Zeffirelli's panoramic opening shot "a tribute to the opening of Olivier's *Henry V*." Olivier's name does not appear in the film's credits, and Paramount's early press releases announced the narrator as Murray Head, a young British rock singer who later gained prominence in *Sunday, Bloody Sunday*. Zeffirelli obviously decided against a youthful reading of the prologue, favoring a traditional and articulate presentation. If is difficult to mistake the beauty and delicacy of Olivier's delivery upon viewing the film. Disturbed by the fact that his name was not in the credits, I wrote to Olivier for confirmation, and reluctant to formally announce his unbilled performance, he replied with a cautious wit, "Dear Mr. Daniels, what you suggest does bear some likelihood."[34]

PARAMOUNT PICTURES presents
A BHE FILM
The
FRANCO ZEFFIRELLI
Production of
ROMEO & JULIET

No ordinary love story….

THE FRANCO ZEFFIRELLI PRODUCTION OF WILLIAM SHAKESPEARE'S "ROMEO & JULIET" / STARRING OLIVIA HUSSEY / LEONARD WHITING / MILO O'SHEA / MICHAEL YORK / JOHN McENERY
PAT HEYWOOD / NATASHA PARRY / ROBERT STEPHENS / ... / SCREENPLAY BY FRANCO BRUSATI and MASOLINO D'AMICO
PRODUCED BY ANTHONY HAVELOCK-ALLAN and JOHN BRABOURNE / ASSOCIATE PRODUCER RICHARD GOODWIN / DIRECTED BY FRANCO ZEFFIRELLI TECHNICOLOR® / A PARAMOUNT PICTURE

Olivia Hussey as Juliet and Leonard Whiting as Romeo.
"Two households both alike in dignity,
In fair Verona where we lay our scene,
From ancient grudge break to new mutiny.
Where civil blood makes civil hands unclean.
From forth the fatal loins of these two foes,
A pair of star-crossed lovers take their life;
Whose misadventured piteous overthrows
Do with their death bury their parent's strife . . ."
   (Prologue, *Romeo and Juliet*, William Shakespeare.)

On April 20, 1969, Olivier attended the annual Antoinette Perry Awards presentation at the Mark Hellinger Theater in New York, to accept a special Tony Award for the National Theatre Company of Great Britain. The honor was presented by American playwright, Arthur Miller, who introduced Olivier as "A man whose name has been spoken with undiminished admiration for several decades now, wherever in the world theater exists. A romantic movie star, a sublime comedian, to many he is the greatest Shakespearean actor of our age. In a time of rockets that light up the theatrical sky and vanish in the night, this is a planet."

"A glooming peace this morning with it brings
The sun for sorrow will not show his head,
For never was a story of more woe
Than this of Juliet and her Romeo."
                    (Epilogue, *Romeo and Juliet.*)

Oh! What a Lovely War

1969, Paramount Pictures presentation and release of an Accord Production; Produced by Brian Duffy and Richard Attenborough; Based on Joan Littlewood's stage production by Charles Chilton; Photography, Gerry Turpin; Editor, Kevin Connor; Choreography, Eleanor Fazan; Songs orchestrated and incidental music by Alfred Ralston; Military advisor, Major-General Sir Douglas Campbell; Directed by Richard Attenborough

CAST

Field Marshal Sir John French	Laurence Olivier
Sir Edward Grey	Ralph Richardson
Count Berchtold	John Gielgud
General Sir Henry Wilson	Michael Redgrave
Field Marshal Sir Douglas Haig	John Mills
Emperor Franz Josef	Jack Hawkins
Stephen	Dirk Bogarde
President Poincare	Ian Holm
Kaiser Wilhelm II	Kenneth More
Music Hall Star	Maggie Smith
Eleanor	Susannah York
Sir John	Cecil Parker
Staff Officer	Robert Flemyng
French Colonel	Jean Pierre Cassel
Lady Grey	Muriel Forbes
Sylvia Pankhurst	Vanessa Redgrave
First Nurse at Station	Juliet Mills
Second Nurse at Station	Nanette Newman
Archduke Franz Ferdinand	Wensley Pithey
Duchess Sophie	Ruth Kettlewell
General von Moltke	John Clements
Tsar Nicholas II	Paul Daneman
Photographer	Joe Melia
Dickie Smith	Kim Smith
Mary Smith	Mary Wimbush
Jack Smith	Paul Shelley
Flo Smith	Wendy Allnutt
Grandpa Smith	John Rae
Edna Smith	Kathleen Wileman

Sir Michael Redgrave as General Sir Henry Wilson (left), director Richard Attenborough, and Olivier on location for *Oh! What a Lovely War.*

Olivier's performance as Field Marshall Sir John French won him the Best Supporting Actor honor from the Society of Film and Television Arts.

Bertie Smith	Corin Redgrave
Freddie Smith	Malcolm McFee
Harry Smith	Colin Farrell
George Smith	Maurice Roeves
Betty Smith	Angela Thorne
Recruiting sergeant	David Lodge
Private Burgess	Peter Gilmore
Sir John French's lady	Isabel Dean
Gen. Sir William Robertson	Guy Middleton
Sir William Robertson's lady	Natasha Perry
Staff Officers	Norman Shelley
	Thorley Walters
Lady Haig	Phyllis Calvert
First Heckler	Clifford Millison
Second Heckler	Dorothy Reynolds
Third Heckler	Harry Locke
Drunken Corporal	Michael Bates
Australian Singer	Vincent Ball
Estaminet Singer	Pia Columbo
Clergyman	Gerald Sim
Soldier Singer	Maurice Arthur

Premiered New York Film Festival, Lincoln Center, October 2, 1969; Opened October 3, Paris Theater, New York

THE FILM

Oh! What a Lovely War was based on Joan Littlewood's London review which opened on Broadway in 1964. The entertainment was a satire on World War I, illustrating the waste and futility of war through a series of period songs and sketches. The film built an elaborate bridge between stage fantasy and movie realism, observing the war and its waste through the eyes of the Smith family, who visit a Brighton amusement pier to see a war exhibit. The Smith boys eventually go to war and are all senselessly destroyed. Military and diplomatic figures, music hall singers, nurses, and suffragettes are woven into the panoramic satire, along with thirty-five wartime songs.

REVIEWS

New York Times, October 4, 1969
"A big, elaborate, sometimes realistic film whose elephantine physical proportions and often brilliant all-star cast simply overwhelm the material with a surfeit of good intentions. Laurence Olivier, John Mills, and Michael Redgrave are staff officers who might have been conceived by Punch, but whose lines are often recorded history."

Judith Crist, *New York* magazine, October 6, 1969
"It is not merely at this point the best film of 1969 but an outstanding film for all time. Attenborough has brought to it the impeccable taste and professionalism that have been the hallmarks of his acting career. Celebrities and dignitaries are portrayed by the crème de la crème of England's acting profession; the result is not the usual cameo-studded spectacular but a unique star-spangled spectacle across which comets flash—here Olivier as the mumblingly blimpish Sir John French of the liquorish eye; there Gielgud, a wily Von Berchtold, manipulating Jack Hawkins as the silent droop-lidded Kaiser; now Maggie Smith, raucous and insidious as a Lilith of the music hall—and hovering over all, reveling in the game and personal consultations with God, John Mills as Haig, supreme commander of the butchery that claims nine million casualties."
Copyright © 1969 by the NYM Corporation. Reprinted with the permission of *New York* magazine.

New York *Daily News,* October 4, 1969
"Olivier is superbly smooth, amusing, properly stuffy as Sir John French, who loses his command of British forces to an upstart, who 'has something to do with whiskey,' Sir Douglas Haig."

New York Post, October 4, 1969
"It gives you half the great acting stars of England, and you should be astounded by the

An actor prepares—Olivier receives dance instruction for the ballroom sequence in *Oh! What a Lovely War.*

189

marvel of Sir Laurence Olivier's Sir John French. It is certainly a masterpiece that will endure and have deep meaning as long as nations have leaders, and wars, and people who go to wars and families who stay behind."

Variety, April 16, 1969
"Dedicated, exhilarating, shrewd, mocking, funny, emotional, witty, poignant and technically brilliant. Laurence Olivier agreed to appear as Field Marshal Sir John French and gives a sly, blimpish performance. After Olivier's okay it was easier for Accord to get the backing and, once he could tie up schedules, for the director to get further plush names to boost marquee and publicity. Four other distinguished knights (Richardson, Clements, Gielgud and Redgrave) play highup martial, royal and diplomatic figures.* It may be a long time before a better, more moving and significant film emanates from a British (or, indeed, any) studio."

The Sun, "n.d."
"The knights of English acting take their places as diplomats or warlords and allow Olivier to steal the scenes away in a brief but brilliant performance."

With the subsequent knighthood of director Attenborough and actor John Mills, the film is quite likely a record holder for its contribution by an assemblage of knighted actors.

COMMENTS

Olivier won a supporting actor award from the Society of Film and Television Arts and commented, "I've been giving support to my fellow artists for years. I'm glad to have won a Supporting Role award. Anyone can get one for a star role."

Richard Attenborough in an interview with Wanda Hale of the *New York Daily News* commented on Olivier's contribution as Sir John French. "Larry is a staggering actor. Sir John was a buffoon and that's how he plays the role, with white hair and moustache. Without padding he becomes the thickset older man merely by the use of his body. At the beginning, Larry came to me and said, 'Dickie, help me, tell me in what style to play Sir John. I need your direction.' It could have been calculated, but if so, it touched me, this greatest of all actors asking for my guidance."

Olivier relished the opportunity to play the broadly comic cartoon portrait of Sir John French. "I love comedy. I like it much better than the dramatic element in the acting world. I've always believed that a comedian can be a greater tragedian than an all-out tragedian. I think that's due to the fact that comedy has more to do, or seems to have more to do, with humanity. I'm sure that the greatest tragedians are all comedians. A tragedian takes himself too seriously. He is inclined to think about the extremely moving and noble nature of his work as a pianist might think about his fingers. There's something more human, more appealing to nature about a comedian and when they come to play tragedy, they give it an element that it doesn't usually have. That's tremendously valuable. They're taught not to take themselves too seriously.

"I keep trying to do comedy myself. I just adore it. *Lovely War* gave me much happiness to do. I'm afraid it's a very extreme ridicule of the character, but that's the office of satire. The point of satire is to set up the high and mighty. Haig, Kitchener, the Kaiser—they're all thrown mud at, but that's the purpose of that realm of drama and we have to accept it. It's been going on since the Greeks right up to the most modern revues. That's the idea—mock the high and mighty."

Battle of Britain

1969, United Artists release of a Harry Saltzman production, Produced by Harry Saltzman and S. Benjamin Fisz; Screenplay by James Kennaway and William Greatorex; Photography, Freddie Young; Music composed by Ron Goodwin; "Battle in the Air" theme by Sir William Walton; Assistant Director, Derek Cracknell; Aerial and Second Unit Director, David Bracknell; Directed by Guy Hamilton

CAST

Air Chief Marshal Sir Hugh Dowding	Laurence Olivier
Flt. Lt. Sqn. Harvey	Christopher Plummer
British Minister in Switzerland	Ralph Richardson
Sqn. Ldr. Skipper	Robert Shaw
Senior Civil Servant	Harry Andrews
Air Vice-marshal Evill	Michael Redgrave
Air Vice-marshal Keith Park	Trevor Howard
Sqn. Ldr. Canfield	Michael Caine
Baron Von Richter	Curt Jurgens
Section Officer Maggie Harvey	Susannah York
Group Captain Hope	Nigel Patrick
Group Captain Baker	Kenneth More
Sgt. Pilot Andy	Ian McShane
Air Vice-marshal Trafford Leigh-Mallory	Patrick Wymark
Warrant Officer Warrick	Michael Bates
Jamie	James Cosmo
Wing Commander Willoughby	Robert Flemyng
Sgn. Ldr. Edwards	Barry Foster
Pilot Officer Archie	Edward Fox
Sqn. Ldr. Evans	W. G. Foxley
Skipper's Wife	Sarah Lawson
Andy's wife	Isla Blair
Farmer	John Bascomb
Willoughby's Asst. Controller	Tom Chatto
Sgt. Pilot Chris	David Griffin
Senior Air Staff Officer	Jack Gwillim
Peter	Myles Hoyle
Pasco	Mark Mahez
French N. C. O.	André Maranne
A minister	Anthony Nichols
Simon	Nicholas Pennell
Ox	Andrzey Scibor
Jean-Jacques	Jean Wladon
Major Brandt	Alexander Allerson
Feldmarschall Milch	Dietrich Frauboes
Brandt's navigator	Alf Jungermann
Bruno	Reinhard Horras
Boehm	Helmut Kircher
Major Foehn	Paul Newhaus
Beppo Schmid	Malte Petzel
Major Falke	Manfred Reddemann
General Osterkamp	Wilfred Van Aacken
Jeschonnek	Karl Otto Alberty
Feldmarschall Kesselring	Peter Hager
General Fink	Wolf Harnish
Reichmarschall Goering	Heim Riess
Hitler	Rolf Stiefel

Opened October 20, 1969, DeMille, Broadway and 86th Street East Theaters, New York

"Battle of Britain"

A Harry Saltzman Production

STARRING IN ALPHABETICAL ORDER:

Harry Andrews Michael Caine Trevor Howard Curt Jurgens Ian McShane Kenneth More Laurence Olivier Nigel Patrick
Christopher Plummer Michael Redgrave Ralph Richardson Robert Shaw Patrick Wymark Susannah York

PRODUCED BY Harry Saltzman AND S. Benjamin Fisz SCREENPLAY BY James Kennaway AND Wilfred Greatorex
DIRECTED BY Guy Hamilton COLOR BY Technicolor® FILMED IN Panavision®

Never in the field of human conflict was so much owed by so many to so few.

Winston Churchill

Two acting knights were reunited to play officers once more for a different war. Sir Michael Redgrave as Air Vice Marshal Evill and Olivier as Sir Hugh Dowding in *Battle of Britain.*

THE FILM

Churchill's immortal words were in tribute to the Royal Air Force and the valiant young fighter pilots who participated in the battle which marked the crucial turning point of World War II for England and the United States. During the last weeks of the summer of 1940, the exhausted pilots of the RAF rose to meet the fury of the Luftwaffe—the most powerful and destructive air force yet built—and beat back Goering's flyers to save Great Britain and certain defeat. The narrative reveals the battle fatigue, the varying opinions on military tactics, and the overwhelming shortage of planes and pilots. Air Chief Marshal Sir Hugh Dowding, realizing the odds against the RAF, persuaded Churchill to keep as many planes as possible in England if Britain were to stand a chance against the pending invasion. Dowding deploys his limited fighters, outnumbered five to one, tricking the mighty Luftwaffe into ultimate defeat. Military strategies are merged with human portraits of British and German pilots, officers, and political figures who took part in the critical sixteen week drama. Included is a generous sampling of vivid aerial combat footage, restaged for the film with an impressive assemblage of more than one hundred reconditioned Spitfires, Hurricanes, Heinkels, and Messerschmitts.

Films in Review, November, 1969

"The first battle ever to be fought completely in the air, which Winston Churchill called 'The Battle of Britain', was the key battle of World War II and one of the decisive battles of history. This film captures the epic quality of it with remarkable accuracy and is one of the finest war films ever produced. Everyone knows the battle was won by young pilots, some barely in their teens, in fragile fighting planes—the graceful Spitfire and the less graceful but more numerous Hurricane. But everyone does not know that the outcome was a near thing, nor know the name of the one man—if *one* is to be singled out—most responsible for the victory: Hugh Dowding, head of the Royal Air Force's Fighter Command. Laurence Olivier here portrays Dowding—called 'Stuffy' in real life by the pilots—with a selfless austerity and an outspoken bluntness that I found convincing and winning. Olivier's Dowding is an unrelievedly worried, but also a competent man. It's a masterly performance."

New York *Daily News,* October 21, 1969

"A fantastic photographic record of the sixteen dark weeks in 1940 when the underdogs, the RAF, cracked Goering's mighty Luftwaffe. Olivier is quietly excellent as Air Chief Marshal Sir Hugh Dowding."

Variety, September 17, 1969

"The entire film has been stunningly photographed. Standouts among the stars are Laurence Olivier as Sir Hugh Dowding, Fighter Command's supremo. Olivier gives a great performance as the realist who sensed what The Few were up against and, refusing to be glibly and overly optimistic, claimed that defeat was round the corner unless more pilots were obtained."

Battle of Britain was a reflection of one of the most glorious periods in English military history; a tribute to the Royal Air Force and the young fighter pilots, who, during sixteen weeks in the summer of 1940, facing odds of five to one, held off the weight of Hitler's Luftwaffe, which was attacking Britain from occupied France. Sir Hugh Dowding, head of Fighter Command, fought Churchill and the cabinet and reluctantly persuaded them not to send any more fighters to France. His strategy was to wait for the mighty Luftwaffe to come to Britain, then attack. His theory proved right, inflicting the first defeat of Hitler's "invincible" war machine and thwarting Operation Sea Lion, the Nazi invasion of England.

The project appealed to many of Great Britain's top performers who remembered England's courage during those dark hours, and they agreed to appear for a fraction of their normal salaries. Olivier received just $20,000. He had been paid $250,000 for eight days work in *Khartoum.* Olivier recalled his first meeting with Dowding, whom he was to portray in the film, in a televised interview. "I was awfully thrilled, naturally. I had admired him very much. It was Lord Dowding who stopped our aircraft going across to France when Churchill was filled with thoughts of our great allies. Acting isn't really a question of 'being,' as long as you think right and give roughly the right sort of appearance of a character it ought to turn out very real. That sounds like an almighty simplification of the work, and it is—but, the thing is if I could have talked to him, which I did, and try to imagine how he spoke, 'cause he's 86 years old now. He's not as he was twenty-five years ago, which is a surprise to no one. I'm only 61 which is very young indeed, and

Sir Ralph Richardson co-starred with Olivier in *The Divorce of Lady X* (1938) and *Q Planes* (1939) in addition to appearances in *Richard III* (1955), *Khartoum* (1966), *Oh! What a Lovely War* (1969), *Battle of Britain* (above, as the British Minister in Switzerland, 1969), *David Copperfield* (1969), *Lady Caroline Lamb* (1972) and *Jesus of Nazareth* (1976). "Olivier's friendship was a great joy and solace to me, especially in the early years. Laurence had a wonderful gaiety, and I never laughed so much with anyone as with him. When we were young, we were, perhaps foolish. There was also a fundamental difference in our natures. It is only now that we can perceive the reasons for the different tracks we followed." When critic and former National Theatre literary manager, Kenneth Tynan asked Richardson how he differed, as an actor, from Olivier, Sir Ralph replied, "I haven't got Laurence's splendid fury."

not very different from what I was twenty-five years ago, but of course he is very much. His nickname was 'Stuffy' and I didn't know whether that was because his name was Dowding and at school in Winchester or somewhere along the way it became dowdy, which meant stuffy. But it wasn't the case. It happened in the air force due to his withdrawn manner. He isn't stuffy at all to meet. He may be stuffy if you don't know him. He'd never mix in the mess at all 'cause he felt it might make the others feel awkward, and that fact made them call him Stuffy.''

Dowding was invited to Pinewood Studios during the filming and to see some of the rushes. Leonard Mosley explained the visit in his account of the making of the film. ''In real life, Olivier is something of an extrovert (though most of his admirers do not seem aware of this fact); he is gay, jokey and convivial, anxious to be liked, full of anecdotes, apt to be daringly shocking if he thinks his particular companions are the least bit squeamish or puritanical. This was a personality exactly contrary to that of Hugh Dowding, an introvert with an inbuilt but invisible volcano if there ever was one. Dowding was a vegetarian, a spiritualist, a character whose lips and very being seemed to be pursed against the utterance of any indiscretion; a man whose life had been one of dedicated restraint.

''It is a measure of Olivier's skill that he has not only recognized this from his researches but was determined that his portrayal of him should not traduce the rigid spirit of the man.'' After watching a scene in which Dowding confronts an official sent by Churchill who reminds the air chief that they are hopelessly outnumbered, the former air chief was visibly moved. Olivier as Dowding replies to the official with an expression of whispered confidence, ''Our young men will just have to shoot down their young men at a rate of five to one.'' The rigidly controlled Dowding wept upon viewing the scene, but not before noting, ''His moustache was a bit sandy, wasn't it? Was mine really as gingery as that?''[35]

David Copperfield

1969, Twentieth Century Fox release of an Omnibus Production; Screenplay by Jack Pulman from Charles Dickens' novel; Music composed by Malcolm Arnold; Photography, Ken Hodges; Editor, Peter Boita; Art Director, Vetchinsky; Costume Design, Antony Mendelson; Produced by Frederick Brogger; Directed by Delbert Mann

CAST

David Copperfield	Robin Phillips
Mr. Creakle	Laurence Olivier
Mr. Micawber	Ralph Richardson
Mr. Peggotty	Michael Redgrave
Mr. Dick	Emlyn Williams
Aunt Betsey	Edith Evans
Mr. Tungay	Richard Attenborough
Barkis	Cyril Cusack
Mrs. Micawber	Wendy Hiller
Uriah Heep	Ron Moody
Agnes Wickfield	Susan Hampshire
Emily	Sinead Cusack
Mr. Murdstone	James Donald
Clara Peggotty	Megs Jenkins
Steerforth	Corin Redgrave
Ham	Andrew McCulloch
Little David	Alastair Mackenzie
Porter at White Swan Inn	James Hayter
Jane Murdstone	Anna Massey
Thomas Traddles	Nicholas Pennell
Mr. Quinion	Liam Redmond
Clara Copperfield	Isobel Black
Mary Ann	Helen Cotterill
Little Emily	Kim Craik
Boy	Brian Tipping
Girl	Alison Blair
Doctor	William Lyon-Brown
Midwife	Christine Ozanne
Prostitute	Phoebe Shaw
Mr. Sharp	Robert Lankesheer
Martha	Ann Stallybrass

Mr. Wickfield	Donald Layne-Smith
Young Steerforth	Christopher Moran
Young Traddles	Jeffrey Chandler
Clergyman	George Woodbridge
Milkman	Gordon Rollings

An NBC television presentation, March 15, 1970, released for commercial film distribution in Great Britain

THE FILM

In the remake of the Charles Dickens' classic, first filmed in 1935 by George Cukor, a mature Copperfield returns to Yarmouth to reflect upon his childhood and seek out some purpose and meaning to his life. In flashbacks, David recalls his misery as an orphan child, his employment at Murdstone's bottle factory, schooling at Salem House Academy with the sadistic Creakle, his romance with Dora and their marriage with its joys and disillusionments, and emergence as a successful novelist. On Dover Cliffs, David is reunited with Agnes Wickfield who has always loved him.

REVIEWS

London Sunday Times, January 4, 1970
"Olivier as Creakle has the menace of distant thunder."

London Daily Mail, December 30, 1969
"As for the ferocious headmaster, Mr. Creakle, hardly have we seen through another of Sir Laurence Olivier's marvelous disguises before he is gone."

Variety, January 14, 1970
"Laurence Olivier as the schoolmaster Creakle, and Richard Attenborough as his cringing, one-legged assistant, Tungay, light up the screen in about sixty seconds flat in their brilliant brief appearances."

New York *Daily News,* March 16, 1970
"Although Olivier is probably the foremost actor of the English-speaking world, he appeared in the comparatively small part of the cruel headmaster of young David's school. But his performance was superb."

New York Times, March 16, 1970
"The film came alive as Sir Laurence Olivier invoked the brutality of the headmaster of Salem School."

COMMENTS

Director Delbert Mann recalled the uncanny skill Olivier demonstrated while filming a brief sequence with the young actor who portrayed David. "In the scene Davy was coming towards him, followed by the camera which was studying Sir L's reactions. As the little boy approached, Olivier could see that he was going to miss the mark on the floor where he was supposed to halt. Taking his cane which he had rested on his shoulder, like a rifle, he reached forward with it and steered the little boy 'home.' However, the gesture was so disguised that it appeared in the scene as anything but a stage direction."[36]

Creakle in *David Copperfield* (1969).

With Richard Attenborough as Mr. Tungay. "A perfect Dickensian double act." (*London Evening Standard.*)

Three Sisters

1970, Lion International Release of Alan Clore Films' presentation of Laurence Olivier's production for the National Theatre Company; Based on Anton Chekhov's play, translated by Moura Budberg; Photography, Geoffrey Unsworth; Art Director, Bill Hutchinson; Costumes, Beatrice Dawson; Music composed by Sir William Walton; Editor, Jack Harris; Executive Producer, Alan Clore; Produced by John Goldstone; Directed by Laurence Olivier

CAST

Vershinin	Alan Bates
Chebutikin	Laurence Olivier
Masha	Joan Plowright
Irina	Louise Purnell
Olga	Jeanne Watts
Andrei	Derek Jacobi
Natasha	Sheila Reid
Kulighin	Kenneth Mackintosh
Anfissa	Daphne Heard
Ferrapont	Harry Lomax
Tusenbach	Ronald Pickup
Solloni	Frank Wylie
Fedotik	Richard Kay
Rode	David Belcher
Orderly	George Selaway
Officers	David Munro, Alan Adams, Robert Walker

Opened March 11, 1974, American Film Theater presentation, selected theaters, Metropolitan New York area

THE FILM

Olga, Masha, and Irina Prozoroff lead lonely and purposeless lives following the death of their father who had commanded the local army post. Olga attempts to find satisfaction in teaching but secretly longs for a home and family. Masha, unhappy in her marriage to a timid schoolmaster, falls hopelessly in love with a married colonel. Irina works in the local telegraph office but longs for gaiety. Their sense of futility is increased by their brother's marriage to Natasha, a coarse peasant girl. She gradually encroaches on the family home until even the private refuge of the sisters is destroyed. They dream of starting a new life in Moscow but are saddled with the practicalities of their quiet existence. Despite their past failures, they resolve to seek some purpose and hope when the army post is withdrawn from the town.

REVIEWS

Variety, September 9, 1970
"A most elegant and important production of the Chekhov classic, as well as marking a welcome return to film direction, after a lengthy hiatus, of Laurence Olivier. Despite the lush physical trappings, it's the performances which ultimately attract, and there's a splendid assortment. Olivier, of course, vastly enjoyable as Chebutikin; Joan Plowright, totally in command as Masha; and Alan Bates, an impressively dosed Vershinin. What cannot be faulted is the overall quality of the production down to the minutest detail, and the rich and lasting contribution it makes in firming a permanent record, for future consultation, discussion and, why not, enjoyment, of another stage gem."

Judith Crist, *New York Magazine,* March 11, 1974
"Olivier, whose direction seems to ebb and flow toward granting both cinema and stage their due, has himself a ball with the role of Chebutikin, the old doctor who is all character." Copyright © 1974 by the NYM Corporation. Reprinted with the permission of *New York* magazine.

New York Times, March 12, 1974
"The film is a tribute to the kind of integrated stage performance we seldom see in this country, and to the play itself. The freedom, automatic in the theater, is so seldom granted in a film, that *Three Sisters* becomes something quite rare."

London Daily Mail, October 28, 1970
"I can think of no other cast that could improve on Sir Laurence Olivier's orchestrally tuned company, with Sir Laurence himself splendidly chunnering on the fringe as a shaggy, Father Christmassy Dr. Chebutikin and striving to relive his youth, plus Alan Bates' dashing Colonel Vershinin."

London Daily Express, October 29, 1970
"The acting is quite superb. Olivier himself plays the part of the extrovert old doctor Chebutikin with enormous relish."

COMMENTS

Olivier directed the film of *Three Sisters* from the National Theatre production, playing the part of Chebutikin, which had been portrayed on the stage by Paul Curran. Alan Bates was added to the film as Vershinin, originally acted by Robert Stephens. *Three Sisters* was the first film Olivier had directed since *The Prince and the Showgirl* in 1957. Filmed at Shepperton Studios in 1970, it was not shown in the United States until four years later, and then received limited distribution as part of Ely Landau's American Film Theater series. Olivier has called the drama "the most beautiful play in the world." His favorite work, both to direct and act in, he admires the play's movement. "It's so subtle, that it's upon you before you know where you are. Before the play is over you could die for these people. It's a chemical process that is perhaps the most subtle in world drama. It is a play of extraordinary perfection of balance."

In June, 1970, Olivier, then 63 years old, became the first actor in British history to be named a life peer and sent to the House of Lords. The peerage was announced in Queen Elizabeth II's birthday honors list. "At first I felt a bit uncomfortable about the title," the actor later confessed. "I didn't want to feel that people regarded me in a strange way, or as being anything apart from either the man in the street or everybody in my profession. I was reminded, however, that as a member of the House of Lords I could do some good for other people. It would give me a chance to plead some causes that I feel strongly about. It gives my profession a forum and that's what finally convinced me it would be a good thing."

The following July he delivered his maiden speech to speak in support of an industrial relations bill that would aid actors. The bill was defeated. The conclusion of the speech was rich with Olivier eloquence.

"I believe in the theatre; I believe in it as the first glamourizer of thought. It restores dramatic dynamics and their relationship to life size. I believe that in a great city, or even a small city or a village, a great theatre is the outward and visible sign of an inward and probable culture."

Actor-director Sir Bernard Miles, founder of the Mermaid Theatre, was the second member of his profession to be named a life peer when he was recognized on the Queen's 1979 New Year's honors list.

In April of 1971 Greater Pacific Production of San Francisco announced intentions to film Oscar Wilde's *De Profundis*. Plans for the two million dollar project included the casting of Paul Scofield, Richard Attenborough, and Anthony Quayle. Olivier was sought to direct the story of Wilde's turbulent life, but the project was discarded.

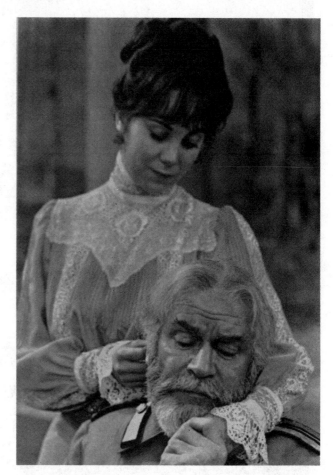

As Chebutikin in *Three Sisters* with Louise Purnell as Irina. Olivier: "The most beautiful play in the world . . . a play of extraordinary perfection of balance."

NICHOLAS
AND
ALEXANDRA <small>A</small>

NICHOLAS and ALEXANDRA
A SAM SPIEGEL-FRANKLIN J. SCHAFFNER PRODUCTION
with MICHAEL JAYSTON as NICHOLAS, JANET SUZMAN as ALEXANDRA,
and HARRY ANDREWS, TOM BAKER, MICHAEL BRYANT,
MAURICE DENHAM, JACK HAWKINS, IAN HOLM, CURT JURGENS,
JOHN McENERY, ERIC PORTER, MICHAEL REDGRAVE, ALAN WEBB,
IRENE WORTH and LAURENCE OLIVIER

Director of Photography Freddie Young
Music Composed by Richard Rodney Bennett
Production Designer and Second Unit Director John Box
Screenplay by James Goldman · From the book by Robert K. Massie
Produced by Sam Spiegel · Directed by Franklin J. Schaffner
Filmed in Panavision® Colour
A Horizon Film · From Columbia Pictures
Released By Columbia-Warner Distributors Ltd.

From Tuesday November 30
SPECIAL 70mm PRESENTATION
ODEON LEICESTER SQ.
TELEPHONE: 930 6111
Separate Performances Daily
ALL SEATS MAY BE BOOKED IN ADVANCE   *BOOK NOW!*

NOVEMBER 29 ROYAL WORLD PREMIERE IN THE PRESENCE OF HER MAJESTY THE QUEEN
in aid of THE SPASTICS SOCIETY, 12 PARK CRESCENT, W.1.

Nicholas and Alexandra

1971, Columbia Pictures release of Sam Spiegel-Franklin J. Schaffner production; Screenplay by James Goldman, based on the book by Robert K. Massie; Additional dialogue, Edward Bond; Photography, Freddie Young; Costumes, Yvonne Blake; Music composed by Richard Rodney Bennett; Production Designer and Second Unit Director, John Box; Directed by Franklin J. Schaffner

CAST

Nicholas	Michael Jayston
Alexandra	Janet Suzman
Count Witte	Laurence Olivier
Sazonov	Michael Redgrave
Count Fredericks	Jack Hawkins
Grand Duke Nicholas	Harry Andrews
Queen Mother Marie Fedorovna	Irene Worth
Yakoviev	Ian Holm
Rasputin	Tom Baker
American Ambassador Root	Alexander Knox
General Alexeiev	Roy Dotrice
German Consul Sklarz	Curt Jurgens
Yurovsky	Alan Webb
Col. Kobylinsky	John Wood
Dr. Botkin	Timothy West
Alexis	Roderic Noble
Anastasia	Fiona Fullerton
Olga	Ania Marson
Tatiana	Lynne Frederick
Marie	Candace Glendenning
Tegleva	Katherine Schofield
Gilliard	Jean Claude Drouot
Nagorny	John Hallam
Dr. Fedorov	Guy Rolfe
Stolypin	Eric Porter
Kokovtsov	Maurice Denham
Rodzianko	Ralph Truman
Guchkov	Gordon Gostelow
Kerensky	John McEnery
Lenin	Michael Bryant
Mme. Krupskaya	Vivian Pickles
Trotsky	Brian Cox
Stalin	James Hazeldine
Martov	Stephen Greif
Pankratov	Steven Berkoff
Plekhanov	Eric Chapman
Avadeyev	Leon Lissek
Goloshchekin	David Giles
Prince Yussoupov	Martin Potter
Grand Duke Dmitry	Richard Warwick
Dr. Lazovert	Vernon Dobtcheff
British Ambassador Buchanan	Ralph Neville
French Ambassador Paleologue	Jorge Rigaud
Gapon	Julian Glover
Petya	John Shrapnel
Sonya	Diana Quick
Col. Voikov	John Forbes Robertson
Flautist	Alan Dalton
Young Bolshevik	David Baxter

Opened December 13, 1971, Criterion Theater, New York (Three consecutive charity premieres: Project Hope, The National Hemophilia Foundation, The Arthritis Foundation, sponsored by Rosalind Russell)

THE FILM

The downfall of the Romanovs begins with the birth, after four girls, of Alexis, the first boy and heir to the Russian throne, who is soon discovered to be hemophilic. The Tsar Nicholas and Empress Alexandra are devoted to one another, but ignorant of the poverty, starvation, and repression in their country. The war against Japan begins against the advice of the Tsar's minister. Russia suffers calamitous defeats, and strikes and violence erupts. With the Tsar's increasing involvement over state affairs, the lonely Alexandra seeks desperately for a friend, accepting spiritual comfort from the self-styled holy man, Rasputin. When the young Alexis suffers internal bleeding and appears to be near death, the monk miraculously arrests the suffering. Alexandra is now convinced that neither she nor the boy can survive without Rasputin close at hand. A mass demonstration to present a petition asking for a constitution, free elections, and a

In costume and make-up for his role as Count Witte in *Nicholas and Alexandra,* **Olivier pauses on the set to chat with producer Sam Spiegel. Witte was perhaps, the ablest administrative brain in Russia. As the leading minister of two tsars, he gave Russia its first parliament and its first constitution.**

minimum wage is organized by the workers' movement. Thousands march upon the Winter Palace on the day which would be remembered as Bloody Sunday, and hundreds are killed by palace troops. Rasputin, who has been banished to his Siberian home for gross debauchery and meddling with government affairs, is summoned again when Alexis is gravely ill. Nicholas assumes command of the military forces, leaving government decisions in the hands of the Empress, who is influenced by Rasputin. Lenin, exiled in Switzerland, returns to Russia as the Imperial state disintegrates and prepares for the Bolshevik takeover. Rasputin is assassinated by the Tsar's cousin in a last desperate attempt to save the state. Abdication is demanded and Nicholas, realizing the disaffection of his entire army, signs a renunciation of the throne. With Alexandra and the children, he is sent to a remote Siberian village, where after a lengthy confinement, they meet their historic death at the hands of a disorganized band of revolutionaries.

New York *Daily News,* December 14, 1971
"The brilliant gem in the mosaic is Laurence Olivier, also by courtesy of the National Theatre. So great was his facial makeup as Count Witte, I had to take a second look into his sad eyes to recognize this greatest of all actors. As the president of the council of ministers, he advises the Tsar against war with Germany. Olivier's cultivated voice is his weapon, soft and purring, raised and ringing in pleading his cause."

New York Post, December 14, 1971
"The great actors of Great Britain are all there in solid ranks. Laurence Olivier as Count Witte is so sunk in his role, you'll not recognize him unless you make an effort."

The Listener, December 9, 1971
"Only Sir Laurence manages to pierce the pantomime by inventing details of performance that trick us into feeling for a moment."

Financial Times, December 3, 1971
"Among the distinguished supporting players only Laurence Olivier as Sergei Witte has authority enough to fix attention on the character rather than on the Lord."

The Dance of Death

1971, British Home Entertainments, National Theatre Company presentation; Translated by C. D. Lecock from the play by August Strindberg; Produced by John Brabourne; Photography, Geoffrey Unsworth; Editor, Reginald Mills; Art director, Herbert Smith; Production manager, Elisabeth Woodthorpe; Set decorations, Helen Thomas; Associate producer, Richard Goodwin; Costumes, Amy C. Binney; Directed for the stage by Glen Byam Shaw; Directed by David Giles; A Paramount Picture

CAST

Edgar	Laurence Olivier
Alice	Geraldine McEwan
Kurt	Robert Lang
Judith	Janina Faye
Allan	Malcolm Reynolds
Jenny	Carolyn Jones
Kristin	Maggie Riley
Lieutenant	Peter Penry-Jones
Old woman	Jeanne Watts
Sentries	Frederick Pyne
	Barry James
	David Ryall

Filmed in 1968; North American premiere, September 10, 1971, Stratford Film Festival, Ontario, Canada; New York premiere, July 13, 1979, D. W. Griffith Theater

THE FILM

An egocentric artillery captain and his venomous wife engage in savage unremitting battles in their isolated island fortress off the coast of Sweden at the turn of the century. Alice, a former actress who sacrificed her career for secluded military life with Edgar, reveals on the occasion of their 25th wedding anniversary, the veritable hell their marriage has been. Edgar, an aging schizoid who refuses to acknowledge his severe illness, struggles to sustain his ferocity and arrogance with an animal disregard for other people. Sensing that Alice together with her cousin and would-be lover, Kurt, may ally against him, he retaliates with vicious force. Alice lures Kurt into the illusion of sharing a passionate assignation and recruits him in a plot to destroy Edgar. With cunning arrogance, Edgar malevolently brings humiliation and ruin to the weaker Kurt. He informs Kurt's son, a young medical officer at the fortress, of his obligation to withdraw advances to his daughter, Judith, and let the girl marry a superior sixty-year old officer. The captain suggests that the influential union will afford the young man to be able to continue his education and career. Judith, who loves the younger officer, destroys her father's measured calculation by insulting the old general. With this revelation, Edgar has a stroke and lies dying in a chair, while tantalized by his wife's triumphant vituperation. In one scorching final counter-attack, Edgar spits in her face and collapses.

Edgar in *The Dance of Death* (1971). When asked which he found the most memorable and impressive of all Olivier performances, Sir John Clements replied, "Without hesitation I'd put his Captain in *The Dance of Death* at the top of the list. It was a staggeringly brilliant performance."

The Observer, July 27, 1969
"One of Laurence Olivier's greatest performances—perhaps his greatest—has been encapsulated in a tin can for posterity."

Financial Times, July 25, 1969
"Olivier's Edgar is unquestionably one of his very best recent performances, viciously comic, painfully truthful. Much of it is only more fascinating when magnified by the camera; yet equally, the camera at times shows up the mechanics of calculation, the self-consciousness of some of his theatrical 'moments,' the occasional retreats into elocutionary devices to cover weaknesses of interpretation."

Pauline Kael, n.d.
"Everytime we single out the feature that makes Olivier a marvel—his lion eyes or the voice or the way it seizes on a phrase—he alters it or casts it off in some new role, and is greater than ever. It is no special asset, it is the devilish audacity and courage of this man. What is extraordinary is inside, and what is even more extraordinary is his determination to give it outer force. He has never leveled off; he goes on soaring."

Films and Filming, October 1969
"The importance of adopting black humor for Edgar has been appreciated to discreet perfection by Laurence Olivier, who exudes a jovial bile, accentuating Edgar's thwarted power-drive, his military fantasy-world, his misogynic spite, and his mad relish of the physical afflictions that repeatedly bring him down. By chuckling in a knowing way (as distinct from giggling with embarrassment), we are able to recognize the truth to the continuing behavior of man."

New York Post, July 13, 1979
"Two groups, anyone who wants to see, appreciate and learn from the greatest acting, and

marital losers who can share the agonies of that classic Battle of the Married Sexes, August Strindberg's *The Dance of Death*, must drop everything and rush to the D. W. Griffith theater. Ten years after the movie was made in England, it has been brought here, a shocking example of exhibitors low-rating the taste of the American movie audiences. It is a picture that grabs and shakes you. It is also an opportunity to see Laurence Olivier as a blustering officer, a browbeating husband, a man torn between hatred and fear of impending death. His performance is magnificent beyond description, and when you contrast it with the current *Dracula*, where he is Van Helsing, an aged Dutch doctor, the opponent of the vampire, it is hard to believe that one man, even with a span of ten years, could be so different.''

Variety, September 29, 1971

"Done with great theatrical skill. A tour de force. The right serious minded film buffs will enjoy its merits.''

STAGE REVIEWS

Saturday Review, July 1, 1967

"The single most splendid performance in the illustrious four-year history of the National Theatre. Olivier's stark portrayal of a schizoid, aging Swedish Army Captain is a superb and mysterious creation. It gives Olivier the opportunity to release himself fully into a hilarious kind of insanity which he makes most entertaining. But ultimately his greatness as an actor makes it possible for him to arrive at a shattering death scene in which the Captain manages to recapture us emotionally. Olivier, at the age of sixty, seems to be entering a new prime period in his acting career.''

New York Times, October 29, 1967

"For Olivier, great heroic actor that he is, has always struck me as being even greater as a character comedian. Hence his triumph as Richard III. His Captain in *Dance of Death* is an even more magnificent creation. The vast seven act play gives him an enormous range of emotions from the boredom of the unsuccessful officer, cooped up with his hated wife in an old fort on a small island, to white-hot hatred, malice, guile, outbreaks of violent rage, collapse in illness; from dejection and humiliation to paroxysms of triumph in revenge over a ruined rival, Olivier encompasses them all. He makes the violent transitions from one mood to another wholly believable.''

Variety, March 8, 1967

"The drama also gives yet another opportunity to Laurence Olivier to extend his almost limitless range. He plays the part with a ferocious panache which turns it into one of his most triumphant achievements. It is a consummate portrayal, superbly thought-out in dramatic terms.''

New York Times, October 19, 1967 (Montreal)

"His performance could have disappointed no one. It was brilliant—the kind of inventive, witty, risky performance that only an Olivier could conceive and fully bring off. He is (has the observation been made before?) the finest actor in the English-speaking world, and this *Dance of Death* only adds to his laurels.''

Olivier on *Dance of Death*.

"I don't find the Strindberg role too exhausting despite its length. The play is a fine one, but it is not really tragedy. The captain's character does not meet the requirements of high tragedy. Some say the play is stylized, grotesque, exaggerated, but I've been married a bit myself and it seems to me to be realistic. Often couples tell me it is almost the story of their marriage—if they had let themselves go. Apparently, many married couples have been on the verge of acting out the big scenes in *The Dance of Death*.

Lady Caroline Lamb

1972, Tomorrow Enterprises release of Nat Cohen's presentation of a Franco Cristaldi-Fernando Ghia production, released by United Artists; Produced by Fernando Ghia; Executive Producer, Franco Cristaldi; Photography, Oswald Morris; Music composed by Richard Rodney Bennett, viola solo by Peter Mark with the New Philharmonia Orchestra; Assistant Director, David Tringham; Art Director, Carmen Dillon; Costumes, David Walker; Editor, Norman Savage; Written and Directed by Robert Bolt

Duke of Wellington in *Lady Caroline Lamb* **(1972).**

CAST

Lady Caroline Lamb	Sarah Miles
William Lamb	Jon Finch
Lord Byron	Richard Chamberlain
Duke of Wellington	Laurence Olivier
The King	Ralph Richardson
Canning	John Mills
Lady Melbourne	Margaret Leighton
Lady Bessborough	Pamela Brown
Miss Milbanke	Silvia Monti
Government Minister	Peter Bull
Lord Holland	Michael Wilding
Mr. Potter	Charles Carson
Lady Pont	Sonia Dresdel
St. John	Nicholas Field
Girl in Blue	Felicity Gibson
Apothecary	Robert Harris
Radical Member	Richard Hurndall
Irish Housekeeper	Paddy Joyce
Benson	Bernard Kay
Miss Fairfax	Janet Kay
First partner	Preston Lockwood
Second partner	John Rapley
Chatsworth Domo	Ivor Slater
Coachman	Mario Maranzana
ADC, to Wellington	Robert Mill
Restaurant Functionary	Norman Mitchell
Murray	John Moffatt
Agent	Trevor Peacock
Mrs. Buller	Maureen Pryor
Lady Holland	Fanny Rowe
Buckham	Stephen Sheppard
Black Pug	Roy Stewart
Admiral	Ralph Truman

Opened Feb. 11, 1973, Fine Arts Theater, New York

A. Wellesley, First Duke of Wellington (T. Heaphy).
National Portrait Gallery, London.

Caroline Lamb is a spoiled, impulsive young beauty, later to scandalize Regency England. Naive and unstable, she is determined to marry William Lamb against the strong objections of his shrewdly antagonistic mother, Lady Melbourne. Lamb, later Lord Melbourne and counsel to the Queen, is attracted by her extravagance and vivid beauty. Caroline is attracted by his poise and consequently, their union is destined to be one of vastly opposing natures. Once married she enters into a tempestuous affair with the flamboyant poet, Lord Byron. It is an absurd and sensational relationship which shocks nineteenth century England. Lord Byron eventually cools toward her, savagely rejecting the desperate Lady Caroline in public. She in turn goes half mad, making a complete fool of herself, while her husband attempts not to notice her tragic behavior. Lord Melbourne sacrifices his political career in an attempt to nurse her back to happiness and good health. To earn favors for the husband she still loves, she lures Lord Wellington into a tryst. That fails and she settles for a divorce to save her husband's career, goes mad, and dies of a broken heart.

REVIEWS

New York Times, February 12, 1973
"*Lady Caroline Lamb* is to cinema what the coffee-table book is to literature: a heavy but insubstantial irrelevancy. Robert Bolt gives us a bit of history—that is, he gives us a corner of the National Portrait Gallery, including Canning (John Mills), George IV (Ralph Richardson), and the Duke of Wellington (Laurence Olivier, in one of his noses)."

Variety, November 29, 1972
"If it's that relative rarity, a lushly, unabashedly romantic—yet tastefully executed—tale that you relish, and there's evidence that a solid niche for such fare exists among world cinemagoers, then

Sarah Miles made her film debut as Shirley in *Term of Trial* (1963), and . . .

was top billed less than a decade later in *Lady Caroline Lamb* in the title role with Olivier as the Duke of Wellington.

England expected an affaire.

Caroline gave them History.

Tomorrow Entertainment presents a Franco Cristaldi-Fernando Ghia production
starring
Sarah Miles   Jon Finch
Richard Chamberlain as "Lord Byron" in
Robert Bolt's

Lady Caroline Lamb

also starring
John Mills   Margaret Leighton   Pamela Brown   Silvia Monti
Ralph Richardson and Laurence Olivier   executive producer Franco Cristaldi
produced by Fernando Ghia   written and directed by Robert Bolt   Panavision®-Color   PG   United Artists

New York Premiere Sunday, February 11th
THE **Fine arts** A WALTER READE THEATRE
58th St. Bet. Park and Lex. • PL 5-6030

Lady Caroline Lamb is your likely cup of tea. Margaret Leighton is one of the many who lend stable support, while two truly upper case cameos are provided by Laurence Olivier as Wellington and especially Ralph Richardson in an even shorter but humorously telling bit as the King."

Judith Crist, *New York Magazine,* February 12, 1973
"It's replete with chandeliers and pages and absolutely delicious moments provided by Sir Laurence Olivier as the plain-spoken Wellington and Sir Ralph Richardson as the slow-spoken George." Copyright © 1973 by the NYM Corporation. Reprinted with the permission of *New York* magazine.

London Times, November 24, 1972
"Laurence Olivier's brief appearance as the Duke of Wellington (is) a beautifully witty and rounded characterization that is worth the price of admission in itself."

Think of the perfect crime... Then go one step further.

PALOMAR PICTURES INTERNATIONAL presents

LAURENCE OLIVIER · MICHAEL CAINE

in JOSEPH L. MANKIEWICZ' Film of

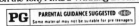"SLEUTH"

To witness the perfect crime you must come on time. No one admitted after "Sleuth" starts.

Based on the play by ANTHONY SHAFFER   Screenplay by ANTHONY SHAFFER
Executive Producer EDGAR J. SCHERICK   Produced by MORTON GOTTLIEB
Directed by JOSEPH L. MANKIEWICZ   PRINTS BY DELUXE®

Based on the Tony Award Winning Broadway Play

PG | PARENTAL GUIDANCE SUGGESTED
Some material may not be suitable for pre-teenagers

20th CENTURY FOX

Sleuth

1972, Twentieth Century Fox release of a Palomar Pictures International presentation; Screenplay by Anthony Shaffer, based upon his play; Executive Producer, Edgar J. Scherick; Produced by Morton Gottlieb; Photography, Oswald Morris; Music composed by John Addison; Editor, Richard Marden; Directed by Joseph L. Mankiewicz

CAST

Andrew Wyke	Laurence Olivier
Milo Tindle	Michael Caine
Inspector Doppler	Alec Cawthorne
Marguerite	Eve Channing
Sergeant Tarrant	John Matthews
Constable Higgs	Teddy Martin
Teva	Karen Monfort-Jones

Opened December 10, 1972, at the Ziegfeld Theater, New York

THE FILM

Andrew Wyke, an affluent and successful mystery novelist and creator of the fictitious detective, St. John Lord Merridewe, invites Milo Tindle to his estate to discuss in a civilized manner, the affair Tindle is having with his estranged wife, Marguerite. The writer is addicted to puzzles, complicated games, and practical jokes. He is a pompous and flamboyant snob, who harbors a particular distaste for those of a working-class background. Tindle, a lowly-born hairdresser of Italian descent, is duped into a fake burglary. Wyke, happy to get Marguerite off his hands, suggests that Tindle steal his wife's jewels and sell them in order to support her expensive demands, while he collects the insurance money. The devious writer's sadistic sense of humor and game plotting lead Tindle into a murderous and elaborate scheme which results in an ultimately devastating conflict.

Andrew Wyke in *Sleuth* (1972).

Olivier on Wyke: "The man's mind is a maze, filled with puzzles and games."

Wyke with Jolly Jack Tar the Jovial Sailor: "He and I have a very good relationship. I make the jokes and he laughs at them." (From *Sleuth*, by Anthony Shaffer.)

REVIEWS

New York Times, December 11, 1972
"To witness Olivier at work is to behold a one-man revue of theatrical excesses—all marvelous. He minces. He bellows. He does exotic things with his tongue. He leaps around as if possessed by the spirit of Errol Flynn, in Flynn's early Warner Brothers days. Suddenly worn out, he slumps into a chair, letting his eyeballs roll slowly up toward immobile lids. Just when you're sure he's had a heart attack, he comes to life again, perhaps with the voice of Edith Evans or Ralph Richardson, sometimes with a gesture that worked well in *Othello.* Olivier's Andrew is hugely funny and extravagant."

New York *Daily News,* December 11, 1972
"Only once in a blue moon is a picture a vast improvement over the play from which it is adapted. *Sleuth* is among the rarities. We get further proof that Olivier is the greatest actor of our lifetime."

New Jersey *Bergen Record,* December 11, 1972
"It seems a bit silly to rave about Olivier at this point in his distinguished career, but his performance is sheer perfection, giving this overly refined, terribly upper class gentleman every twitch that makes him alive."

Newsweek magazine, December 18, 1972
"The incomparable Sir Laurence Olivier in a role that allows him to deliver a classic, multilevel performance. Olivier's aristocrat is a spellbinding figure, at once the keen player, the gentleman, the sadist and the madman—all gathered into a logical whole."

Cue magazine, December 16, 1972

"Sir Laurence Olivier brings his unique powers to the part of Wyke, the aristocratic mystery writer. Olivier's performance is a memorable lesson in what a great actor can accomplish."

Time magazine, December 25, 1972

"Of late, Olivier's movie activity has been confined to playing a variety of cameos in top-heavy histories like *Nicholas and Alexandra*. It is good to see him again in a role of size, if not of substance, and he makes wonderful sport of it. His face is a study in split-second metamorphoses. He does so much with it so fast that sometimes, in a closeup, he gives the impression of a multiple exposure. Caine seems not in the least daunted by acting with a legend incarnate. To say that he matches Olivier in every way is to pay him the highest of compliments."

Variety, December 13, 1972

"Terrific. Anthony Shaffer's topnotch screenplay of his legit hit provides Laurence Olivier and especially Michael Caine with their best roles in years. Olivier is outstanding as the famed mystery writer and society figure who is galled at the prospect of losing his wife to Caine. Could it be possible that greater professionalism is again returning to motion pictures?"

London *Sunday Times,* July 15, 1973

"Sir Laurence is called on to act a theatrical character in a theatrical film. He subdues the theatrical element, but not so much as to disturb the artifices of the narrative; and we are left with a performance of exquisite professionalism, the portrait of a middle-aged literary show-off—defensively vain, finicky, waspish, with the cruelty and the concealed self-doubts of the solitary. To see him deliberately fixing himself a caviar snack is in itself a pleasure."

COMMENTS

Sleuth, the suspenseful thriller by Anthony Shaffer opened February 12, 1970, at St. Martin's Theatre in London with Anthony Quayle as Andrew Wyke and Keith Baxter as Milo Tindle. The play ran for more than five years in London, playing a total of 2,358 performances at three West End theatres. Quayle and Baxter also appeared in the Broadway production which had a 1,222 performance run, winning a Tony Award as Best Play. When the play closed at New York's Music Box Theater, a small obituary appeared on the entertainment page of the *New York Times*:

WYKE, ANDREW, Beloved creation of Anthony Shaffer. Devoted "Sleuth" of Morton Gottlieb and friends. Born: St. Martin's Theatre, London, Feb. 12, 1970. Final New York curtain, Music Box Theater, Oct. 13, 1973, 8:00 P.M.

The character of Andrew Wyke fascinated Olivier from the moment he first saw the play during its pre-London tryout in Brighton, where the actor resided. "The man's mind is a maze, filled with puzzles and games. He's completely self-sufficient, because all his games can be played alone. However, when played against someone, the games can become more exciting. That's what happens when he decides to play murder. All he needs is another player and, in Milo, he is surprised and delighted to find one worthy of him."

In an interview with radio personality Fred Robbins, Olivier explained his return to the screen in a major role and described the drawbacks of appearing in too many cameo roles. "I'd been a very good boy about nonabsenteeism for the past ten years with the National Theatre, and it was about time I played a leading part. It is awfully nice, all these cameos that come along, but after you've done about six of them, there is a whole generation of people who think you're a small part actor. That's all right. I don't mind being a small part actor, but after a while if you aren't very careful, you'll find that they begin to consider you in terms of a small part actor's salary. Now *there* is a difference. That's a different kettle of fish entirely. And that makes you think of it and I thought, well, perhaps I ought to pretend I'm a leading actor then after all."

Olivier obviously had an enormously good time playing the mystery writer with a devious childish streak. A veritable tour de force, the dialogue offered a field day of impersonations, and Olivier as Wyke seized the opportunity to taunt his victim with various puns in the guises of American gangsters, cowboys, and fops. Director Joseph Mankiewicz planted all sorts of red herrings

"There is no actor in the world who can do as much with a peruke and snuff box as Larry." (Joseph L. Mankiewicz.)

If it was murder, where's the body?
If it was for a woman, which woman?
If it's only a game, why the blood?

PALOMAR PICTURES INTERNATIONAL presents

LAURENCE OLIVIER MICHAEL CAINE

in JOSEPH L. MANKIEWICZ Film of

"Sleuth"

To witness the perfect crime you must come on time. No one admitted after "Sleuth" starts.

Based on the play by ANTHONY SHAFFER   Screenplay by ANTHONY SHAFFER
Executive Producer EDGAR J. SCHERICK   Produced by MORTON GOTTLIEB
Directed by JOSEPH L. MANKIEWICZ   PRINTS BY DELUXE®

Based on the Tony Award Winning Broadway Play

PG   PARENTAL GUIDANCE SUGGESTED
Some material may not be suitable for pre-teenagers

219

throughout the film in addition to those already ingeniously created by the author. A supporting actress bears the pseudonym of Eve Channing, a composite of Eve Harrington and Margo Channing, the principle antagonists of Mankiewicz' 1950 masterpiece, *All About Eve*. Also a portrait of Wyke's wife, Marguerite, and a photograph on the wall turn out to be that of actress Joanne Woodward, who once won an Oscar for *The Three Faces Of Eve*.

Wyke: "You're going to die and no one will suspect murder."

with Michael Caine as Milo Tindle. The only film in which the entire cast was nominated for Academy Awards.

In his accustomed quest for perfection, Olivier took the trouble to sink most of his shots in a billiard sequence, even though the actual trick shots were to be inserted at a later date by a professional player. The character of Wyke is one of the longest roles in modern drama, and Olivier was somewhat discouraged by his difficulty in learning lines. With the exception of *Othello* and *The Dance of Death*, which had been performed on the stage many times prior to filming, he had not played a sizeable screen role since *Term of Trial*, nearly ten years earlier.

Delays caused by Olivier's "drying up" were unnerving to director and crew, but "despite the costly fluffs Mankiewicz maintained that 'there is no actor in the world who can do as much, from all his work in Restoration comedy, with a peruke and snuff box as Larry.' The scene he was referring to is one in which Olivier models a Monsieur Beaucaire outfit and then a monk's cowl as possible costumes for Caine's burglary getup. Olivier's droll camping is countered by Caine's own deft drag bit; he extends a limp wrist and clutches a flapper's dress to his chest."[37]

Trivia experts will note that the film marked the only time in Academy Award history that an entire cast received Oscar nominations. The names of the other actors in the title credits are completely fictitious. Billing additional players was an inspired gimmick which began when the play was originally presented, to dupe audiences against the identity of a principal character. Michael Caine and Olivier were cited for their tandem performance. It was Olivier's eighth nomination. Marlon Brando won his second Oscar for his performance in *The Godfather*. Coincidentally, Olivier had been considered for the role of the warlord Don Corleone in the film of Mario Puzo's best seller. He believes the inquiry was made to his agent who replied that Olivier was too busy. "I was immensely flattered," he told Robbins, adding, "I wish to God I'd done it. I'd have adored to do it." Olivier did win the Best Actor award for 1972 from the New York Film Critics, however, capturing thirty votes on the fifth ballot to Brando's twenty-seven.

"It is the most difficult role I have ever played. But I wanted to work with Olivier. If you want to better yourself, you must always work with the best. Olivier is probably one of the greatest actors in the world." (Michael Caine, 1972.)

"We play off each other perfectly. We had never met, Olivier and I, before the first rehearsal. There are masses of wonderful surfaces to bounce anything off that you want to. You bounce a table-tennis ball off Larry's surface and it comes back a diamond." (Michael Caine, 1972.)

Marathon Man

1976, A Paramount Pictures presentation of a Robert Evans-Sidney Beckerman production; Screenplay by William Goldman, based on his novel; Photography, Conrad Hall; Editor, Jim Clark; Production Design, Richard MacDonald; Art Direction, Jack de Shields; Set Decoration, George Gaines; Music scored by Michael Small; Directed by John Schlesinger

CAST

Babe Levy	Dustin Hoffman
Dr. Christian Szell	Laurence Olivier
Doc Levy	Roy Scheider
Janeway	William Devane
Elsa	Marthe Keller
Professor	Fritz Weaver
Karl	Richard Bright
Erhard	Marc Lawrence
Mr. Levy	Allen Joseph
Melendez	Tito Goya
Szell's Brother	Ben Dova
Rosenbaum	Lou Gilbert
LeClerc	Jacques Marin
Chen	James Wing Woo
Nicole	Nicole Deslauriers
Old Lady in Street	Lotta Andor-Palfi
Laundress	Alma Beltran
Bank Guard	William Martel
Plainclothesmen	Glenn Robards, Ric Carrott

Street Gang—Lionel Pina, Church, Tricoche, Jaime Tirelli, Wilfredo Hernandez

Jewelry Salesmen—Harry Goz, Michael Vale, Fred Stuthman, Lee Steele

Opened October 6, 1976, Loews State and Loews Tower East theaters, New York

THE FILM

Dr. Christian Szell, a wanted war criminal and former Nazi dentist, has amassed a fortune extracting gold from the teeth of prisoners in a German concentration camp. "The white angel of Auschwitz," so called because of his rich, snow-white hair, later had the gold converted into diamonds, which were stored in a New York safe deposit box by his brother. When the brother is killed in a bizarre auto accident, Szell emerges, head shaven, from his jungle hideaway in Uruguay to reclaim his treasure. Distrustful of Doc Levy, a government double agent who had served as a diamond courier, Szell murders him. Doc's brother, Babe, an amateur marathon runner and Columbia graduate student, whose historian father committed suicide during the McCarthy era, is kidnapped by Szell and his henchmen. Babe Levy, unaware of his brother's espionage activities and diamond smuggling, is brutally tortured. He escapes and seeks help from his brother's associate, Janeway, and an attractive Swiss student, both of whom turn out to be in Szell's employ. A final confrontation between Levy and Szell begins in Manhattan's diamond selling district where the dentist is attempting to assess the value of his horde and climaxes in a Central Park water plant.

REVIEWS

New York Times, October 7, 1976
"Lord Olivier, one of the great ornaments of the English-speaking theater and cinema, helps to make *Marathon Man* a film that you won't want to miss."

New Jersey *Bergen Record,* October 7, 1976
"Laurence Olivier gives us, as the villain, a monster worthy of appearance in our own nightmares. He is a giant presence—totally the man he plays, nothing of the actor—in a perfectly calibrated, cosmic performance that illustrates the banality of evil. It is one of the great screen performances of all time."

Newsweek magazine, October 11, 1976
"The most satisfying element is the work of Olivier, one of the few who turn acting into one of the great humane professions of Western civilization. It's wonderful to see how Olivier invests everything he does, no matter how small a role, with the same care, preparation, and resourcefulness that he gives to *Othello* or *Long Day's Journey Into Night.* Olivier shows us that a great actor is the sculptor of his self, turning his body into a sign, a symbol, and a force that jolts us into a higher consciousness."

Dr. Christian Szell in *Marathon Man* **(1972).**

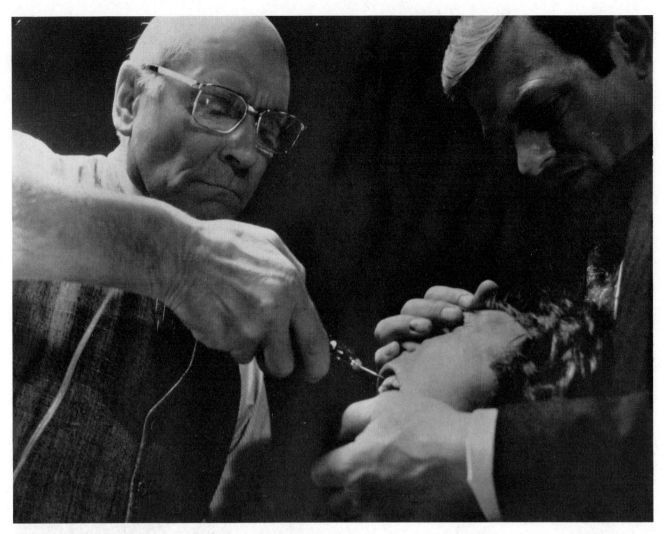

Several cuts were made in *Marathon Man* prior to the
film's general release. Patrons at advance screenings
objected to the excessive violence. In the final version,
Nazi dentist Christian Szell (Olivier), tortures student
Babe Levy (Dustin Hoffman), by drilling into a healthy
front tooth, but this scene in which the drill is displayed
clearly lodged against the tooth was omitted. The sound
of the drill and Levy's agonized scream left enough for
the imagination.

Time magazine, October 18, 1976
"*Marathon Man* is the year's most cunning entertainment, a thriller full of spills and shootings, double-dealings and triple betrayals. It is lavishly mounted and loaded with flash. The movie also offers Dustin Hoffman, giving one of his best performances, up against Laurence Olivier, who is in fine form playing an arch-villain."

Playboy magazine, November 1976
"*Marathon Man's* chief attention-getter, bar-none, is Laurence Olivier—probably the greatest actor in the world, proving it once again with his insidious, sly, and mesmerizing performance as an unregenerate Nazi war criminal."

COMMENTS

Olivier resigned as artistic director of the National Theatre at the end of 1973, after a ten year reign, turning over the directorship to Peter Hall. In October, he appeared as Antonio, the senile patriarch in Eduardo de Filippo's comedy, *Saturday, Sunday, Monday. Punch Magazine* praised Olivier's doddering grandfather: "Olivier gives this proud but now incompetent old craftsman a mad dignity." His last role for the National was as John Tagg in *The Party* by Trevor Griffiths, in which he portrayed a dying Trotskyite delivering an eighteen minute monologue, prompting *Variety* to report, "Olivier turns his usual considerable trick of making an audience forget he's a legend." His final performance before a live audience, was as Tagg on March 21, 1974.

The National Theatre's long awaited new home on London's South Bank began performances in March of 1976, celebrated a Royal opening in October, and became fully operational in March of 1977. The modern sprawling complex contains three theatres, bars, buffets, a restaurant, bookshops, terraces, and river walks providing a stunning view of London by day or night. The largest theatre, accommodating 1,160 people is named after Olivier, who continues to serve as board consultant.

In 1975, Olivier began filming *Marathon Man,* in which he portrayed a sadistic, Nazi dentist who tortures his victims with a drill. It had been sixteen years since he made a film in the United

Szell murders government agent Doc Levy (Roy Scheider) with a blade concealed in a wrist bracelet. Audiences saw only the impact of Szell's sudden thrust and were spared the following shot in which the cameras panned downward to reveal a large pool of crimson blood at Levy's feet.

Szell: "You have to shoot me. Come on, shoot. You won't - you can't - you're too weak. Your father was weak in his way, your brother in his, now you in yours. You're all so predictable." (From *Marathon Man* by William Goldman.)

Szell: "Isn't that remarkable? Simple oil of cloves and how amazing the results. Life can be that simple. Relief - discomfort; now which of these I next apply, that decision is in your hands, so take your time and tell me . . . is it safe?" (From *Marathon Man*.)

Olivier: "I really don't mind what I play, but this villain is really horrific. They tell me that's the fashion."

States. Olivier relied on the advice Charles Laughton had given him at that time, during the filming of *Spartacus* in 1959. "If you really want to do the heavies, do them well," Laughton had advised. "They will pay you much more than if you make them sympathetic." Olivier approached his monstrous villain with the Laughton spirit, but confessed, "the best villains are the ones that are amusing. I really don't mind what I play, but this villain is really horrific. They tell me that's the fashion."

At age 68, Olivier was battling another serious illness. "I had to turn things down for more than a year, because of my gorgeous, lovely, smashing illness, which is the worst I've ever had, just because it's so mysterious. I mean cancer was one thing. I just treated it very rough and hardened my mind against it. Then three years later, came the thrombosis, and I thought 'Christ, two of these major ones in three years, come on, now,' and I got angry with fate, and thought, 'What do you want now?' The new illness was a wasting inflammation of the muscles which hospitalized him in the winter of 1975 before chemicals and therapy got him on his feet again. "Some enzymes which are supposed to be nice to you turned into wicked little fellows and attacked me."

Olivier gave himself a test by taking a small part in *The Seven-Per-Cent Solution* to see if he had the strength to film *Marathon Man*. "I wanted to be sure that I would not burst into tears and run crying off the set, or that I would not be able to memorize one line." His performance as Dr. Szell brought him a ninth Academy Award nomination, his first in the category of supporting actor. The award went to Jason Robards, who played a Washington newspaper editor in *All the President's Men*. The British Variety Clubs honored Olivier as Best Actor for his performance in *Marathon Man*.

The Seven-Per-Cent Solution

1976, A Universal Picture, Screenplay by Nicholas Meyer, based on his novel; Music composed by John Addison; Executive Producers, Arlene

Sellers and Alex Winitsky; Associate Producer, Stanley O'Toole; Photography, Oswald Morris; Editors, William Reynolds, Chris Barnes; Production Design, Ken Adam; Art Direction, Peter Lamont; Set Decoration, Peter James; Song, "I Never Do Anything Twice" by Stephen Sondheim; Produced and Directed by Herbert Ross

CAST

Sherlock Holmes	Nicol Williamson
Dr. Watson	Robert Duvall
Professor Moriarty	Laurence Olivier
Sigmund Freud	Alan Arkin
Lola Deveraux	Vanessa Redgrave
Lowenstein	Joel Grey
Mrs. Watson	Samantha Eggar
Mycroft Holmes	Charles Gray
Baron von Leinsdorf	Jeremy Kemp
Mrs. Freud	Georgia Brown
Madame	Regine
Freda	Anna Quayle
Mrs. Holmes	Jill Townsend
Berger	John Bird
Mrs. Hudson	Alison Leggatt
Marker	Frederick Jaeger
Butler	Eric Chitty

Opened, October 24, 1976, Plaza Theater, New York

THE FILM

The faithful Dr. John Watson, concerned by Sherlock Holmes' increasing drug addiction, plots with Professor Moriarty and Holmes' brother Mycroft, to lure the great detective to Vienna and the ministrations of Sigmund Freud. Holmes becomes paranoid in his attempt to outwit his old enemy, Moriarty, portrayed here as a nervous, old mathematics professor and hardly the devious nemesis of the famous sleuth's earlier adventures. Freud probes the drug-addicted complexities of Holmes' subconscious and reveals the hidden meanings behind his recurrent dream images. Explanations are offered concerning his hatred of Moriarty, his aversion to women, and the reason he became a detective.

Freud and Holmes join forces to solve the mysterious disappearance of an actress, Lola Deveraux, eventually rescuing the woman in a perilous, climactic duel and train chase.

REVIEWS

Time magazine, November 1, 1976
"The ace in this poorly shuffled deck, is, no surprise, Olivier. He has not often done comedy on screen, but his extravagantly funny Moriarty is a creation of wit and invention."

Hollywood Reporter, October 6, 1976
"As that arch-villain Moriarty, as it turns out, Olivier is correctly ambiguous. It's an adventure tale told with a deliciously light tongue-in-cheekiness."

New York Times, October 25, 1976
"Nothing less than the most exhilarating entertainment of the film year to date. Laurence Olivier is marvelous as Professor Moriarty, an extremely tentative, timid old fellow to be such a tycoon of crime."

Stanley Kauffmann, *New Republic,* October 30, 1976
"Olivier is Professor Moriarty—but what a Moriarty! Not the Fritz Langian archfiend. It seems that Moriarty was really a wispy old schoolteacher who had once been the tutor of the Holmes boys, Sherlock and Mycroft, and who had unintentionally had a traumatic effect on the psyche of the young Sherlock. Because of the boyhood experience the great detective now *imagines* that Moriarty is an archfiend. But as Olivier plays him, with neat quick comic pathos, Moriarty is a man whose chief aim in life is to be indistinguishable from the wallpaper."

London *Daily Mail,* May 20, 1977
"His Professor Moriarty is the most memorable feature in this curious combination of fact and fictitious fiction. As Holmes' nemesis Moriarty, who may be just a figment of his drugged imagination or a memory from the past, Olivier gives a performance of majestically comic and alarming proportions."

Professor Moriarty in *The Seven-Per-Cent Solution* **(1976).**

Olivier's meek Moriarty was hardly Conan Doyle's "Napoleon of crime."

COMMENTS

Next to the master detective himself, and the faithful Dr. John Watson, Professor Moriarty is the best-known character to emerge from the adventures of Sherlock Holmes, although he appears in only one story and is referred to in two others. Moriarty has risen from the pages of detective fiction as one of the most intriguing master criminals of all time. Conan Doyle's cunning villain was created as the controlling brain of a vast underworld network of crime. Several notable stage, screen, and radio actors have found the character a fascinating challenge. Among those well served by the role of Moriarty are Henry Daniel, Clive Revill, Martin Gabel, Orson Welles, Lionel Atwill, and George Zucco. Nicholas Meyer provided a surprising twist in his novel and subsequent screenplay, *The Seven-Per-Cent Solution*, turning Moriarty into a timid mathematics professor who is wronged and severely harassed by a deluded, drug-addicted Holmes. Olivier, in a few brief moments, contributes a witty cameo as he rehabilitates Holmes' archenemy.

Jesus of Nazareth

1976, Produced by Vincenzo Labella, Written by Anthony Burgess, Suso Cecchi d'Amico, and Franco Zeffirelli; Executive Producer, Bernard J. Kingham; Associate Producer, Dyson Lovell; Music composed and conducted by Maurice Jarre; Directed by Franco Zeffirelli; Distributed by I.T.C. Entertainment Limited

CAST

Jesus	Robert Powell
Jesus (as a boy)	Lorenzo Monet
Yehuda the Rabbi	Cyril Cusack
Herod the Great	Peter Ustinov
Proculus	Robert Beatty
Saturninus	Norman Bowler
Naso	John Phillips
Joseph	Yorgo Voyagis
Mary	Olivia Hussey
Elisabeth	Marina Berti
Anna	Regina Bianchi
Abigal	Nancy Nevison
The Shepherds:	Jonathan Adams
	Roy Holder
	Renato Terra
Simeon	Ralph Richardson
The Magi:	
Gaspar	Fernando Rey
Melchior	Donald Pleasance
Balthazar	James Earl Jones
John the Baptist	Michael York
Herod Antipas	Christopher Plummer
Herodias	Valentina Cortese
Mad Boy	Keith Skinner
Salome	Isabel Mestres
Mary of Magdala	Anne Bancroft
Joseph of Arimathea	James Mason
The Adulteress	Claudia Cardinale
Simon the Pharisee	Francis de Wolfe
The Zealots:	
Amos	Ian Bannen
Joel	Oliver Tobias
Hosias	George Camiller
Saul	Oliver Smith

Robert Powell (center) as *Jesus of Nazareth;* Anne Bancroft (bottom center) as Mary Magdalene and (clockwise) Rod Steiger as Pontius Pilate, Ernest Borgnine as the Centurion, Anthony Quinn as Caiaphas, Laurence Olivier as Nicodemus, Peter Ustinov as Herod the Great, James Farentino as Simon Peter and Ralph Richardson as Simeon.

Daniel	Robert Davey
The Apostles:	
Simon Peter	James Farentino
Andrew his brother	Tony Vogel
James the son of	
Zebedee	Jonathan Muller
John his brother	John Duttine
Philip	Steve Gardner
Bartholomew	John Eastham
Thomas	Bruce Lidington
Matthew the tax	
collector	Keith Washington
James the son of	
Alphaeus	Sergio Nicolai
Thaddeus	Mimmo Crao
Simon the Zealot	Murray Salem
Judas Iscariot	Ian McShane
Martha	Maria Carta
Zerah	Ian Holm
Barabbas	Stacy Keach
The centurion	Ernest Borgnine
The blind man	Renato Raschel
Caiaphas	Anthony Quinn
Habbakuk	Lee Montague
Nicodemus	Laurence Olivier
Pontius Pilate	Rod Steiger
Quintillius	Tony Lo Bianco

THE FILM

"The cross-beam was lifted and roped to Jesus's lacerated back. In intense pain and weakness he began the walk to Calvary. The tragic procession had to pass under some arches that opened on to the streets of Jerusalem, close to the fortress. Nicodemus was lurking behind one of the pillars, watching with a bursting heart as Jesus dragged past. Jesus looked at him, and Nicodemus's eyes filled with tears. The recognition caused Jesus to falter for a moment, and a guard pushed him brutally forward. Nicodemus clasped his hands together and broke into uncontrollable weeping. A verse of scripture echoed in his mind '. . . like a lamb led to the slaughter.' It was intensely hot. The sun scorched down from a sky that was like a dome of beaten copper. Then the murmur of a sad lament made itself heard. Nicodemus, conscious only of the tragic figure of Jesus, was reciting the prophecy of Isaiah:

'He was despised and rejected of men; a man of sorrows and acquainted with grief. He was oppressed and afflicted, yet he opened not his mouth. He was brought as a lamb to slaughter, as a sheep before its shearer is dumb. Surely he has borne our griefs and carried our sorrows. Yet, we did esteem him, stricken, smitted of God and afflicted. But he was wounded for our transgressions. He was abused for our transgressions and through his wounds we are healed, and born again.' "[38]

Jesus of Nazareth was presented by NBC-TV as The Big Event on April 10, 1977, Easter Sunday, and commercially released to theatres in Great Britain

COMMENTS

Jesus of Nazareth became the center of a storm of controversy when General Motors withdrew as sponsor of the telecast prompted by protests over Franco Zeffirelli's statement that Christ would be depicted as a man rather than a divine miracle worker. "I see Jesus as an ordinary man, gentle, fragile, simple," the director commented in an Associated Press interview, adding, "Of course, the public is going to be annoyed that I am destroying their myths."

Proctor and Gamble agreed to assume full sponsorship for the program and the film was critically acclaimed despite the objections of a handful of fundamentalist religious leaders and groups who hadn't even seen it. Consultants to the project included the Archbishop of Canterbury and representatives of the Vatican.

John J. O'Connor reviewing the film in the *New York Times* praised Zeffirelli's gift for detail. "As with all of Zeffirelli's work, from the film *Romeo and Juliet* to his theater and opera stagings, this new production combines minute details with rich visual effects. Olivier and Richardson are superb in their small roles."

NBC encored the film in 1979 as a pre-Easter miniseries, adding a number of outtakes into the negative, so the original six-and-a-half hour telecast of 1977 became an eight hour epic.

Dr. Spaander in *A Bridge Too Far* (1977).

Liv Ullmann as Kate ter Horst, a Dutch mother of five who gave her elegant home to the British wounded, confers with the courageous Dr. Spaander (Olivier), who spent day and night in the makeshift hospital to attend the injured and dying.

A Bridge Too Far

1977, United Artists Release of a Joseph E. Levine Production, Produced by Joseph E. Levine, Richard P. Levine; Screenplay by William Goldman, based on the book by Cornelius Ryan; Photography, Geoffrey Unsworth; Associate Producer, John Palmer; Music composed and conducted by John Addison; Editor, Anthony Gibbs; Art Directors, Roy Stannard, Stuart Craig; Special effects, John Richardson; Costume Designer, Anthony Mendleson; Directed by Richard Attenborough

CAST

Lt. General Browning	Dirk Bogarde
Lt. Colonel Joe Vandeleur	Michael Caine
Lt. Colonel John Frost	Anthony Hopkins
Dr. Spaander	Laurence Olivier
Staff Sergeant Eddie Dohun	James Caan
Major General Robert Urquhart	Sean Connery
Lt. General Brian Horrocks	Edward Fox
Colonel Bobby Stout	Elliott Gould
Major General Sosabowski	Gene Hackman
General Ludwig	Hardy Kruger
Brig. General James M. Gavin	Ryan O'Neal
Major Julian Cook	Robert Redford
Lt. General Bittrich	Maximilian Schell
Kate ter Horst	Liv Ullmann
Tough colonel	Arthur Hill
Field Marshal von Rundstedt	Wolfgang Preiss
Underground leader	Siem Vroom
Kid with glasses	Eric Van't Wout
Old Dutch lady	Mary Smithuysen
Wife	Marlies Van Alcmaer
Captain Glass	Nicholas Campbell
Major Carlyle	Christopher Good
Lt. Cornish	Keith Drinkel
Captain Harry	Peter Faber

Opened June 15, 1977, at the Rivoli, Eastside Cinema, Columbia I and II Theaters in New York

Leaving the battered village, Mrs. ter Horst and Spaander survey the holocaust and waste in the film's powerful closing moments.

A Bridge Too Far is an account of Field Marshal Montgomery's plan to end World War II by flying thirty-five thousand Allied paratroopers, mainly American, three hundred miles and drop them behind German lines in Holland, where they were to capture and hold a series of vital bridges. Simultaneously, a British armored corps of thirty thousand vehicles was to crash through German lines, cross the successive bridges, wheel across the final and most crucial one, Arnhem Bridge, and roar straight into the industrial heart of Germany, crippling the German forces and bringing surrender. Operation Market-Garden, as it was called, began on a Sunday, the seventeenth of September and ended tragically, ten days later.

REVIEWS

New York Times, June 16, 1977
"The battle scenes are as spectacular as any you've ever seen and may ever see again. As an example of big-budget, literal-minded movie-making, *A Bridge Too Far* is as good as one can get."

New York Post, June 16, 1977
"Epic in size. Everything is first class, the realism of those shots of parachutists filling the sky, the tank battles, the vicious little fire-fights in narrow streets, and even the conversations between generals and their subordinates on both sides. This is the hell that war becomes up close. It would be unfair to single out performances from among so many fine ones. Despite their too well-known faces and personalities, they all make you feel they are those soldiers, those particular civilians. If it succeeds as a major epic film of our time, that will be because it underlines so dreadfully war's worst waste."

Olivier portrayed Doctor Spaander, a courageous Dutch doctor in his sixties, who spends day and night treating the British wounded in the home of Kate ter Horst, played by Liv Ullmann, who converted her beautiful fourteen room, two-hundred-year-old home into a makeshift hospital. In the film's closing moments Kate and Spaander leave town carrying a few rescued possessions in a cart. As they pass through the street, cluttered with the rubble of a devastated village, they survey the terrible reminders of the holocaust. Olivier discussed the character in William Goldman's account of the filming in the *Story of a Bridge Too Far.* "When a character runs all the way through a film, you've got an intimate knowledge of a great many things that happen to him, and in this instance you just have intimate knowledge of a very, very few things. You're much in the hands of your director, which, in this particular case, is a very, very nice and very good thing to be. I suppose it's (the film) a very salutary thing. But I've no doubt at all that even as an epic it's going to have exceptional qualities, very exceptional indeed. The story is quite a terrifying one. One's learned a lot actually through the book and studying the story that one didn't know at the time. If you think you're going to be involved, which we constantly were thinking, on and off anyhow, for some years—you never really think what it is going to be like, not really. Nature's merciful in that way. I think (the film is) rather beautiful in its majestically ghastly way. It's very true. I've no doubt that a lot of people will find faults in the translation or the interpretation of certain facts or certain personalities. No doubt it'll be the subject of after-meal arguments for a long time."

The Betsy

1978, Presented by Emanuel L. Wolf; Produced by Robert R. Weston; Associate producer, Jack Grossberg; Screenplay by Walter Bernstein and William Bast from the novel by Harold Robbins; Music by John Barry; Director of Photography, Mario Tosi; Editor, Rita Roland; Production designer, Herman A. Blumenthal; Costume designer, Dorothy Jeakins; Set decorators, James Payne, Sal Blydenburgh; Assistant director, Wolfgang Glattes; Directed by Daniel Petrie; An Allied Artists Harold Robbins International Production; An Allied Artists Release

CAST

Loren Hardeman, Sr. (Number One)	Laurence Olivier
Loren Hardeman III	Robert Duvall
Sally Hardeman	Katharine Ross
Angelo Perino	Tommy Lee Jones
Alicia Hardeman	Jane Alexander
Lady Bobby Ayres	Lesley-Anne Down
Jake Weinstein	Joseph Wiseman
Betsy Hardeman	Kathleen Beller
Dan Weyman	Edward Herrmann
Loren Hardeman, Jr.	Paul Rudd
Duncan	Roy Poole
Mark Sampson	Richard Venture
Angelo Luigi Perino	Titos Vandis
Joe Warren	Clifford David
Mrs. Craddock	Inga Swenson
Elizabeth Hardeman	Whitney Blake
Roxanne	Carol Williard
Donald	Read Morgan
Loren III (as a boy)	Charlie Fields
Man	Robert Phalen
Bellhop	Nick Czmyr
Boardmember #1	Norman Palmer
Boardmember #3	Fred Carney
Boardmember #4	Maury Cooper
Boardmember #5	Russell Porter
Hotel clerk	Teri Ralston
Security Guard	Warney H. Ruhl
Helicopter Pilot	Patrick J. Monks
Secretary of Commerce	William Roerick
Butler	William B. Cain
Chauffeur	Edward C. Higgins
Nurse	Mary Petrie
Male Guest	H. August Kuehl
Retired Man	Robert Hawkins
Retired Woman	Sadie Hawkins
Car Driver	Anthony Steere

Opened February 10, 1978, National Theater, New York

THE FILM

Loren Hardeman, Sr. (Number One), is the founder of the giant Bethlehem Motor Corporation. In the twenties he is a colorful auto magnate and an incorrigible womanizer. He is disappointed in his son, Junior, a delicate young man under the influence of a conniving friend, Joe Warren, who is attempting to control the company. Junior's wife, Sally, is troubled by her husband's disinterest in her and finds comfort with Number One. To avert family complications, Number One takes an extended European trip and returns to find the company on strike and in a state of crisis under the influence of Warren. Number One fires Warren and resumes his close relationship with Sally, which culminates in tragedy for Junior.

In the seventies Bethlehem is being run by Loren Hardeman III, who since childhood, has suppressed his hatred for his grandfather. Number One, now nearly ninety, is still alert and shrewd in the use of power. He cannot give up his passion for innovating a new automobile, de-

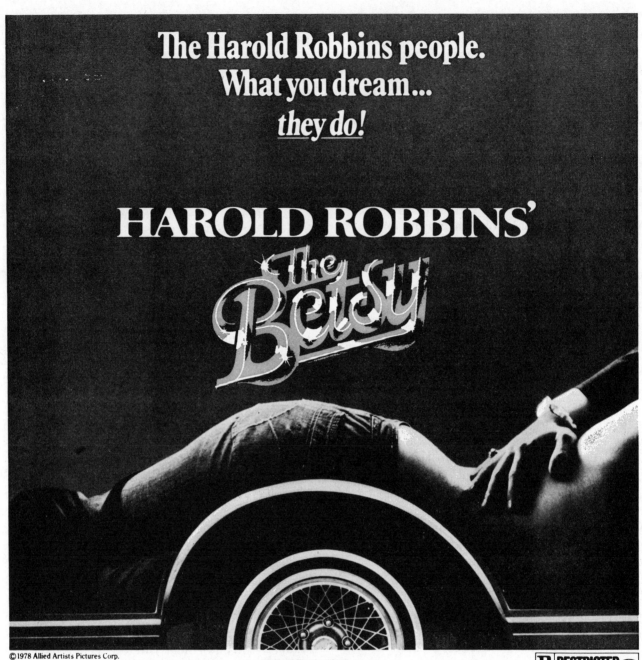

The Harold Robbins people.
What you dream...
they do!

HAROLD ROBBINS'
The Betsy

©1978 Allied Artists Pictures Corp.

EMANUEL L. WOLF Presents
LAURENCE OLIVIER
ROBERT DUVALL   KATHARINE ROSS   TOMMY LEE JONES   JANE ALEXANDER
in HAROLD ROBBINS' THE BETSY
LESLEY-ANNE DOWN   JOSEPH WISEMAN   EDWARD HERRMANN
PAUL RUDD   KATHLEEN BELLER
Screenplay by WILLIAM BAST and WALTER BERNSTEIN   Music JOHN BARRY
Produced by ROBERT R. WESTON   Associate Producer JACK GROSSBERG   Directed by DANIEL PETRIE
An Allied Artists / Harold Robbins International Production   An Allied Artists Release

signed by a flamboyant race driver, Angelo Perino, and named the Betsy, after his great-granddaughter.

Angelo is consumed with the construction of the new car, despite interference from Loren III. Number One decides to give up on the Betsy, but Angelo refuses to accept defeat, despite being brutally assaulted. He persuades Betsy and Loren III's wife to support him and enlists the aid of an old family friend and attorney with underworld connections. A final confrontation among Angelo, Number One, and Loren III determines the fate of the Betsy and the control of Bethlehem.

REVIEWS

Jack Kroll, *Newsweek* magazine, February 20, 1978
"*The Larry*. God bless Laurence Olivier. And God only knows what the incomparable actor of the Western world is doing in a piece of hilarious idiocy like *The Betsy*. Taking away a zillion dollars, one hopes. This is no cameo role; the great septuagenarian is playing the lead. And lead he does, in the greatest put-on performance you've ever seen. Having plumbed the depths of Shakespeare and Chekhov, Olivier has little trouble probing the nookies and crannies of Harold Robbins (the thinking man's Sidney Sheldon) from whose best seller this farrago was farragoed. Only the great Hamlet could create the great Loren Hardeman Sr., mighty Detroit automobile tycoon and founder of the silliest industrial dynasty in junk-novel history. Having dealt many times with the primal sin of Oedipus, Olivier has no trouble committing incest with his daughter-in-law. In the crystalline winter of his glorious career, Olivier reaches new heights as horny old Hardeman, humping a chambermaid furiously right before your boggled eyes. See Olivier chew out his homosexual son. Watch him try, at the age of 86, to put the make on a juicy broad. See him in flashbacks become a man in his 40s, still handsome and graceful. Listen to him invent the most endearingly wacked-out Midwestern-Scots accent you've ever heard. Watch him show the suffering cast how to kid a ridiculous script without losing your integrity." Copyright 1978 by Newsweek, Inc. All rights reserved. Reprinted by permission."

Loren Hardeman in *The Betsy* (1978).

Olivier portrays the creator of a mighty automobile dynasty. Here, Hardeman is in his forties.

239

Here he appears as the nearly ninety year old patriarch.

New York *Daily News,* February 10, 1978
"Laurence Olivier, as the auto magnate, spends the entire picture searching for the proper American accent and trying to master a Midwestern twang. At times, he sounds like a cross between Walter Brennan and Billy Carter. What makes this movie especially painful is that it exposes this brilliant actor at his very worst in a performance totally out of control."

New York Tribune, February 10, 1978
"Laurence Olivier seems to be having a good time, but never gets a grip on his accent, sounding at times like Joseph Cotten, at times like Lionel Barrymore."

New York Times, February 10, 1978
"Only Olivier manages to play his role and wink at it simultaneously, and his is surely the most sensible approach."

Rex Reed, New York *Daily News,* February 10, 1978
"It is abysmally depressing to see Laurence Olivier hobbling through this jetsam chuckling and croaking like Frank Morgan in *The Wizard of Oz.*"

New Jersey *Bergen Record,* February 10, 1978
"Olivier turns in the best performance as the crusty patriarch. He provides the cement that holds the movie together, but even he has his share of problems. He must have picked up his accent at the United Nations; it sounds part Scottish, part Amish and part silliness."

COMMENTS

Olivier expressed his enjoyment playing the lecherous auto magnate in an interview with *TV Guide.* "You can say what you like about that film, but it was very enjoyable to do. It was a filthily vulgar part, the most awful character I've ever played in my life and I enjoyed it highly." Later in a *New York Times* interview he elaborated on the acceleration of his film career. "Thank God for the movies. I can no longer be a stage actor, because I don't feel I've got the power . . . the physical attributes that are absolutely necessary to be a very good, powerful, meaningful actor. So we have the movies, and I

**Granddaughter Betsy Hardeman (Kathleen Beller) has a
new automobile named after her.**

**It was designed by race driver, Angelo Perrino (Tommy
Lee Jones).**

241

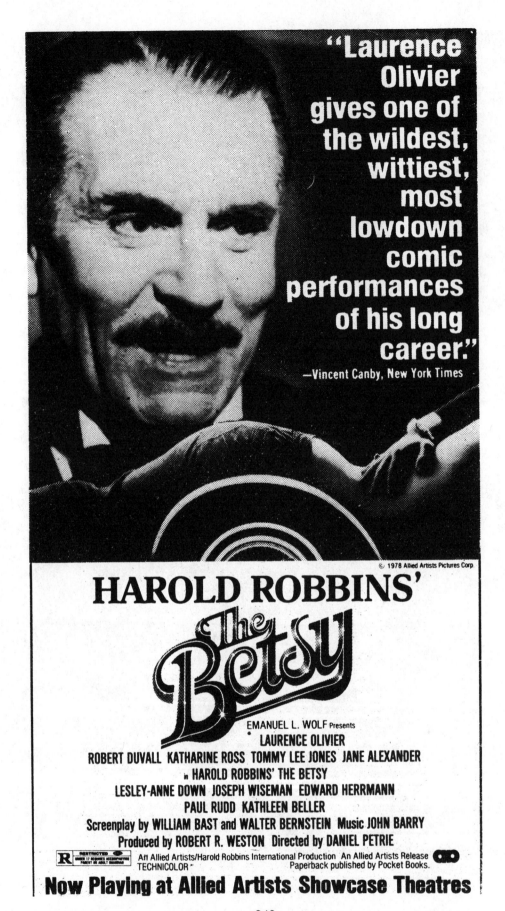

242

Hardeman becomes involved in an incestual relationship with his daughter-in-law Sally (Katharine Ross).

Olivier on Hardeman: "The most awful character I've ever played in my life, and I enjoyed it highly."

get a fortune for doing it, which is absolutely what I'm after because I've always overspent in my life and now I'd better get with it.

"They criticize me in the papers. 'Why's he doing such muck?' I'll tell you why . . . to pay for three children in school, for a family, and their future. So what should I do? Write the critics and ask them to support us? Would that satisfy them?"[39]

The Gentleman Tramp
(The Chaplin Biography)

1978, A Tinc Production Corp. Release in association with Marvin Films, Inc.; Written and Directed by Richard Patterson; Produced by Bert Schneider; Original music by Charles Chaplin; Narrated by Walter Matthau, Laurence Olivier, and Jack Lemmon

THE FILM

Olivier reads excerpts from Charles Chaplin's 1964 autobiography in a documentary including scenes from seventeen of the comedian's films and rare footage from the Chaplin private collection and home movies. The film opened April 26, 1978, at the New Yorker, Trans-Lux 85 Street and the Waverly theaters in New York.

REVIEWS

New York Post, April 26, 1978
"The must-see movie of the moment—and, I suspect, any old or new time—is *The Gentleman Tramp*. This delightful film has captured the quintessence of the artist and his art and done so in terms accessible to everyone."

New York *Daily News*, April 26, 1978
"A touching tribute to his genius."

The Boys from Brazil

1978, Sir Lew Grade Presentation of a Producer Circle Production, Produced by Martin Richards and Stanley O'Toole; Executive Producer, Robert Fryer; Screenplay by Heywood Gould from the novel by Ira Levin; Editor, Robert E. Swink; Sound, Derek Ball; Music by Jerry Goldsmith; Production Design, Gil Parrondo; Art Direction, Peter Lamont; Assistant Director, Jose Lopez Rodero; Costumes, Anthony Mendleson; Production Supervisor, Ron Carr; Director of Photography, Henri Decae; Camera, Jimmy Davis; Technical Advisor, Dr. Derek Bromhall; Special Effects, Roy Whybrow; Directed by Franklin J. Schaffner; A Twentieth Century Fox Release from I.T.C. Entertainment

CAST

Josef Mengele	Gregory Peck
Ezra Lieberman	Laurence Olivier
Eduard Siebert	James Mason
Esther Lieberman	Lilli Palmer
Frieda Maloney	Uta Hagen
Barry Kohler	Steven Guttenberg
Sidney Benyon	Denholm Elliott
Mrs. Doring	Rosemary Harris
Henry Wheelock	John Dehner
David Bennett	John Rubinstein
Mrs. Curry	Anne Meara
Jack/Simon/Bobby /Erich	Jeremy Black
Strasser	David Hurst
Bruckner	Bruno Ganz
Harrington	Michael Gough
Nancy	Linda Hayden
Hessen	Guy Dumont
Gunther	Georg Marishka
Farnbach	Gunter Meisner
Kleist	Jurgen Andersen
Schwimmer	Wolf Kahler
Trausteiner	Carl Duering
Mundt	Walter Gotell
Schmidt	David Brandon
Stroop	Mervin Nelson
Gertrud	Monica Gearson
Fassler	Joachim Hansen

SIR LEW GRADE Presents
A PRODUCER CIRCLE PRODUCTION

**GREGORY
PECK**   and   **LAURENCE
OLIVIER**

**JAMES
MASON**

A FRANKLIN J. SCHAFFNER FILM

THE
BOYS
FROM
BRAZIL

if they survive...will we?

and starring LILLI PALMER

"THE BOYS FROM BRAZIL" Executive Producer ROBERT FRYER
Music by JERRY GOLDSMITH Screenplay by HEYWOOD GOULD
From the novel by IRA LEVIN Produced by MARTIN RICHARDS
and STANLEY O'TOOLE Directed by FRANKLIN J. SCHAFFNER

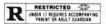 Original Soundtrack Recording Available on A&M Records and Tapes

© 1978 Twentieth Century-Fox   "We're Home Again" Sung by Elaine Paige

Lieberman in *The Boys from Brazil* **(1978).**

Lofquist	Wolfgang Preiss
Ismael	Raul Faustino Saldanha
Mrs. Harrington	Prunella Scales
Doring	Richard Marner
Berthe	Gerti Gordon
Blonde Lady	Guida De Carlo

Opened October 5, 1978, Ziegfeld Theater, New York

THE FILM

Dr. Josef Mengele, formerly the "angel of death" at Auschwitz, holds a secret meeting in a South American country with a group of former colleagues in the Third Reich at which he announces a devious plan to assassinate 94 civil servants—all aged 65, and all male. Barry Kohler a young American has overheard the plan and phones Ezra Lieberman, a famed Vienna-based Nazi war criminal hunter. Lieberman is reluctant to get involved, but when Kohler is murdered he is motivated to investigate further. As Mengele's henchmen begin their methodical assassinations, Lieberman persuades a journalist to send cuttings of all mysterious deaths of 65 year old men but cannot understand why deaths of middle-aged men—Christians at that—should be part of a big Nazi plot. The significance of the case is that Mengele, a man who killed hundreds of thousands in genetic experiments—often with twins—is masterminding it.

Lieberman begins to trace deaths which appear to be accidents but cannot find the link. While in the United States on a lecture tour, he investigates one of the recent deaths and discovers a fourteen-year-old boy to be the exact double of a boy he met while following up a German death. The boy's mother explains that her son was adopted. This fact leads Lieberman to question a former Nazi, Frieda Maloney, about her illegal work after the war for an American adoption agency. Mengele is disturbed by the interference of the Nazi hunter and continues alone on his murderous project when his superior halts the plan and recalls the assassination team.

Mengele and Lieberman have a final confrontation in a small Pennsylvania town where their fate is controlled by Bobby Wheelock, another

During a break while filming *The Boys from Brazil*, Olivier serves a comforting cup of tea to co-star Gregory Peck who portrayed the villainous Dr. Mengele.

The character of Ezra Lieberman was inspired by Simon Wiesenthal, the celebrated real-life hunter of Nazi war criminals.

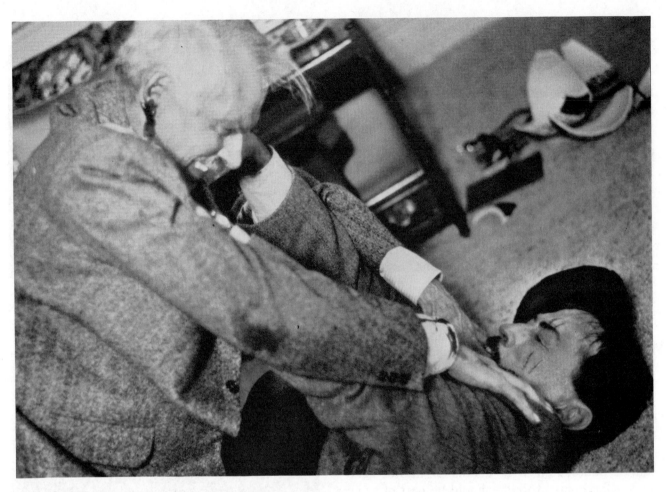

Though plagued by a painful disorder which seriously
affected his nerve endings, Olivier insisted on perfection
during the filming of the climactic fight sequence with
Peck.

fourteen-year-old duplicate and a pack of Doberman guard dogs. Mengele's plan was to recreate, by cloning, 94 young Hitler's from samples of the Führer's blood drawn during his lifetime. The identical environment of the 'Boys' was to approximate Hitler's own: Nordic Christian families where the husband, a civil servant was considerably older than his spouse and who died at age 65, leaving a fourteen-year-old child and wife who would die five years later.

REVIEWS

Variety magazine, September 27, 1978
"With two excellent antagonists in Gregory Peck and Lord Laurence Olivier, *The Boys from Brazil* presents a gripping, suspenseful drama for nearly all of its two hours. In a fine shift from his usual roles, Peck plays the evil Josef Mengele, a real-life character who murdered thousands of Jews, including many children, carrying out bizarre genetic experiments at Auschwitz in Poland. Olivier, slipping completely into the role of an elderly Jewish gentleman, is the Nazi hunter who brings him to bay. (The real Mengele, if living, has never been found.)"

Newsweek magazine, October 9, 1978
"The movie's meat is the bravura acting of Laurence Olivier, Gregory Peck, and James Mason. Olivier's ironic, subtle acting as usual has a thousand nuances. His performance looks like a homage to the great old German actor Albert Bassermann, a refugee from Hitler who was in so many American movies, such as Alfred Hitchcock's *Foreign Correspondent*. Olivier's acting has the same sweet, strong, lilting rhythms—the tonality of the Middle European humanism that Hitler almost destroyed."

Time magazine, October 9, 1978
"Olivier relishes playing the old Jew. Wise and crusty, frail of frame but stout of heart, Lieberman is one of those movie character roles that the great actor visibly enjoys doing and that one cannot help enjoying along with him."

In the film of Ira Levin's best selling novel, *The Boys from Brazil,* Olivier offered a sharp contrast to the vicious Nazi dentist enacted in *Marathon Man*. The actor switched sides to play Nazi hunter Ezra Lieberman, a character inspired by real life war criminal sleuth, Simon Wiesenthal. His antagonist, the infamous Dr. Josef Mengele, is portrayed by Gregory Peck who seldom played an unsympathetic role in his long motion picture career. His cruel cowhand in *Duel in the Sun* and the possessed Captain Ahab of *Moby Dick* were tormented souls driven by passion and revenge, and were his only "heavies" to date. Mengele, a Nazi physician who sent millions to death in gas chambers and destroyed thousands more in laboratory experiments is fictionalized as a scientist who discovers a way to clone a number of Hitlers in his South American hideout.

Filming was extremely arduous for Olivier who continued to be plagued by dermatomyositis which affected his nerve endings so seriously that it became difficult to engage in a simple handshake. Executive Producer Robert Fryer watched Olivier walk down a flight of steep stairs without holding the banister during filming at Wien Studios in Vienna and had the impression the actor was in "holy agony." In a climactic fight between Mengele and Lieberman, Olivier demanded perfection despite obvious pain. He suggested an elaborate fall to director Franklin Schaffner who advised him against it, but Olivier insisted it would be effective and proceeded to execute the maneuver with alarming finesse, never once complaining.

Film critic Bernard Drew observed the filming of the fight. He had witnessed Olivier's *Oedipus* thirty years earlier and never forgot the piercing cry the actor gave at the end of the play. Drew notes that Olivier's cry as he falls to the floor after being shot by Peck was "a smaller version of the one he emitted in *Oedipus,* which might be the apotheosis of his career."

Uta Hagen, the celebrated stage actress, author and teacher, made a rare screen appearance in *The Boys from Brazil* as Frieda Maloney, an ex-Nazi who is awaiting trial in Germany for her

With Lilli Palmer as Esther Lieberman, sister of the crusading Nazi hunter.

Peck and Olivier are confronted by Jeremy Black as Bobby Wheelock who controls some dangerous Doberman guard dogs. Mr. Peck has referred to Olivier as "the heavyweight champ among actors."

illegal participation after the war in an American adoption agency. An interrogation scene in which Lieberman attempts to discover a link in Mengele's murderous master plan, required but three days of shooting for the actress and Olivier. "Since everyone knows he's a great actor," Miss Hagen writes, "I can only add that he's a superb, courteous and considerate colleague as well."

Olivier received his eleventh Academy Award nomination for his role as the Nazi hunter. With the recognition of ten acting nominations, the actor set a new record, topping nine such honors accumulated by his old friend, Spencer Tracy. Jon Voight won the 1978 Oscar for his performance as a Vietnamese war veteran in *Coming Home*. The National Board of Review announced a tie for the Best Actor honor of the year, citing both Voight and Olivier.

Upon the completion of filming *Boys from Brazil*, Olivier rested for several months following a new battle with pneumonia. "I am not supposed to undertake work of any kind," he wrote the author of this book in April of 1978. On the eve of his seventy-first birthday he made a surprise appearance at London's Court Theatre in support of the Sunday Night Cabaret for the George Devine Award presentation. Among those present were John Gielgud, Dame Peggy Ashcroft and Janet Suzman. Lady Olivier performed a scene by N. F. Simpson.

Soon after trade papers announced that Olivier would appear as Professor Van Helsing in a new film of *Dracula*, scheduled to begin filming in July with Frank Langella, who had received considerable acclaim for his performance in the title role of a Broadway revival. Production plans were postponed until October while Langella extended his New York appearance until actor Raul Julia would be available to replace him. In the meantime, though still weak from his recent illness, Olivier accepted the invitation of director George Roy Hill to appear as a gentlemanly pick-pocket in his romantic comedy, *A Little Romance*. Filming began in Paris and Venice during the summer months, and the courageous actor, defiantly ignoring the annoying interruptions of failing health, began the job of creating Julius, one of the warmest and most endearing characters yet in the already astounding parade of impressive screen portrayals.

For his performance as Ezra Lieberman in *The Boys from Brazil*, Olivier was cited as Best Actor of the year by the National Board of Review. The role also brought him his eleventh Academy Award nomination, ten of which were for acting, topping the previous record of nine nominations set by Spencer Tracy.

AMERICA IS HAVING A LOVE AFFAIR WITH "A LITTLE ROMANCE"

PAN ARTS Presents

A GEORGE ROY HILL FILM
"A LITTLE ROMANCE"

Starring

LAURENCE OLIVIER

ARTHUR HILL   SALLY KELLERMAN   DIANE LANE and THELONIOUS BERNARD as the lovers

Produced by YVES ROUSSET-ROUARD and ROBERT L. CRAWFORD   Executive Producer PATRICK KELLEY

Screenplay by ALLAN BURNS   Directed by GEORGE ROY HILL   Original Music by GEORGES DELERUE

Based on the novel "E=MC², MON AMOUR" by PATRICK CAUVIN   Published by the EDITIONS JEAN-CLAUDE LATTES

Prints by TECHNICOLOR®   An ORION PICTURES Release   Thru WARNER BROS ⊙ A Warner Communications Company   PG PARENTAL GUIDANCE SUGGESTED ⬛ SOME MATERIAL MAY NOT BE SUITABLE FOR CHILDREN

252

A Little Romance

1979, a Pan Arts Foundation, Produced by Yves Rousset-Rouard and Robert L. Crawford; Executive Producer, Patrick Kelley; Directed by George Roy Hill; Screenplay by Allan Burns; based on the novel $E = MC^2$, *Mon Amour* by Patrick Cauvin; Original Music Composed and Conducted by Georges Delerue; Director of Photography, Pierre William Glenn; Film Editor, William Reynolds; Production Design, Henry Bumstead; Art Director, Francois De Lamothe; Set Decoration, Robert Christides; Wardrobe Designer, Rosine Delamare; An Orion Pictures Release, through Warner Bros.

CAST

Julius	Laurence Olivier
Daniel	Thelonious Bernard
Lauren	Diane Lane
Richard King	Arthur Hill
Kay King	Sally Kellerman
Brod	Broderick Crawford
George de Marco	David Dukes
Bob Duryea	Andrew Duncan
Janet Duryea	Claudette Sutherland
Londet	Graham Fletcher-Cook
Natalie	Ashby Semple
Michel Michon	Claude Brosset
Inspector Leclerc	Jacques Maury
Ms. Siegel	Anna Massey
Martin	Peter Maloney
First Assistant Director	Mike Marshall
French Ambassador	Michel Bardinet
French Representative	Alain David Gabison
Monique	Isabelle Duby
Make-up Man	Jeffrey Carey
Second Assistant Director	John Pepper
Woman Critic	Denise Glaser
Woman in Metro	Jeanne Herviale
Tour Guide	Carlo Lastricati
Secretary	Judy Mullen
Theater Manager	Philippe Brigaud
Cashier	Lucienne Legrand

Opened April 27, 1979, Sutton Theater, New York

THE FILM

Lauren, a lonely, gifted American girl who lives in Paris with her flighty and fickle mother and understanding step-father, is easily attracted to Daniel, a French boy who shares an I.Q. equally as lofty, and a passion for American motion pictures, soccer, philosophy and mathematics. The girl is out of touch with her flamboyant and sophisticated mother, who is suddenly enamored by an "auteur" film director. Daniel is also alienated by his hard-drinking, ill-humored, cab driver father. Their new found friendship with each other and the accidental acquaintanceship of a raffish old boulevardier, inspires an adventurous journey in search of a romantic ideal. Julius charms the youngsters with fanciful tales of old-world romance, particularly a legend concerning lovers who kiss beneath the Bridge of Sighs in Venice to pledge eternal love. The beguiling old Frenchman becomes an unwitting accomplice in the pilgrimage, and is ultimately accused of kidnapping the teen-agers. In reality, Julius turns out to be an experienced pickpocket with a long criminal record, whose crafty methods help finance the journey. To elude the police in Verona, the trio enter a cross country bicycle race. With parents and authorities in hot pursuit, the young couple travel by gondola towards the fabled bridge to keep the romantic rendezvous which will seal their vow to love each other forever.

REVIEWS

Cue magazine, May 11, 1979
". . . director George Roy Hill has imbued his handsomely mounted, sprightly paced *A Little Romance* with humor, sophisticated charm, and a sly wink . . . played with sentiment and flair by Laurence Olivier."

Variety, April 4, 1979
". . . a classy winner. A charming blend of youthful innocence and guile. Fulcrum in Burns' script is the beneficent boulevardier limned by Laurence Olivier in a modern refashioning of the old Maurice Chevalier role. The prototypical lov-

Julius Edmond Santorin in *A Little Romance* (1979).

With Thelonious Bernard as Daniel and Diane Lane as Lauren.

Julius: "Lovers who kiss beneath the Bridge of Sighs in Venice, at sunset as the bells of Campanile toll, will love each other forever."

Julius: "I may be an old fraud, but I know this much is true. Something that two people who are in love create together . . . against impossible odds . . . can hold them together. Forever."

255

A special bicycle was designed for non-cyclist Olivier, who as a pickpocket being pursued by the police, escapes from Verona as a participant in a cross country race. Olivier insisted on doing the scene himself, as his stand-in, Harry van Engel watched several strenuous takes.

able scoundrel. Olivier hams it up unmercifully, the latest of his recent dialectician roles. It's his 60th screen role, and the well-rounded nature of his characterization still astounds.''

Newsweek magazine, April 30, 1979
''On paper, these precocious lovers must have seemed too good to be true; as incarnated by (Diane) Lane and (Thelonious) Bernard they are too true to be resisted. Even Lord Olivier—who delivers a shamelessly theatrical but nonetheless endearing performance—is in constant danger of having his scenes stolen.''

Women's Wear Daily, April 23, 1979
''If Shakespeare had been in our times and had opted for films rather than the theater, he probably would have made movies like *A Little Romance*. It has all the basic ingredients for a perfect romantic film. Laurence Olivier stars as a charming liaison between the romantic past and a pragmatic present, and there are colorful scenes of Paris, Venice and Verona that manage to be lovely without being lavish.''

New York *Daily News,* April 27, 1979
''It is a jaunty, good-humored and refreshingly tart movie. Olivier, who is looking more and more frail, seems to have poured all of his energy into the role of a boulevardier who turns out to be a practiced con man. But although one delights in the crafty and impish way he steals a scene, he seems to be straining too hard and his efforts tend to kill the light-hearted mood of the movie.''

New York Times, April 27, 1979
''Mr. Olivier plays the Maurice Chevalier role, a role in which even Mr. Chevalier finally became tiresome. Mr. Olivier is never tiresome—sometimes he is quite funny—but he does seem desperate. As an elderly, extremely soft-hearted, French pick-pocket who befriends the young lovers, Mr. Olivier is required to be not much more than cute.''

Time magazine, May 7, 1979
''One of the consistent joys of '70s moviegoing has been Laurence Olivier's game, witty performances in otherwise terrible films. Even junk like *The Betsy* and *The Boys from Brazil* became memorable in his hands: Who could forget his

parody of a Midwestern accent in the former or his rapturous cigarette smoking in the latter? Olivier is such a sly devil that he could make his Oscar acceptance speech, a riotous stream of sheer poppycock, sound as though it were a Shakespearean soliloquy. As TV audiences saw, it was enough to addle Fellow Oscar Winner Jon Voight's brain for the rest of the night. In *A Little Romance*, Olivier has another crusty character: a suave old coot of a Frenchman who plays fairy godfather to a pair of star-crossed lovers who are just thirteen. He is in delightful fettle and creates one classic bit, a gasping fit while reading a newspaper. Yet this is one latter-day Olivier film that has more going for it than its star."

Penelope Gilliatt, *New Yorker*, May 7, 1979
"The film is assumptively about a modern-world Romeo and Juliet, but the day does not belong to the capering children. It belongs to Laurence Olivier, cast as a dapper Frenchman who takes up with the children in the street and entertains them with hot chocolate; and Olivier gives himself, and us, the fun of which he is uniquely capable. His tongue seems to be lolling in his cheek like a hot spaniel's, as it often does when he is calling with ease on his genius and working at the top of his form. The man played by Sir Laurence speaks to the children's heart. The performance is sauced with the peculiar daintiness that Olivier brings to mischievously trivial parts. He endows this one with some of the debonair alertness he gives to Restoration comedy. The film is fortunate to have him: perhaps most of all fortunate for his importation of implicit centuries of European learning and merriment, just as the children—this latter-day Romeo and Juliet—are very lucky in their Friar Laurence." From an article in *The New Yorker*. Reprinted by permission; © 1979. The New Yorker Magazine, Inc.

The Aquarian, May 2, 1979
"W. C. Fields advised that no actor in his right mind would ever co-star with children or animals. Fields once evened the odds in his favor by spiking Baby LeRoy's orange juice with gin, but Olivier has no need for such subterfuge. He more than holds his own against the two young leads. The role of Julius has been tailor-made in the style of the comedic second banana, the kind of part played to perfection by Arthur Treacher or the immortal Edward Everett Horton. Olivier, who has recently proven his ability to appear both menacing and feeble, turns his talents here toward the finer points of comedy: double-takes, pauses, a whole world of shtick. Watching Olivier in any role is like taking acting lessons; in *A Little Romance,* the lesson is in comedy, and Olivier is very, very funny."

Filming in Verona held a special significance for Olivier, as it is the city in which Shakespeare set *Romeo and Juliet*. The actor's long association with the tragedy includes the British record of 186 successive performances as Romeo at London's New Theatre. He is also one of the world's few actors who has been equally successful in both the roles of Romeo and Mercutio. His last association with the timeless romance was when he served as narrator for Zeffirelli's 1968 film.

At the Los Angeles premiere of *A Little Romance*, Olivier became the second recipient of the Filmex Trustees Award at the International Film Exposition. First awarded to director Alfred Hitchcock in 1976, the honor recognizes talent which has "materially advanced the art of film."

Olivier's "leading lady" was fourteen year old Diane Lane, herself a veteran of classic theatre, having appeared at the La Mama Theater in New York in productions of *Medea, The Trojan Women, Electra, The Good Woman of Setzuan* and *As You Like It*. Her off-Broadway success brought her to the attention of producer Joseph Papp who cast her in New York Shakespeare Festival productions of *Agamemnon* and *The Cherry Orchard* at Lincoln Center, and as Jackie in Elizabeth Swados' contemporary musical, *Runaways*, on Broadway.

Olivier brings a touch of seedy grandeur to his role as an aging gentleman crook who poses as a worldly diplomat.

258

He meets the youngsters unexpectedly while strolling in a Paris park when Daniel sends him sprawling from the impact of a wayward soccer ball. Winded, but never at a loss for words, the old charmer invites his new friends for hot chocolate to regale them with his lifetime of romantic adventures.

Inspired by the romantic legend which Julius has charmed them with, Daniel and Lauren travel by gon-dola towards the fabled Bridge of Sighs in Venice to pledge eternal love.

COMMENTS

The world premiere of *A Little Romance*, the first film released by Orion Pictures, was held on March 30, 1979 at the ABC Entertainment Center in Los Angeles. The event was marked by the presentation of the Filmex Trustees Award to Olivier. The award is voted in recognition of a major creative talent, whose contributions have not only been distinguished in their own right, but have also materially advanced the art of film. Olivier was the second recipient of the honor, the first having been given to Alfred Hitchcock in 1976.

Variety reported the evening to be "reminiscent of some of his famous Shakespearean roles. There was a bit of King Lear, a measure of Hamlet and a great deal of courage in Olivier's last minute arrival." The actor was temporarily delayed on a Concorde jet in New York. "But when the stage lights came on and the curtain rose, there was Olivier." Presenting the award, Gregory Peck noted Olivier's "heightened awareness, robust judgment, keen intelligence and noble sensibility," adding, "we're all better off because of him."

It was a simple tribute which visibly moved Olivier who, with tears in his eyes, told the crowd, "I'm quite aware that my voice is a little shaky, and my composure less than perfect, but this is a most rare experience, and an honor I shall treasure for the rest of my days. I am at the point where I wish I had more of those days with which to enjoy it." The actor was accorded several standing ovations and a prolonged one at the conclusion of the screening when a fan shouted, "God bless Sir Laurence."

On the same evening a ninety minute retrospective of Olivier's fifty year film career was shown at the Plitt Century Plaza Theatre in Hollywood. The film tribute featured twenty-five separate clips, assembled by David Chierichetti, with the aid of David Koenigsberg, Richard Simonton Jr. and David Weiss. Variety observed that "the development of his character from a slick-haired roue in *The Yellow Ticket* in 1931 to his portrayal of the sinister Nazi in *Marathon Man*, gave proof that the Olivier legend is grounded in reality."

260

One week later at the presentation of the fifty-first Academy Awards ceremony, Olivier received a special achievement award for "the full body of his work, the unique achievements of his entire career and his lifetime of contribution to the art of film." Columnist Liz Smith hailed Olivier's acceptance speech as the show stopping moment of the long evening. "It surely will live as the all-time uplifting, gracious and stunning apex of what one wishes all acceptance speeches might be. Everything after that seemed gross and trivial." Film critic Vincent Canby noted that "Olivier added class to the proceedings, giving the show the aura of the public event it always wants but seldom achieves."

"Mr. president, and governors of the academy, committee members, fellows, my very noble and approved good masters, my colleagues, my friends, my fellow students, in the great wealth—the great firmament of your nation's generosity, this particular choice may perhaps, be found by future generations as a trifle eccentric, but the mere fact of it, the prodigal, pure human kindness of it, must be seen as a beautiful star in that firmament which shines upon me at this moment, dazzling me a little, but filling me with warmth and the extraordinary elation, the euphoria that happens to so many of us at the first breath of the majestic glow of a new tomorrow.

From the top of this moment, in the solace, in the kindly emotion that is charging my soul and my heart at this moment, I thank you for this great gift which lends me such a very splendid part in this your glorious occasion. Thank you."

Laurence Olivier
April 9, 1979
Dorothy Chandler Pavilion
Los Angeles Music Center

In a summation of the gala evening, commenting on the climactic appearances of Lord Olivier and John Wayne (just three months after surgery which involved the removal of his stomach), the New York Post reported; "But the climax had come before this climax, or Wayne's. It had come when they showed five minutes of Laurence Olivier as Hamlet, Heathcliff, Archie Rice, Max de Winter, Richard III, Henry V—five breathtaking and glorious minutes when time stood still for a little touch of Larry in the night."

261

Professor Van Helsing in *Dracula* **(1979).**

Dracula

1979, The Mirisch Corporation, A Walter Mirisch—John Badham Production; Screenplay by W. D. Richter; Based on the stage play by Hamilton Deane and John L. Balderston from the novel by Bram Stoker; Music by John Williams; Photography, Gilbert Taylor; Costumes, Julie Harris; Art Director, Peter Young; Editor, John Bloom; Executive Producer, Marvin E. Mirisch; Produced by Walter Mirisch; Directed by John Badham; A Universal Picture

CAST

Count Dracula	Frank Langella
Professor Van Helsing	Laurence Olivier
Dr. Seward	Donald Pleasence
Lucy Seward	Kate Nelligan
Jonathan Harker	Trevor Eve
Mina Van Helsing	Jan Francis
Annie	Janine Duvitski
Renfield	Tony Haygarth
Swales	Teddy Turner
Walter	Sylveste McCoy
Mrs. Galloway	Kristine Howarth
Tom Hindley	Joe Belcher
Scarborough sailor	Ted Carroll
Harbourmaster	Frank Birch
Captain of Demeter	Gabor Vernon
Demeter sailor	Frank Henson
Priest	Peter Wallis

Opened July 13, 1979, Ziegfeld Theater, New York and 62 Universal Blue Ribbon Theaters in New York and New Jersey

THE FILM

The sailing ship Demeter founders off the rugged Yorkshire coast, eventually crashing upon the jagged rocks. The ship's captain is found lashed to the wheel, rosary in hand, with his throat torn apart. The only survivor is the mysterious Count Dracula, discovered in a cave at the foot of the stormy cliffs by Mina Van Helsing, a guest at Billerbeck Hall, a nearby sanatorium for the insane. The Count is invited to dinner by the asylum's supervisor, Dr. Jack Seward and his daughter Lucy. Jonathan Harker, a young Lon-

Frank Langella repeated his Broadway success as a sensuous and sinister Prince of Darkness in *Dracula*. Praising Langella's performance in the New York *Daily News*, Tom McMorrow observed that the actor "takes a legendary character of super-human proportions and makes him human."

don solicitor has arranged for the Count to lease Carfax Abbey, a long deserted, almost uninhabitable mansion. The fragile Mina, whose health has been progressively declining, suddenly passes away following a futile struggle for breath in the night. Her death is seemingly unexplained by Seward, save for two small punctures in her neck. Seward's old colleague, Professor Abraham Van Helsing arrives from Holland and begins an intense investigation of the circumstances which have led to his daughter's death. His knowledge of the supernatural leads him to a reluctant but inevitable conclusion that there is a vampire within their midst; a creature dead and yet not dead, a creature who lives by night upon a diet of

263

human blood. The usual antidotes to the powers of a vampire—garlic, the Christian cross and a yew stake driven through the monster's heart—have only a minimal effect on the Prince of Darkness. Van Helsing has a bizarre confrontation with his dead daughter, struggles to release Lucy Seward from the clutches of the Count and joins Seward and Harker in a frantic crosscountry dash to Scarborough port. Van Helsing and Dracula engage in a violent death battle on the open sea as Harker rescues the abducted Lucy Seward.

"Frank Langella applies his formidable technique to the role while exulting in the surface playing and showmanship it demands. He is flamboyant, aristocratic and swashbuckling when in control of situations, a raging beast when cornered. Sheathed in black velvet, his cape a bat wing, he is bravura itself." (Martin Gottfried, *New York Post*, October 21, 1977.)

REVIEWS

Time magazine, July 23, 1979
"Laurence Olivier contributes another of his shrewd Germanic foxes to the proceedings as Van Helsing."

New York, *Daily News,* July 13, 1979
"It's fascinating to observe Olivier, perhaps in homage to his mentor (*Rebecca* director, Alfred Hitchcock), portraying the evangelical Professor Van Helsing as a near carbon copy of Albert Basserman's memorably whiny Dr. van Meer in Hitchcock's *Foreign Correspondent*."

COMMENTS

Dracula, the most famous of all vampires, was created at the end of the nineteenth century by Bram Stoker in his masterful gothic novel. So effective was his monster that it passed into modern folklore, stirring the imagination of film makers, novelists, and dramatists for decades to follow.

The 1927 play, *Dracula,* was adapted for the stage by Hamilton Deane, who directed the London production and appeared as Van Helsing. The play opened on Broadway at the Fulton Theater on October 5, 1927, with Bela Lugosi in the title role. Lugosi, a Hungarian-born actor, became the definitive bloodsucker for thirty-five years. In his last years, plagued by ill health and drug addiction, the actor toured neighborhood film houses making personal appearances as Dracula in midnight magic and horror stage shows.

When the play first opened in New York, slight revisions in Deane's dramatization were made by John L. Balderston. It was this version which was successfully revived fifty years later at the Martin Beck Theater in New York starring Frank Langella as the Count and Jerome Dempsey as Abraham Van Helsing. Langella, a dark and handsome classic actor, brought new life to the timeless monster with his graceful, near-balletic performance. Edward Gorey was praised for his atmospheric costumes and decor, and the critically acclaimed production was recognized with a Tony Award as the most innovative production of a revival.

The role of Professor Van Helsing is one of the most appealing and knowledgeable sleuths in modern literature. Olivier followed a group of notable actors who, as the foremost vampire authority, put an end to the legend by driving a stake into the heart of Count Dracula. The character was first played on the screen in 1931 by Edward von Sloane opposite Lugosi in the durable film classic. Five years later, von Sloane repeated the role in a low budget sequel, *Dracula's Daughter* with Otto Kruger. Herbert Lom, the harassed Inspector Dreyfus of the Pink Panther series, essayed the Dutch metaphysician and philosopher in a 1968 British remake with Christopher Lee, as did Peter Cushing in another update four years later. Frank Finlay (Iago to Olivier's *Othello* in 1965) took a turn at destroying Dracula in a 1978 television mini-series which featured Louis Jourdan as the vampire.

In the contemporary comedy, *Love at First Bite*, a 1979 satire released by American International Pictures, Richard Benjamin portrayed the grandson of Van Helsing, who changes his name to Jeff Rosenberg, "for professional reasons."

The concept of the Langella-Olivier *Dracula* varied considerably from the Broadway revival. The whimsical black and white settings by Edward Gorey which might have served a Charles Addams family quite nicely were replaced with opulent production values including picturesque Cornish cliffs, majestic castles, and gloomy graveyards. Langella's Byronic Count remained sensual, fangless, and elegant. His portrayal was that of a quietly menacing aristocrat and much of the satire which dominated his performance on the stage was replaced by a darkly malevolent mood accented by John Williams' chilling Wagnerian score and several violent episodes.

Mina Van Helsing, who was Mina Harker in Stoker's novel, became the professor's daughter.

Consequently the Van Helsing as played by Olivier became an avenging father determined to destroy the monster who transformed his daughter into a ghoul. This new relationship heightened the conflict between Van Helsing and Dracula and strengthened the role for an actor of Olivier's dimension. When his hideously deformed daughter is impaled by a stake, Olivier is afforded the opportunity to deliver one of his great tragic cries; a piercing echo of his Shylock and Othello.

Langella, delighted to have an opportunity to work with Olivier, accepted the senior actor's invitation to address him as "Larry", but cautioned, "Only if you call me Lord Langella on occasion."

The film grossed over three million dollars in the first three days of its release in 500 theatres. Opening, appropriately enough, on Friday the thirteenth, it also set a new first day record at New York's Ziegfeld Theater. On the same day, *The Dance of Death,* filmed in 1968, made its long overdue New York debut at the D. W. Griffith Theater on Manhattan's eastside. At other theaters in the city, *A Little Romance* was celebrating its eleventh week. The name of Laurence Olivier could be found on marquees all over town and there were more films on the way.

In the spring of 1979, Olivier began preparations for his role in *Clash of the Titans*, a spectacular film about the legendary Gods and heroes of Greek mythology. The film, a combination of live action and special visual effects, featured Olivier in the role of the supreme ruler, Zeus, a power greater than that of all the other divinities. The epic also reunited Olivier with two of his former Shakespearean leading ladies, Maggie Smith, his Desdemona in *Othello* and Claire Bloom, who appeared as Lady Anne in *Richard III.*

Upon completion of *Clash of the Titans*, Olivier accepted an invitation to appear as General Douglas MacArthur in Terence Young's film about the historic landing during the Korean War at *Inchon.*

Olivier, as Professor Van Helsing, the world's leading vampire authority, destroys his possessed daughter, Mina (Jan Francis) to release her soul from the domination of Count Dracula.

The Jazz Singer

1980, EMI Films; A Jerry Leider Production; Written by Stephen H. Foreman, Herbert Baker; Original score by Neil Diamond; Produced by Jerry Leider; Directed by Richard Fleischer; Released by Associated Films Distribution

CAST

Neil Diamond, Laurence Olivier, Lucy Arnaz, Catlin Adams, Franklyn Ajye

Clash of the Titans

1981, Produced by Charles H. Schneer and Ray Harryhausen; Screenplay by Beverley Cross; Directed by Desmond David, An M-G-M Picture

CAST

Laurence Olivier, Burgess Meredith, Maggie Smith, Claire Bloom, Ursula Andress, Sian Phillips, Harry Hamlin, Judi Bowker, Susan Fleetwood, Pat Roach, Tim Piggot-Smith, Flora Robson

Inchon

1980, A Terence Young Film, Produced by Mitsuharu Ishi; Written by Robin Moore, Laird Koenig, Barry Beckerman; Directed by Terence Young; One Way Productions Inc.

CAST

Laurence Olivier, Jacqueline Bisset, Ben Gazzara, Omar Sharif, Toshiro Mifune, David Janssen, Richard Roundtree

Olivier on Television

Discounting an appearance in a production of *Macbeth* made in the experimental days of 1937 when London claimed only a few thousand viewers, Olivier made his official television debut in Henrik Ibsen's dark drama, *John Gabriel Borkman,* presented in Great Britain on November 19, 1958. The somber and humorless play lacked popular appeal, and the critical reception was less than enthusiastic.

Olivier recalled the live telecast some years later in an interview with Mike Douglas. "I once did live television. Never again. It was a rather turgid piece by Ibsen. I didn't really know it and I was thinking, well, I'll be very 'method' about this, and then right in the middle of a line I hadn't the faintest idea of what to say next, or what I was talking about, or what followed, or what scene had just gone on. For a ghastly ten hours, which is what one second can feel like, I was absolutely high and dry. I never felt so dreadful in my life. I was in my fifties and already the memory was beginning to play tricks and you can't memorize very well. As you get older it gets to be a bigger problem."

In March of 1956, *Richard III* was presented by NBC on a Sunday afternoon, marking the first time that a motion picture had its premiere in the two media on the same day. The three hour presentation was also the longest on record for television at that time. NBC paid $500,000 for the right to use the film once.

Olivier's American television debut was on October 30, 1959, in a ninety-minute color production of W. Somerset Maugham's *The Moon and Sixpence* produced by David Susskind and directed by Robert Mulligan. The story was adapted for television by S. Lee Pogostin and featured a prestigious supporting cast including Judith Anderson, Jessica Tandy, Hume Cronyn, Geraldine Fitzgerald, Denholm Elliot, Jean Marsh, Cyril Cusak, and Murray Matheson. "A towering accomplishment" hailed the *New York Times* and the *New York Herald Tribune* called it, "the closest thing to dramatic perfection ever known on television . . . adjectives alone cannot describe the haunting beauty of the production and particularly the performance by Sir Laurence Olivier, a towering craftsman, whose portrayal of the Gauguin-like hero had a brilliance and magnetism unmatched in the annals of television." His official American television debut brought Olivier the Emmy award for the best acting performance of the year.

The actor next appeared in *The Power and the Glory,* also produced by David Susskind, on October 29, 1961, for CBS-TV. The film was commercially released to theaters in Great Britain.

In a 1969 *TV Guide* interview, Olivier candidly commented on his displeasure of the medium. "I'm not very happy about television. It's tearing the theater apart. I've never seen the classics well done on TV. People are surrounded by drama nowadays because of television. It's there all day and every day by simply turning a knob. It's good for actors, of course. They must live. It's good for people, too—as long as they discriminate. But at the moment they tend not to. It's easy to sit at home and take what's given—good, bad, or indifferent. This lack of discrimination will always be a threat (to the theater) and if because of television, people give up going to the theater any more, I'd be very sad indeed."

Following the filming of *Long Day's Journey into Night,* he told *TV Times,* "Television is essentially an intimate medium and classical plays weren't written for close scrutiny; they were written to assault the senses. Television invites the audience in, shows them the tiniest details. Therefore, the more dramatic the dialogue, the more majestic the poetry, the harder it is to communicate in miniature. Television has developed its own classics—programs like *Upstairs, Downstairs,* which is marvelous. And TV has rightly developed its own school of actors. Unless an actor is highly experienced, it's too much to ask him to suddenly alternate between the understated performance needed for the screen or 'box,' and the broad, open style associated with the stage in its classics."

In 1972, Olivier filmed a series of Polaroid camera commercials for which he reportedly received $500,000 for five one-minute spots. "I never worried about doing advertisements in this country. At home they'd be shocked. They've set up that ridiculous image of me. I had to say to Polaroid, 'I'm sorry, but you can't show them in Britain.'"

In January of 1976, it was announced that Olivier would be artistic director and host of a series of dramas by twentieth century playwrights, to be produced by Granada Television of Britain and carried in the United States by NBC-TV as "A Tribute to the American Theater." Olivier's personal choices of plays written since 1900 were to be selected from the works of Eugene O'Neill, Tennessee Williams, Arthur Miller, Lillian Hellman, George S. Kaufman, and Robert E. Sherwood, among others. At the age of seventy, Olivier began a new career as a full-time working television producer.

In addition to Tennessee Williams' *Cat on a Hot Tin Roof* and William Inge's *Come Back Little Sheba,* the first two productions in the series, he produced with Derek Granger, *The Collection* by Harold Pinter, and produced and directed with June Howson, a production of Stanley Houghton's *Hindle Wakes,* starring Donald Pleasence and Roy Dotrice.

Olivier announced indefinite postponement of "A Tribute to the American Theater" in February, 1978, claiming a heavy load of motion picture assignments. While Olivier's arrangement with Britain's Granada Television in association with NBC, called for a continuing number of projects, the network agreed to declare a temporary hiatus.

Unable to return to the vigorous demands of stage acting, Olivier's screen career in the seventies accelerated with his appearances in *Sleuth, Marathon Man,* and *The Betsy.* Despite a profitable new decade as a movie star once again, the actor remained a dedicated supporter of the theater, suggesting a reversal in the trends of cultural life. "There will be revivals of interest in the theatre. People will understand and begin to appreciate the difference. Color and third dimension won't be enough. Something eventually will make them want to see something life-style. Something will make them want to get their drama back into human experience—provided, of course, you can obtain a measure of proportion on human terms, where you can see from every seat in the house the expression on the face and can hear every word, and can get a perfect view of the action. I would swear that was better value in the entertainment world than anything you can get on the box or screen."

Television

John Gabriel Borkman, November 19, 1958 (Great Britain)
The Moon and Sixpence, October 30, 1959

The Power and the Glory, October 29, 1961
Uncle Vanya, February 10, 1967
Male of the Species, Host and narrator, January 3, 1969
David Copperfield, March 15, 1970
Long Day's Journey into Night, March 10, 1973
The World at War, Narrator, Series premiere September 23, 1973
The Merchant of Venice, March 16, 1974
Love among the Ruins, March 6, 1975 (Great Britain, December, 1976)
The Collection, December 5, 1976 (Great Britain)
Cat on a Hot Tin Roof, December 6, 1976
Jesus of Nazareth, April 3 and 10, 1977
Come Back Little Sheba, December 31, 1977
The Collection, October 25, 1978 (U.S. premiere)
Brideshead Revisited, 1980 (miniseries)

The Moon and Sixpence

NBC-TV, October 30, 1959. Produced by David Susskind; Adapted by S. Lee Pogostin from the novel by W. Somerset Maugham; Directed by Robert Mulligan

CAST

Charles Strickland — Laurence Olivier
Dirk Stroeve — Hume Cronyn
Blanche Stroeve — Jessica Tandy
and Judith Anderson, Geraldine Fitzgerald, Denholm Elliott, Jean Marsh, Cyril Cusak, Murray Matheson

REVIEW

Variety, November 4, 1959
"It isn't very often that television through fusing of its skills and talents, can achieve a level of beauty and perfection that can stand on a par with the finest artistic standards of stage and films on all counts, but principally [by] Olivier's magnificent portrayal of the tragic artist."

Male of the Species

NBC-TV Prudential On Stage presentation, January 3, 1969. Written by Alun Owen; Executive Producer, Cecil Clarke; Directed by Charles Jarrott

CAST

Host/Narrator	Laurence Olivier
MacNeil	Sean Connery
Dooley	Michael Caine
Bowen	Paul Scofield
The Girl	Anna Calder-Marshall

THE FILM

Three episodes involving a girl and her relationships with three predatory males: her scoundrel father, whose compulsive girl chasing and deceit scars the girl's psyche, an office casanova looking for an equal match, and a middle-aged barrister who in matters of sex and law cares more about winning than about justice.

REVIEW

Variety, January 15, 1969
"A skillful and absorbing little play. Miss Calder-Marshall's captivating performance was one level of interest, the separate contributions of the name male cast another, and the terse narration by Olivier still another. The narration which laced the segments together did not require an Olivier delivery, but it was quite a bonus that he did it."

Long Day's Journey into Night

March 10, 1973, by Eugene O'Neill, adapted by Michael Blakemore and Peter Wood; Executive Producer, Cecil Clarke; National Theatre Production, Directed by Peter Wood

CAST

James Tyrone	Laurence Olivier
Mary Tyrone	Constance Cummings
Jamie	Denis Quilley
Edmund	Ronald Pickup
Cathleen	Maureen Lipman

THE FILM

A day in the turbulent life of the Tyrone family, set in Connecticut in 1912. James Tyrone reviews his financially successful but artistically shallow career on the stage. Mary, his wife, slips back into drug addiction, while the oldest son, Jamie, takes refuge in drinks and prostitutes. Edmund, the youngest, is preparing to enter a public hospital for tuberculosis treatment.

REVIEWS

New York Times, March 10, 1973
"The performances maintain a rare level of acting excellence. And with Lord Olivier as James Tyrone, that level rises to the magnificent. With hair slicked down, sporting a theatrical handkerchief and the air of a gentleman-rogue, the former Sir Laurence displays the entire artistic inheritance of his fifty years as an outstanding actor. It is a memorable performance. And Lord Olivier gives Tyrone a slight Irish brogue that is devilishly Irish-American. The production is recommended without qualifications."

Variety, March 14, 1973
"An uncommonly high level of sustained acting excellence. Olivier utilized all of the actor's gifts and techniques at his disposal, especially his great command of the upper registers of his voice, and breathed life into the rather rigid role of the miserly, rusting-out matinee idol. For the skeptics who feel that his reputation as the greatest living actor on the English-language stage is based on what he's done in the past rather than what he's doing now, his mercurial, breath-taking performance of his major scene must surely have been a revelation. Olivier's excellence must give new hope to the cause of TV drama."

New York *Daily News,* March 10, 1973
"There are too few memorable theatrical experi-

ences in a lifetime to pass up the opportunity to see Sir Laurence Olivier in the National Theatre production of Eugene O'Neill's *Long Day's Journey into Night.* His agonizing performance of James Tyrone, a penny-pinching patriarch, so desperately in love with his wife that his guts are torn from him when she slips back into the drug habit, is a classic portrayal of a man trying to keep the threads of his life together. It's a remarkable sympathetic, compassionate drama, beautifully acted and produced. ABC can be proud of having made this commitment.''

New Jersey *Bergen Evening Record,* March 9, 1973
"It is worth giving up a Saturday night to stay home tomorrow and watch Laurence Olivier. Olivier has said that O'Neill is the greatest of all American playwrights and he considers *Long Day's Journey into Night* O'Neill's greatest work. For that reason, despite age and recent illness, he plunged into the gripping and arduous drama with great feeling.''

(National Theatre production) *New York Times,* December 22, 1971
"Olivier's Tyrone is unrivaled in technical and personal fascination—personal because James Tyrone (alias James O'Neill) was an actor with the kind of career that Olivier has spent his life avoiding: a strong young talent destroyed by years of imprisonment in profitable typecasting.''

Variety, December 29, 1971
"Olivier, as the boozy father gives a performance of modulated intensity that seems perfectly in tune. It also reaffirms his extraordinary ability to submerge his own towering presence into a stage character.''

London *Daily Telegraph,* December 22, 1971
"Laurence Olivier, as the father, uses no tricks of makeup. The American accent seems his own. Repeatedly he galvanizes attention. It is a funny, dazzling, searing, heart-breaking exhibition.''

The play which ran well over three hours when presented on the stage, was trimmed to two hours and ten minutes, with commercial breaks added for the two and one-half hour telecast. Agreement with the O'Neill estate was reached with the condition that any editing would be subject to final approval by Olivier. "Cutting never improves anything," Olivier said at a press conference. "It does not improve Hamlet, nor Beethoven's Ninth. In theater, length of this production achieves its purpose in a majestic sense. It has a great sweep. A television audience isn't geared for things of that length. I can't imagine an American audience sitting that long. So it will be cut and we hope we make it palatable. It still is long, but if you're religious, it's like being in church on Good Friday.''*

Olivier's chief concern in playing James Tyrone for American audiences was the American accent. "Being British does make it difficult and imperfections will be noticeable to the American viewer. The play is set in 1912 and certain words were pronounced with accents that differ from today. In those days it was EElectricity, with the accent on the first syllable, and autoMObile, with the accent on the middle syllable, and so on. Tyrone, on the other hand, is no stranger to me. I didn't have to invent his eccentricities. I knew them all. There are some things, which, as James Tyrone found, one never forgets. When I first became a professional actor, I lacked for food. I was hungry, out of work and terrified. My father was a parson—or a priest, as he liked to call himself—and we were very poor. I had to use my father's bath water after him to save water. There's something about being brought up in an atmosphere of genteel poverty that makes you feel, 'I'll show them. I've got to show them'.''*

Olivier received an Emmy Award as the best actor for his performance as James Tyrone by the National Academy of Television Arts and Sciences.

*New Jersey *Bergen Record,* Dan Lewis, October, 22, 1972
**TV Times* by Ian Cotton, April 21, 1973

Narrating *The World at War*.

A scene from *Alone*, **part four of** *The World at War*.
Rallied by Churchill after Dunkirk, the British wait
alone for an invasion which never comes. The cities are
bombed and the RAF triumphs in the aerial Battle of
Britain. Following the defeat at Dunkirk in 1940, British
Expeditionary Force Troops are evacuated on any kind
of floating troop ship.

The World at War

Premiere September 23, 1973, The story of the Second World War in 26 one-hour episodes; A Thames Television Production; Produced by Jeremy Isaacs; Chief historical adviser, Dr. Noble Frankland DFC, Director of the Imperial War Museum, London; Music, Carl Davis; Narrator, Laurence Olivier

COMMENTS

The World at War tells the story of the Second World War, using dramatic film from national and private sources, including much which had never been screened before. The films combined archive footage and contemporary interviews with statesmen and military leaders of the time, illustrating the experiences of ordinary men and women—British and German, American, Japanese and Russian, in uniform and out—who lived and fought through the most momentous conflict in world history.

London's *Evening Standard* praised the series as "the definitive documentary on World War II." The entire series was screened at the National Film Theatre on London's South Bank beginning July 29 and continuing through August 3, 1974.

The Merchant of Venice

March 16, 1974, A National Theatre Production of William Shakespeare's play; Executive producer, Cecil Clarke; Produced and Directed for ABC Theater by Jonathan Miller

CAST

Shylock	Laurence Olivier
Portia	Joan Plowright
Bassanio	Jeremy Brett
Gratiano	Michael Jayston
Jessica	Louise Purnell
Antonio	Anthony Nicholls

THE FILM

Antonio, a merchant, to assist his friend Bassanio's courtship of the heiress Portia, is forced to borrow money from the Jewish usurer Shylock. Because he nurses a grudge against all Christians, Shylock forgoes his usual interest and asks for a pound of flesh in the event the loan is not repaid in three months. Bassanio manages to win his heiress, but Antonio's richest ships are lost, and he is forced to repay the debt. Portia assumes lawyer's robes and disguised in a Venetian court of justice defends Antonio and defeats Shylock by insisting that he take his pound of flesh without spilling any blood.

New York *Daily News,* March 16, 1974
"Laurence Olivier is powerful and superb in the role of Shylock. Olivier has very definitely lived up to his avowed commitment neither to sentimentalize nor caricature Shylock. On the contrary, Shylock comes over with great dignity, intellect, and human feeling."

Variety, March 20, 1974
"A handsome literate production."

New York Times, March 15, 1974
"Lord Olivier is superb as Shylock. He does avoid caricature, brilliantly, using his inimitable pyrotechnics to compose an unforgettable portrait."

National Theatre production - *Punch,* May 6, 1970
"Olivier's Shylock is, as one would expect, rich in apt physical and vocal details—the slight bend at the hip, the curious lips, the memorable *smack* of the lips, the saintly grey hair around his skullcap. Shylock's end, broken and ill at the bar of the court, takes us suddenly into tragedy—made perfect by his offstage wail of grief some seconds later."

Time magazine, May 18, 1970
"A provocative new production. Olivier makes no easy appeal to the audience's sympathies, but holds to an avid, harshly funny portrayal of the cruelty of human justice and the bitter ironies of human mercy. At the end of Shakespeare's text, Jessica and the merchant, the two characters whose triumphs have been bought at the cost of Shylock's downfall, pause alone and silently before the final curtain. The moment apparently is intended to evoke Shylock, and it works. Such is the flinty power of Olivier's unorthodox performance that his unseen presence dominates the stage at that moment as few actors ever do when they are actually on it."

Frank Marcus, *New York Times,* May 10, 1970
"Kenneth Tynan likened Olivier's appearance on the stage to tigers being unleashed in the arena. Shylock is the most tigerish performance since his captain in *Dance of Death.* I have never seen him give a more dangerous performance: he is a man corroded by passion. A performance of stunning magnitude. Sir Laurence transcends period settings, directorial notions, words and theater itself. His wail, issuing from the wings, is eternal. It has haunted history; it is present like original sin, hovering over the world stage. Those who hear it will never forget it."

COMMENTS

The famous howl of anguish which Olivier delivered off-stage in the original production was successfully repeated in the television presentation. After Shylock stumbles from the courtroom and delivers his unearthly moan, the camera jumped from one face to the next, uncovering the terrible realization of what the others have done to him. Olivier was voted Best Actor for his performance as Shylock by the London theatre critics as announced in *Plays and Players* magazine.

With the filming of *The Merchant of Venice,* six of the National Theatre productions made during Olivier's tenure as artistic director were preserved for posterity. These include *Uncle Vanya* (1963), *Othello* (1965), *Three Sisters* (1970), *The Dance of Death* (1971), *Long Day's Journey into Night* (1973) and *Merchant* (1974).

Love among the Ruins

March 6, 1975, Produced by Allan Davis; Written by James Costigan; Directed by George Cukor; ABC Circle Films

CAST

Sir Arthur Granville-Jones	Laurence Olivier
Jessica Medlicott	Katharine Hepburn
Devine	Colin Blakely
Druce	Richard Pearson
Pratt	Leigh Lawson
Mrs. Pratt	Joan Sims

THE FILM

In turn-of-the-century London, a rich and spirited widow, Jessica Medlicott, is being sued for breach of promise by a young former fiancé. Sir Arthur Granville-Jones is hired to defend her in court. Unknown to his client, the normally staid barrister is elated at the thought of representing the widow, as he loved her for over forty years, ever since a blissful three-day affair she can't even recall.

REVIEWS

Variety, March 12, 1975
"Katharine Hepburn and Laurence Olivier did their turns in the romantic comedy with great flair, and the result was amusing, offbeat, high-quality television. The extravagant gifts of Hepburn and Olivier were under the direction of George Cukor, and the three together have more show business experience than the Atlantic has water."

COMMENTS

When Dick Cavett interviewed Katharine Hepburn, he asked why she had never appeared with Olivier. The actress indicated that their careers were far from over, and there was still a likelihood of a collaboration. Inspired by the suggestion, they were teamed for *Love among the Ruins* and were voted outstanding actress and actor by the National Academy of Television Arts and Sciences. Writer James Costigan also won an Emmy Award for his original drama.

Sir Arthur Granville-Jones in *Love Among the Ruins* (1975).

With Katharine Hepburn as Jessica Medlicott. Between them—six Oscars and twenty-two Academy Award nominations.

Big Daddy in *Cat on a Hot Tin Roof* (1976).

December 6, 1976, by Tennessee Williams; Produced by Derek Granger and Laurençe Olivier; Directed by Robert Moore

CAST

Maggie	Natalie Wood
Brick	Robert Wagner
Big Daddy	Laurence Olivier
Big Mama	Maureen Stapleton
Gooper	Jack Hedley
Mae	Mary Peach
Doctor	David Healy
Dixie	Heidi Rundt
Sonny	Sean Saxon

REVIEW

Commercial Appeal, Memphis, December 6, 1976

"Laurence Olivier is not only the greatest actor of our time, he is a genius, and his towering gifts energize and dominate this searing story about lust, greed, and sexual perversity in the Old South. Olivier is breathtaking in the middle scenes during his dialogue with son, Brick."

COMMENTS

Tennessee Williams' drama about a cannibalistic Southern family won the 1955 Pulitzer Prize and the New York Drama Critics' Circle Award. The original production starred Barbara Bel Geddes as Maggie, the "cat," a passionate and desperate young wife struggling to save her marriage. Ben Gazzara portrayed Brick, the troubled, alcoholic husband, and Burl Ives was Big Daddy, a blustering self-made millionaire who is dying of cancer. Ives repeated the role in a 1958 film with Paul Newman and Elizabeth Taylor. The play was revived on Broadway in 1974 with Elizabeth Ashley, Keir Dullea, and Fred Gwynne.

Natalie Wood expressed her astonishment and delight when invited by Olivier to appear with him in *Cat on a Hot Tin Roof,* along with her husband, actor Robert Wagner, in a *Los Angeles Times* interview. "R.J. (Wagner) has always idolized Olivier. But neither of us had dreamed of

Natalie Wood as the tempestuous Maggie, "the cat", Olivier as Big Daddy and Robert Wagner as the alcoholic Brick. "He's a brilliant technician, but he never does the same thing twice." (Natalie Wood.)

working with him. You know the structure of the play, it's like a series of arias—the first act is all Maggie, the second is Big Daddy, and the third is Brick. I used to slip down and stand in the back in the dark and watch Olivier and R.J. do that second act. It was incredible. Olivier doesn't play Big Daddy as physically big, no padding, no big belly, not like Burl Ives. Burl was wonderful but this is quite different. The bigness is that he was a Mississippi redneck who has become a Southern gentleman and a millionaire—that's what makes him Big Daddy! You know that speech where he talks about getting himself a choice woman, he'd wrap her in diamonds and smother her in mink? Well, he'd wind up for that speech like a baseball pitcher doing his thing. He's a brilliant technician but he never does the same thing twice, he never locks it in. In the third act when Maggie tells him she has Brick's baby in her body, he played it differently every time. Once he just looked at me. And looked and looked. It went on so long I began to feel faint. Later Maureen Stapleton told me: 'One thing, honey, when you've been looked at by Olivier, you know you've been looked at!' "[1]

Doc Delaney in *Come Back, Little Sheba* **(1977).**

Come Back Little Sheba

December 31, 1977, by William Inge; Produced by Derek Granger and Laurence Olivier, an NBC presentation in association with Granada Television; Directed by Silvio Marizzano

CAST

Doc Delaney	Laurence Olivier
Lola	Joanne Woodward
Marie	Carrie Fisher
Turk	Nicholas Campbell
Mrs. Coffman	Patience Collier

THE FILM

A teleplay of William Inge's 1950 drama, which starred Shirley Booth and Sidney Blackmer. Shirley Booth recreated the role of Lola for a 1952 film, for which she won an Academy Award. Burt Lancaster appeared as Doc in the film directed by Daniel Mann. The play concerns a slatternly middle-aged housewife and her alcoholic husband struggling to come to terms with their empty lives.

REVIEWS

Judith Crist, *TV Guide,* December 31, 1977
"The play itself seems dated and obvious, but Woodward is deeply affecting as the empty-headed beauty grown 'old and sloppy.' Olivier, now 70, is impressive as the alcoholic husband and Carrie Fisher is charming as the lodger who disrupts their lives."

John J. O'Connor, *New York Times,* December 30, 1977
"The machinery of William Inge's play creaks rather badly, but the story of a drab marriage in a small Middle Western town is still strangely moving. The project itself, though, overseen by Lord Olivier, remains puzzling. It is always interesting to see this superb actor do anything. But perhaps there are some things best left undone as a legacy for mass audiences (one is hawking cameras for hefty salesman fees). If television is going to undertake a rare series of major American plays, is it really necessary that they star Britain's most distinguished actor? The result

With Joanne Woodward as Lola.

Doc: "We gotta keep on living, don't we? I can't stop just 'cause I made a few mistakes. I gotta keep goin' . . . somehow."

(*Come Back Little Sheba*, William Inge.)

inevitably becomes a curiosity. Lord Olivier's Middle Western accent is distressingly close to his Southern drawl in the Tennessee Williams play. There is much to admire in his performance, but the whole amounts to little more than an odd turn."

Kay Gardella, New York *Daily News,* December 25, 1977
"You begin to suspect the worst of the television adaptation of *Come Back Little Sheba* when you realize NBC has seen fit despite a cast headed by Joanne Woodward and Laurence Olivier, to schedule the production on New Year's Eve. Unless, of course, the network is cashing in on the fact that Olivier plays the part of a reformed alcoholic and member of AA. To be blunt as one can be, Miss Woodward, who gets top billing as the credits roll, turns in a mediocre performance as the middle-aged wife of a man who felt trapped from the day she became pregnant, and he was forced to give up his medical career and become a chiropractor instead. (It) is a work that calls for many levels of acting, something Olivier achieves and Miss Woodward does not. Still perhaps she is not to be blamed. Since Olivier is the artistic and creative producer of the series, any faults to be found with the telecast rightfully should be laid at his doorstep."

Harriet Van Horne, *New York Post,* December 31, 1977
"Sir Laurence Olivier—a last minute replacement for Robert Mitchum—plays Doc, the MD fallen to chiropractor. He is about as credible in the part as Bob Mitchum would be as King Lear. Joanne Woodward, a lovely, gifted actress, gives an embarrassing performance in the role Shirley Booth played with such divine skill. Sir Laurence, in truth, is the only member of the company whose word is knife-clean. Not that it matters really . . . If you've anything else to do tonight at 9—do it!"

Olivier discussed the various American dialects which he encountered in 1977 in a television interview with Mike Douglas. "I don't pick it up by myself. I always have a teacher. I'm very careful if I'm trying to play an American part, which I love to do. I don't know why, but I have a special dialectician about when playing an American if I can, because if I get away with it, all the better. I had a very good teacher when I used a North Michigan accent in a film I did called *The Betsy,* and that was a little difficult because I had just done a Kansas accent and they're a little bit close. I was acting with darling, wonderful Joanne Woodward and of course she inclines to be a little, wee bit southern, and as I had just done a southern accent playing in *Cat on a Hot Tin Roof* as Big Daddy, I'm afraid it was terribly close work for me to keep away from that with a Kansas accent, which is the most southernish of all the central southwestern states."

The Collection

By Harold Pinter; Televised December 5, 1976, in Great Britain; United States Premiere, Great Performances, October 25, 1978—PBS/WNET; Produced by Laurence Olivier and Derek Granger for Granada Television; Designed by Michael Grimes; Coordinating Producer, Peter Weinberg; Theme by Purcell; Executive Producer for Great Performances, Jac Venza; Directed by Michael Apted

CAST

Harry Kane	Laurence Olivier
James	Alan Bates
Bill	Malcolm McDowell
Stella	Helen Mirren

282

Harry Kane is an affluent, aging designer who shares a house with Bill, a promising young figure in the fashion world whom Kane discovered. Early one morning, the routine of their lives is shattered at 4 A.M. by a mysterious phone call for Bill. The next day, James appears on the doorstep and asks to see Bill, refusing to state the nature of his business with Harry. He returns at a later time and forces his way into the house confronting Bill with a suspected indiscretion with his wife, Helen. Harry, confused by the nature of the relationship between Bill and James visits Helen to find out exactly what took place at a hotel in Leeds. The jealous husband is subjected to a series of different accounts of the meeting by Bill, Harry, and his wife. The quartet becomes involved in a dangerous game of jealousy, suspicion, and revenge.

Harry Kane in *The Collection* (1976).

REVIEWS

Variety, December 22, 1976
"Olivier rounds out a curious quadrangle as a man of evident wealth. The part has a certain ambiguity, but the Olivier stamp of authority is, per usual, sharp and compelling. But not overwhelming, which is one of the actor's virtues."

Sunday People, London, December 12, 1976
"If you have never really watched a great actor, catch Laurence Olivier in *The Collection*—and have something to tell your grandchildren."

New York Post, October 25, 1978
"Olivier, who also served as co-producer, has the smaller role of Harry, and he is perhaps too old for the character described by Pinter as in his forties. But Olivier's every expression and gesture is a model of the actor's art as he moves from petulant bewilderment at a disruption in his routine to apparent mastery of the situation, excoriating Bill in the play's most scathing speech as 'a slum slug . . . (who) crawls all over the walls of nice houses, leaving slime'."

With Helen Mirren as Stella
Harry: "I found him in a slum, you know, by accident. Just happened to be in a slum one day and there he was. I realized he had talent straight away. I gave him a roof, gave him a job and he came up trumps. We've been close friends for a year."

(*The Collection*, **Harold Pinter**.)

Alan Bates (left) as James and Malcolm McDowell as Bill.

Pinter's arresting short play is crowded with an intangible menace. Words left unspoken provide fierce theatrical intensity. It is a masterful chamber piece orchestrated for a perfectly tuned quartet of actors. Olivier joined Alan Bates, Malcolm McDowell, and Helen Mirren in an extraordinary display of adroit ensemble acting. The actor analyzed the dark secrets of Pinter's disturbing drama in an interview with *TV Guide*. "I had seen it done by the Royal Shakespeare Company in London and thought, my God, that's a beautiful little play. Without exception, it was one of the most exquisite pieces of work I had ever seen. And so I said, I'll do that one day. As every single day of rehearsal went by, we found more and more and more in the play. It's not a darling bit of froth along the top of the wavelets, you know. It is as deep as can be, and absolutely filled with cross-references of every kind. With a fellow like Pinter, you don't by any means get it all on the first hearing."

"Each person in the play is terrified of losing what he's got—and in each case that is another person. The Alan Bates character is terrified of losing his wife. His wife is terrified of losing Alan Bates, although she plays around and has been found to be doing so. My character is simply terrified of the moment that the young boy (McDowell) falls in love with a female. I don't want to lose that boy, and the boy doesn't want to lose what he gets out of me, which is a very comfortable means of livelihood."

"It's so pathetic when I try to explain my situation to the girl. I say 'I picked him up in a slum, you see. I just happened to be in a slum and there he was with no roof over his head.' She knows perfectly well what the truth behind all this is, and she pretends to be ever so innocent. And that's what's wonderful—the way people think they have a hope of kidding each other. But they're all sensitive and highly sophisticated, and

Helen Mirren

by Evelyn Waugh; 1980; Produced by Derek Granger for Granada Television; Directed by Charles Sturridge; Cast: Laurence Olivier, Claire Bloom, Jeremy Irons, Anthony Andrews, Diana Quick

they all cling manfully to the hope that they can pull the wool over the others' eyes, and of course they can't. And they really know they can't, and at the end it's clear they haven't. You're left in a state of absolute flux, not sure whether they've managed to keep for themselves what it is they're terrified of losing. I think it's the most beautiful bit of work I've ever had anything to do with. And I don't think I've ever been so happy in any job before.''[2]

The Theater of Laurence Olivier

Awards, foreign decorations, honorary degrees, have been showered upon him. No English actor, living or dead, can begin to compete with or challenge him. A Garrick, a Kean, a Henry Irving, merely enjoyed a small local reputation when compared with his. His career has been fantastic, as if a young actor had been visited by a wild dream.

J. B. Priestley,
Particular Pleasures
(New York: Stein and Day, 1975),
p. 132.

1916—Brutus in *Julius Caesar* by William Shakespeare, All Saints School, Marylebone

1922—Katharine in *The Taming of the Shrew* by William Shakesspeare, All Saints Choir School presentation, Stratford Memorial Theatre, Stratford-on-Avon

1924—Professional debut as Suloit Officer in *Byron*, Century Threatre, London

1925—*The Ghost Train*, Brighton Hippodrome

Lennox in *Macbeth* by William Shakespeare, St. Christopher Theatre, Letchworth

Flavius in *Julius Caesar* by William Shakespeare, Lena Ashwell Players, Century Theatre, London

The Cenci, Empire Theatre, London

Thomas of Clarence and Snare in *Henry IV, Part 2*, Regent Theatre, London

1926—Birmingham Repertory Company:

Minstrel in *The Marvelous History of St. Bernard*

The Barber and the Cow

Richard Coaker in *The Farmer's Wife* by

Eden Phillpots

Guy Sydney in *Something to Talk About*

1927–Vanya in *Uncle Vanya* by Anton Chekhov

Parolles in *All's Well That Ends Well* by William Shakespeare

Tony Lumpkin in *She Stoops to Conquer* by Oliver Goldsmith

1928—Birmingham Repertory Company, Royal Court Theatre, London:

Young Man in *The Adding Machine* by Elmer Rice

Malcolm in Macbeth by William Shakespeare

Title role in *Harold* by Alfred Lord Tennyson

The Lord in *The Taming of the Shrew* by William Shakespeare

Martellus in *Back to Methuselah* by Bernard Shaw

Gerald Arnwood in *Bird in Hand* by Drinkwater, Royalty Theatre, London

Stanhope in *Journey's End* by R. C. Sherriff, Appollo Theatre, London

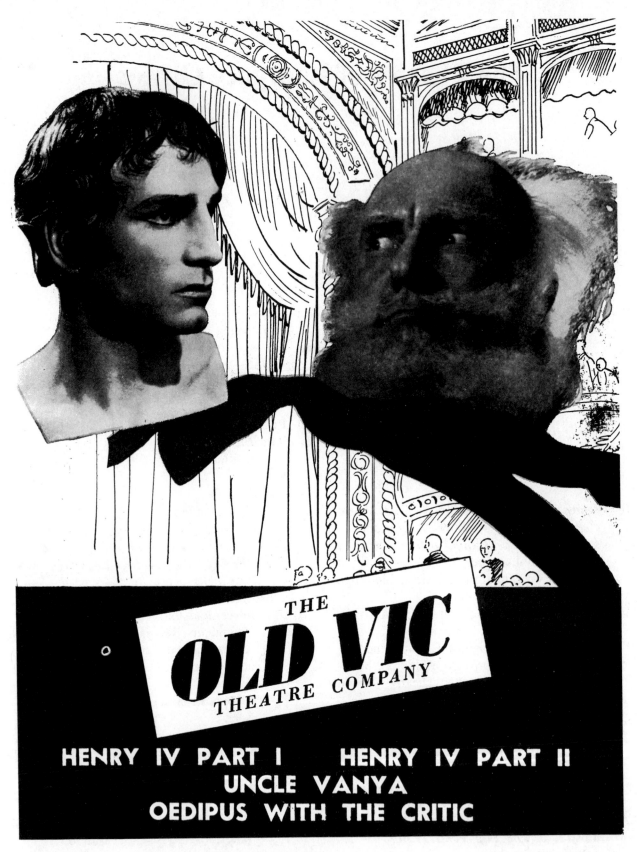

THE OLD VIC THEATRE COMPANY

HENRY IV PART I   HENRY IV PART II
UNCLE VANYA
OEDIPUS WITH THE CRITIC

CAESAR AND CLEOPATRA

ANTONY AND CLEOPATRA

The

PLAYBILL

®

for the Ziegfeld Theatre

THE
ENTERTAINER

PLAYBILL

a weekly magazine for theatregoers

BECKET

Hamlet, with Vivien Leigh at Elsinore (1937).

1929—Title role in *Beau Geste* by Basil Dean, Her Majesty's Theatre, London

Prince Pao in *The Circle of Chalk,* New Theatre, London

Richard Parish in *Paris Bound,* Lyric Theatre, London

John Hardy in *A The Stranger Within,* Garrick Theatre, London

Hugh Bromilow in *Murder on the Second Floor* by Frank Vosper, (American debut), Eltinge Theater, New York

Jerry Warrender in *The Last Enemy* by Frank Harvey, Fortune Theatre, London

Ralph in *After All,* Arts Theatre

1930—Victor Prynne in *Private Lives* by Noel Coward, Phoenix Theatre, London

1931—*Private Lives,* Times Square Theater, New York

1933—Stevan Beringer in *The Rats of Norway* by Keith Winter, Playhouse Theatre, London

Julian Dulcimer in *The Green Bay Tree,* Cort Theater, New York

1934—Richard Kurt in *Biography* by S. N. Behrman, Globe Theatre, London

Bothwell in *Queen of Scots* by Gordon Daviot, New Theatre, London

Tony Cavendish in *Theatre Royal* by Edna Ferber and George S. Kaufman, Lyric Theatre, London

1935—Peter Hammond in *The Ringmaster* by Keith Winter, Shaftesbury Theatre, London

Richard Harben in *Golden Arrow* by Sylvia Thompson with Victor Cunard, Whitehall Theatre, London

Romeo and Mercutio (exchanging roles with John Gielgud) in *Romeo and Juliet* by William Shakespeare, New Theatre, London

1936—Bob Patch in *Bees on the Boatdeck* by J. B. Priestley, Lyric Theatre, London

1937—Old Vic Company:

Title role in *Hamlet* by William Shakespeare

Sir Toby Belch in *Twelfth Night* by William Shakespeare

Title role in *Henry V* by William Shakespeare

Title role in *Macbeth* by William Shakespeare

Title role in *Hamlet*, with Vivien Leigh, Kronborg Castle, Elsinore, Denmark

293

Hotspur in *Henry IV, Part One* (1946).

1938—Iago in *Othello* by William Shakespeare
Vivaldi in *King of Nowhere* by James Bridie
Title role in *Coriolanus* by William Shakespeare

1939—Gaylord Easterbrook in *No Time for Comedy* by S. N. Behrman, Ethel Barrymore Theater, New York

1940—Romeo in *Romeo and Juliet* with Vivien Leigh, San Francisco, Chicago, and New York

1944—Old Vic Company: (appointed codirector)
Sergius in *Arms and the Man by* Bernard Shaw, New Theatre, London
Button Moulder in *Peer Gynt* by Henrik Ibsen, New Theatre, London
Title role in *Richard III* by William Shakespeare, New Theatre, London

1945—Directed *The Skin of Our Teeth* by Thornton Wilder, with Vivien Leigh, Phoenix Theatre, London
Old Vic Company, New Theatre, London:
Astrov in *Uncle Vanya* by Anton Chekhov
Justice Shallow in *Henry IV, Part 2* by William Shakespeare
Title role in *Oedipus* by Sophocles
Mr. Puff in *The Critic* by Richard Sheridan
Arms and the Man, Peer Gynt, Richard III—tour of Belgium, Holland, Germany, and France

1946—*Henry IV, Parts One and Two, Oedipus, The Critic, Uncle Vanya*—Century Theater, New York
Title role in *King Lear* by William Shakespeare, New Theatre, London

1947—Presented and directed *Born Yesterday* by Garson Kanin, Garrick Theatre, London

1948—Australian tour, Old Vic Company:
Sir Peter Teazle in *The School for Scandal* by Richard Sheridan, also directed, with Vivien Leigh
Mr. Antrobus in *The Skin of Our Teeth* by Thornton Wilder, also directed, with Vivien Leigh
Title role in *Richard III* by William Shakespeare

1949—Old Vic season, New Theatre, London
The School for Scandal
Chorus in *Antigone* by Jean Anouilh, also directed, with Vivien Leigh

294

Directed *The Proposal* by Anton Chekhov

Title role in *Richard III*

Directed *A Streetcar Named Desire* by Tennessee Williams, with Vivien Leigh, Aldwych Theatre, London

1950—Actor-Manager at St. James's Theatre, London:

Duke of Altair in *Venus Observed* by Christopher Fry, also directed

1951—Caesar in *Caesar and Cleopatra* by Bernard Shaw, with Vivien Leigh

Antony in *Antony and Cleopatra* by William Shakespeare, with Vivien Leigh

Caesar and Cleopatra, Antony and Cleopatra, Ziegfeld Theater, New York

1952—Directed *Venus Observed,* New Century Theater, New York

1953—Grand Duke in *The Sleeping Prince* by Terence Rattigan, also directed, with Vivien Leigh

1955—Shakespeare Memorial Theatre, Stratford-on-Avon:

Malvolio in *Twelfth Night* by William Shakespeare, with Vivien Leigh

Title role in *Macbeth* with Vivien Leigh

Title role in *Titus Andronicus* by William Shakespeare, with Vivien Leigh

1957—Archie Rice in *The Entertainer* by John Osborne, Royal Court Theatre, London

Titus Andronicus—tour to Paris, Venice, Belgrade, Zagreb, Vienna, Warsaw, and Stoll Theatre, London

The Entertainer, Palace Theatre, London

1958—*The Entertainer,* Royale Theater, New York

1959—Title role in *Cariolanus* by William Shakespeare, Shakespeare Memorial Theatre, Stratford-on-Avon

1960—Berenger in *Rhinoceros* by Eugene Ionesco, Royal Court Theatre, London

Becket in *Becket* by Jean Anouilh (opposite Anthony Quinn as King Henry) St. James Theater, New York

Directed *The Tumbler* by Benn W. Levy, Helen Hayes Theater, New York

1961—Toured as Henry II in *Becket*

Henry II in *Becket* (opposite Arthur Kennedy as Becket) Hudson Theater, New York

1962—Director of Chichester Festival Theatre:

Caesar and Cleopatra, **with Vivien Leigh as the Queen of the Nile (1951).**

Directed *The Chances* by John Fletcher

Prologue and Bassanes in *The Broken Heart* by John Ford, also directed

Astrov in *Uncle Vanya*, also directed Fred Midway in *Semi-Detached* by David Turner, Saville Theatre, London

1963—Director of National Theatre, at Old Vic

Directed *Hamlet*

Astrov in *Uncle Vanya,* also directed

Captain Brazen in *The Recruiting Officer* by Farquhar

1964—Title role in *Othello* by William Shakespeare

Solness in *The Master Builder* by Henrik Ibsen

1965—Directed *The Crucible* by Arthur Miller

Tattle in *Love for Love* by William Congreve and *Othello,* National Theatre tour, Berlin and Moscow

Love for Love, Old Vic

As *Titus Andronicus*, with Vivien Leigh as Lavinia
(1955).

1966—Directed *Juno and the Paycock*

1967–Edgar in *The Dance of Death* by August
Strindberg

    Plucheux in *A Flea in Her Ear*—National
Theatre Company, tour, Canada, including
O'Keefe Center, Toronto

1968—Directed *Love's Labour's Lost* by William
Shakespeare

    Codirected with Donald MacKechnie, *The
Advertisement* by Natalia Ginsburg

1970—Shylock in *The Merchant of Venice* by William Shakespeare

1971—Directed Amphitryon 38 by Jean Giraudoux,
New Theatre, London

    James Tyrone in *Long Day's Journey into
Night* by Eugene O'Neill, New Theatre
London

1972—*Long Day's Journey into Night,* Old Vic

1973—Antonio in *Saturday, Sunday, Monday* by
Eduardo de Filippo Old Vic

    John Tagg in *The Party* by Trevor
Griffiths, Old Vic

1974—Directed *Eden End*

1980—Directed *Filumena* by Eduardo de Filippo,
with Joan Plowright and Frank Finlay,
New York

"He was a man, take him for all in all, I shall not look upon his like again." (Hamlet, Act 1, Scene 2.)

"I've often thought how I wished I'd been a cricketeer instead of an actor from time to time. How much better a life I would have had . . . a healthier existence, a better man altogether . . . and much more miserable." (Laurence Olivier.)

Olivier on Record

Recordings

It seems incredible that the man considered by many to be the finest English-speaking actor of our time has a recorded legacy of less than a dozen selections, half of which are soundtracks and fragmentary contributions. *Othello* is the only complete Shakespearean performance produced for records and his readings from the Old Testament, a twelve volume set, remains the most ambitious recorded presentation.

SHAKESPEARE

Othello. A presentation of the National Theatre of Great Britain, with Laurence Olivier as Othello, Frank Finlay as Iago, Maggie Smith as Desdemona, Derek Jacobi as Cassio, and Joyce Redman as Emilia; Produced for records by George R. Marek and Charles Gerhardt; RCA Victor VDS 100 (RCA SER 5520—3)*

Richard III. Soundtrack from the motion picture with Laurence Olivier, Ralph Richardson, John Gielgud, Claire Boom, Cedric Hardwicke, Alec Clunes, Stanley Baker; RCA Victor LM 6126 (complete), LM 1940 (excerpts)

Olivier in scenes from *Hamlet* and *Henry V,* with Stanley Holloway, Harcourt Williams, Basil Sydney; Music by Sir William Walton; RCA Victor LM 1924 (RCA RB 16144)*

Romeo and Juliet. Complete motion picture soundtrack recording of the production by Franco Zeffirelli, with Leonard Whiting as Romeo, Olivia Hussey as Juliet, Milo O'Shea as Friar Laurence, Michael York as Tybalt, Pat Heywood as Nurse, Robert Stephens as Prince of Verona, and Laurence Olivier, narrator (unbilled); Capitol Records SWDR 289

Homage to Shakespeare. Devised and Directed by George Rylands, Recorded in association with the Shakespeare Exhibition in 1964. Scenes and speeches from plays, Tributes in poetry, prose, and music with Peggy Ashcroft, Alan Bates, Judi Dench, Edith Evans, John Gielgud, Richard Johnson, Peter McEnery, Laurence Olivier, Michael Redgrave, Vanessa Redgrave, Ralph Richardson, Paul Scofield, John Stride, Sybil Thorndike, Dorothy Tutin, Irene Worth, Lewis Casson, Donald Wolfit, Peter Pears, Jaye Consort of Viols, Kneller Hall Trumpeters. (Olivier is heard presenting the speech to the Senate from *Othello*) Argo Records, ZNF 4

Uncle Vanya by Anton Chekhov. British Home Entertainment presentation in association with the Chichester Festival Theatre; with Max Adrian, Lewis Casson, Fay Comton, Rosemary Harris, Robert Lang, Laurence Olivier, Joan Plowright, Michael Redgrave, Sybil Thorndike; Complete play on two discs, Philips PHM 2–301; Reissued Caedmon Records TRS 303 (Philips AL 3448/9)*

Love for Love by William Congreve. National Theatre of Great Britain, Production directed by Peter Wood; Cast: Laurence Olivier as Tattle,

Geraldine McEwan, Madge Ryan, Joyce Redman, Lynn Redgrave, John Stride, Robert Lang, Colin Blakely, Miles Malleson, and Anthony Nicholls. Complete play on three discs, RCA Victor VDS 112

On the Death of King George VI. The Services at Windsor Chapel, Written and read by Laurence Olivier, Recorded in New York, February 22, 1952, Caedmon Records TC 1003

A Robert Louis Stevenson Collection. The Suicide Club and *The Strange Case of Dr. Jekyll*

*Great Britain

and Mr. Hyde; Laurence Olivier, London 5425

A Christmas Carol by Charles Dickens. Laurence Olivier as narrator and Scrooge, plus Mr. Micawber's "Difficulties" from *David Copperfield,* Towers of London production, Limited Edition distributed by the Pepsi Cola company

Sleuth. Music and dialogue from the film; Laurence Olivier as Andrew Wyke, Michael Caine as Milo, Music composed and conducted by John Addison, Columbia Records S 32154

The Living Bible. Laurence Olivier reads from the Old Testament, with music from the Holy Land; Presented by Douglas Fairbanks Jr., Production directed by Fiona Bentley, Music research and supervision by Cyril Ornadel, Recorded for Mercury Records

Vol. 1. *In the Beginning* (The Creation, Adam and Eve, Cain and Abel, The Flood)

Vol. 2. *Except Thou Bless Me* (Abraham, Sodom and Gomorrah, Isaac, Jacob, and Esau)

Vol. 3. *This Dreamer Cometh* (Joseph and His Brothers, Moses)

Vol. 4. *Let My People Go* (The Flight from Egypt, The Ten Commandments,

Jericho, The Song of Deborah)

Vol. 5. *Whither Thou Goest* (Samson and Delilah, Ruth and Naomi)

Vol. 6. *The Lord's Anointed* (Samuel, Saul, David and Goliath)

Vol. 7. *A Still Small Voice* (The Death of Jonathan, David and Bathsheba, Absalom, Solomon, Elijah)

Vol. 8. *A Chariot of Fire* (Naboth's Vineyard, Ahab and Jezebel, Elisha, Naaman, Job)

Vol. 9. *Thy Kingdom is Divided* (Shadrach, Meshach and Abednego, Daniel, Jonah)

Vol. 10. *The Lord is My Shepherd* (The Psalms)*

Vol. 11. *Comfort Ye My People* (The Vision of Isaiah)

Vol. 12. *Let Us Now Praise* (Jeremiah, The Apocrypha—The Wisdom of Solomon, Ecclesiasticus, Ecclesiastes)

*also released separately, Philips Records PHC 9047 Excerpts, Great Britain, HMV ALP 1933–1944

Homage to T.S. Eliot. Recorded at the Globe Theatre, June 13, 1965 with Laurence Olivier, Paul Scofield, George Devine, Ian Richardson, Alec McCowen, and Groucho Marx. *Sweeney Agonistes;* Music by John Dankworth, with Nicol Williamson, Cleo Laine, Anna Quayle, Clive Revill, Alec McCowen, Bernard Cribbins, John Le Mesurier. (Olivier reads "Little Gidding," 1942, Section One from Four Quartets) HMV CLP1924

Churchill in His Own Voice. Quotations selected from the speeches of Winston Churchill delivered in his own voice with comments from his contemporaries; with Laurence Olivier, John Gielgud, Franklin D. Roosevelt, Harry S. Truman, King of England George VI, Dwight D. Eisenhower, Neville Chamberlain, Eleanor Roosevelt, George Patton. Caedmon TC 2018

Command Performance—Highlights from *Night of 100 Stars* featuring, Laurence Olivier, Vivien Leigh, Bob Hope, Jack Benny and others. DRG Records, Archive series DARC–2–1104

Hollywood on the Air presents *The Feminine Touch*—Excerpts from radio broadcasts featuring Jean Harlow, Marilyn Monroe, Alice Faye, Ingrid Bergman, plus a segment from the Gulf Radio Theater production of *Private Lives* by Noel Coward, starring Vivien Leigh and Laurence Olivier. Limited edition for collectors, Star-tone Records ST 205

Music from the Films of Laurence Olivier

Some of the screen's most exciting and memorable music has been created for the films of Laurence Olivier. Alfred Newman's melodic score for *Wuthering Heights* is rich with gothic beauty and haunting romantic themes. The score was nominated for an Academy Award, as was Franz Waxman's for *Rebecca*. Waxman's sensuous recurring theme subtly summons the presence and mystery which surrounds the first Mrs. de Winter.

The composer most closely associated with the Olivier films is Sir William Walton who provided scores for *As You Like It, Three Sisters,* and the great Shakespearean trilogy, *Hamlet, Henry V,* and *Richard III.* The splendor and pageantry the Walton music evokes enriches the Shakespearean tapestry with a majestic and regal dignity. Walton originally composed the entire score for *Battle of Britain,* but prior to the film's release, the music was withdrawn and replaced by Ron Goodwin's score. Only Walton's graphic "Battle in the Air" remains in the film. The composer "regarded his collaboration with Olivier as the most rewarding of his experiences in films. He characterized Olivier as a man who invariably knew what he wanted as a director—and who was nearly always right."[1]

Jack J. Jorgens in his incisive study, *Shakespeare on Film,* states while "it sometimes seems that the director is striving with full orchestra to provide the emotional power which his actors cannot" goes on to cite Walton's successful underscoring of *Henry V's* great variety of visual styles, the festive ceremonial music in *Hamlet* which dies off when the observers realize the climactic duel is in earnest, and the ironic religious music of *Richard III.*

Making one of his rare contributions to motion pictures was the great British composer, Sir Ralph Vaughan Williams, who wrote a pastoral prologue for *The 49th Parallel.* The original release of the film marks one of the few occasions, and might very well be the only time, when the composer's name appeared in the opening credits prior to the film's title. The principal actors and the composer each had their own frame:

LAURENCE OLIVIER
LESLIE HOWARD
RAYMOND MASSEY
and the music of RALPH VAUGHAN WILLIAMS
in
THE 49TH PARALLEL

When the film was distributed in the United States by Columbia Pictures as *The Invaders,* the composer's name appeared with the music credits, crowded into a single frame and dwarfed by that of the London Philharmonic Orchestra in larger letters.

John Addison has scored four of the Olivier films, beginning with *The Entertainer* in 1960. His stirring military motifs for *A Bridge Too Far* area bold contrast to the amusing quizzical themes created for *Sleuth* and *The Seven Percent Solution.*

Richard Addinsell, known for his *Warsaw Concerto,* a composition which became a milestone in the history of film music, contributed a sweeping heroic score for *Fire over England.* Long before the epic scores he composed for *Ben Hur, Quo Vadis,* and *Julius Caesar,* Hungarian composer Miklos Rozsa wrote some of his earliest and most delicately wistful themes for *The Divorce of Lady X* and *That Hamilton Woman.*

One of England's most acclaimed contemporary film composers is Richard Rodney Bennett who won an Oscar nomination for his regal score in *Nicholas and Alexandra.* He also contributed the whimsical military motifs for *The Devil's Disciple* and the evocative themes for *Lady Caroline Lamb.*

Also nominated for Academy Awards were the Alex North scores for *The Shoes of the Fisherman* and *Spartacus.* The pounding percussive accompaniment for the latter thrillingly captures the barbaric and ruthless thrust of the epic.

In *The Boys from Brazil,* Jerry Goldsmith uses a lilting Viennese waltz to illustrate the old world humanism in vivid contrast to menacing themes which define the hunted Nazi war criminal and his butchering henchmen.

With his triumphant award winning music for *Star Wars* and *Superman,* John Williams brought back to the screen a gallant symphonic richness missing from films since the golden era of Erich Wolfgang Korngold, Max Steiner, and Alfred Newman. His classic mold for *Dracula* frames the vampire legend with chilling musical atmosphere.

The distinctive film scores associated with Olivier's film work offer an invaluable musical portrait of his unforgettable screen characterizations.

Recorded Music from the Films of Laurence Olivier

Wuthering Heights (1939). Composed by Alfred Newman, Conducted by Elmer Bernstein, Elmer Bernstein's Filmmusic Collection, FMC 6

Rebecca (1940). Suite, Composed by Franz Waxman, Charles Gerhardt conducting the National Philharmonic Orchestra, RCA ARL1-0708

That Hamilton Woman (1941). Love Theme (Lady Hamilton). Composed and Conducted by Miklos Rozsa, Polydor 2383440

The 49th Parallel (1941). Prelude, Composed by Ralph Vaughan Williams, Bernard Herrmann conducting the National Philharmonic Orchestra, Great British Film Scores, London SPC 21149

Henry V (1945), *Hamlet* (1948), *Richard III* (1955). Music from Sir Laurence Olivier's Shakespearean Films, Composed and Conducted by Sir William Walton, Angel S 36198, reissued Seraphim 60205

Spartacus (1960). Composed and Conducted by Alex North, Decca DL 79092

Bunny Lake Is Missing (1965). Composed and Conducted by Paul Glass, RCA LSO 1115

Khartoum (1966). Composed and Conducted by Frank Cordell, United Artists UAS 5140

The Shoes of the Fisherman (1968). Composed by Alex North, MGM S1E 15

Romeo and Juliet (1968). Composed and Conducted by Nino Rota, Capitol ST 400

Battle of Britain (1969). Music Composed and Conducted by Ron Goodwin, "Battle in the Air" composed by Sir William Walton, conducted by Malcolm Arnold, United Artists UAS 5201

David Copperfield (1969). Composed and Conducted by Malcolm Arnold, GRT 10008

Oh! What a Lovely War (1969). Paramount PAS 5008

Nicholas and Alexandra (1971). Music composed by Richard Rodney Bennett, New Philharmonia Orchestra of London, Conducted by Marcus Dods, Bell 1103

Lady Caroline Lamb (1972). Composed by Richard Rodney Bennett, New Philharmonia Orchestra, Conducted by Marcus Dods, Angel 36946

Sleuth (1972). Composed and Conducted by John Addison, Columbia S 32154

Jesus of Nazareth (1976). Composed and Conducted by Maurice Jarre, Pye NSPH 28504

The Seven-Per-Cent Solution (1976). Composed and Conducted by John Addison, Citadel CT JA 1

A Bridge Too Far (1977). Composed and Conducted by John Addison, United Artists UA-LA 762H

The Boys from Brazil (1978). Composed and Conducted by Jerry Goldsmith, A & M SP 4731

Dracula (1979). Composed and Conducted by John Williams, MCA 3166

A Little Romance (1979). Composed and Conducted by Georges Delerue, Varese Sarabande STV 81109

Appendix

Olivier's Cinema - Chronological List

Too Many Crooks—1930
The Temporary Widow—1930
Potiphar's Wife (Her Strange Desire)—1931
Friends and Lovers—1931
The Yellow Passport (The Yellow Ticket)—1931
Westward Passage—1932
Perfect Understanding—1933
No Funny Business—1934
Moscow Nights (I Stand Condemned)—1935
As You Like It—1936
Fire Over England—1937
The Divorce of Lady X—1938
Q Planes (Clouds Over Europe)—1939
Wuthering Heights—1939
Twenty-One Days (Twenty-One Days Together)—1940
Conquest of the Air—1940
Rebecca—1940
Pride and Prejudice—1940
That Hamilton Woman (Lady Hamilton)—1941
The 49th Parallel (The Invaders)—1942
The Demi-Paradise (Adventure for Two)—1943
Henry V—1945

Hamlet—1948
Carrie—1952
The Magic Box—1952
The Beggar's Opera—1953
A Queen Is Crowned—1953
Richard III—1956
The Prince and the Showgirl—1957
The Devil's Disciple—1959
The Entertainer—1960
Spartacus—1960
The Power and the Glory—1961
Term of Trial—1963
Uncle Vanya—1963
Bunny Lake Is Missing—1965
Othello—1965
Khartoum—1966
The Shoes of the Fisherman—1968
Romeo and Juliet—1968
Oh, What a Lovely War—1969
Battle of Britain—1969
David Copperfield—1969
Three Sisters—1970
Nicholas and Alexandra—1971
The Dance of Death—1971
Lady Caroline Lamb—1972

Sleuth—1972
Marathon Man—1976
The Seven-Per-Cent Solution—1976
Jesus of Nazareth—1976
A Bridge Too Far—1977
The Betsy—1978
The Gentleman Tramp—1978
The Boys from Brazil—1978
A Little Romance—1979
Dracula—1979
Inchon—1980
Clash Of The Titans—1981
The Jazz Singer—1981

Academy Award Nominations

1939—Heathcliff in *Wuthering Heights*
1940—Maxim de Winter in *Rebecca*
1946—King Henry V in *Henry V*
    Honorary award to Laurence Olivier for
    his outstanding achievement as actor, pro-
    ducer, and director in bringing *Henry V* to
    the screen.
1948—Prince Hamlet in *Hamlet*
    Winner – Best Actor
    Winner – Best Motion Picture
    Nomination – Best Director
1956—Richard III in *Richard III*
1960—Archie Rice in *The Entertainer*
1965—Othello in *Othello*
1972—Andrew Wyke in *Sleuth*

1976—Dr. Christian Szell in *Marathon Man*
    (Supporting Actor)
1978—Ezra Lieberman in *The Boys from Brazil*
    Special award to Laurence Olivier for the
    full body of his work, the unique achieve-
    ments of his entire career and his lifetime
    of contribution to the art of film.

New York Film Critics Best Actor

1946—*Henry V*
1948—*Hamlet*
1972—*Sleuth*

Olivier's Performances—Cinema and Television—Alphabetical List

Adventure for Two (The Demi Paradise)
As You Like It
Battle of Britain
Beggar's Opera, The
Betsy, The
Boys from Brazil, The
Brideshead Revisited
Bridge Too Far, A
Bunny Lake is Missing
Cat on a Hot Tin Roof
Clash of the Titans
Clouds Over Europe (Q Planes)
Collection, The

Come Back, Little Sheba
Conquest of the Air
Dance of Death, The
David Copperfield
Demi Paradise, The (Adventure for Two)
Devil's Disciple, The
Divorce of Lady X.
Dracula
Entertainer, The
Fire Over England
49th Parallel, The (The Invaders)
Friends and Lovers
Gentleman Tramp, The
Hamlet
Henry V
Her Strange Desire (Potiphar's Wife)
Inchon
Invaders, The (The 49th Parallel)
I Stand Condemned (Moscow Nights)
Jazz Singer, The
Jesus of Nazareth
John Gabriel Borkman
Khartoum
Lady Caroline Lamb
Lady Hamilton (That Hamilton Woman)
Little Romance, A
Long Day's Journey Into Night
Love Among the Ruins
Magic Box, The
Male of the Species

Marathon Man
Merchant of Venice, The
Moscow Nights (I Stand Condemned)
Nicholas and Alexandra
No Funny Business
Oh! What a Lovely War
Othello
Perfect Understanding
Potiphar's Wife (Her Strange Desire)
Power and the Glory, The
Pride and Prejudice
Prince and the Showgirl, The
Q Planes (Clouds Over Europe)
Rebecca
Richard III
Romeo and Juliet
Seven-Per-Cent-Solution, The
Sleuth
Spartacus
Temporary Widow, The
Term of Trial
That Hamilton Woman (Lady Hamilton)
Three Sisters
Too Many Crooks
Twenty-one Days (Twenty One Days Together)
Uncle Vanya
Westward Passage
World at War, The
Wuthering Heights
Yellow Passport, The (The Yellow Ticket)

Notes

Introduction

1. Richard Meryman, "The Great Sir Laurence," *Life* magazine (May 1, 1964): p. 80 a.
2. Hal Burton, ed., *Great Acting* (New York: Hill and Wang, 1967), p. 12.
3. *Ibid.*, p. 14.
4. *Ibid.*, p. 15.
5. Richard Findlater, *The Player Kings* (New York: Stein and Day, 1971), p. 229.
6. Logan Gourley, ed., *Olivier* (London: Weidenfeld and Nicolson, 1973), p. 115.
7. Tyrone Guthrie, *A Life in the Theatre* (New York: McGraw Hill, Inc., 1959), p. 186.
8. Logan Gourley, ed., *Olivier* (London: Weidenfeld and Nicholson, 1973), p. 115.

The Cinema of Laurence Olivier

1. Felix Barker, *The Oliviers* (Philadelphia and New York: J. B. Lippincott, 1953), p. 68.
2. Terry Coleman, "Olivier Now," California: *Show* Magazine (June, 1970): p. 45.
3. Charles Champlin, "Olivier Better Than Ever," *Los Angeles Times* News Service (January 19, 1976).
4. Barker, *The Oliviers*, p. 70.
5. *Ibid.*, p. 78.
6. Norman Zierold, *Garbo* (New York: Stein and Day, 1969), p. 122.
7. Brooks Atkinson, *Broadway* (New York: Macmillan Co., 1970), p. 378.

8. R. J. Minney, *The Films of Anthony Asquith* (South Brunswick, N.J. and New York: A. S. Barnes and Co., 1975), p. 104.
9. R. W. Apple, "At 75, John Gielgud Looks Back—and to the Future," *New York Times* (April 15, 1979).
10. Janet Dunbar, *Flora Robson* (London: George G. Harrap and Co. and Curtis Brown Ltd., 1961), p. 195.
11. Alan Dent, *Vivien Leigh: A Bouquet* (London: Hamish Hamilton Ltd., 1969), p. 109.
12. Logan Gourley, ed., *Olivier* (London: Weidenfeld and Nicholson, 1973), p. 85.
13. Kenneth Harris, "All the Stage Is His World," *New York Post* (February 22, 1969).
14. Dent, *Vivien Leigh: A Bouquet*, p. 113.
15. *Time* magazine (December 29, 1975): p. 58.
16. Atkinson, *Broadway*, p. 379.
17. Rudy Behlmer, ed., *Memo from David O. Selznick* (New York: Viking Press, 1972), p. 282.
18. Karol Kulik, *Alexander Korda, The Man Who Could Work Miracles* (London: W. H. Allen and Co., 1975), p. 246.
19. Minney, *The Films of Anthony Asquith*, p. 105.
20. Daniel Schwarz, "The Present and Future of Shakespeare," *New York Times* (May 12, 1946).
21. Behlmer, ed., *Memo from David O. Selznick*, p. 390.
22. J. C. Trewin, *Robert Donat* (London: Heinemann, 1968), p. 198.
23. *Ibid.*, p. 204.
24. Herbert Wilcox, *Twenty-Five Thousand Sunsets* (South Brunswick, N. J. and New York: A. S. Barnes and Co., 1967), p. 164.
25. Edwin P. Hoyt, *Marilyn, The Tragic Venus* (New York: Duell, Sloan and Pearce, 1965), p. 191.
26. Fred Robbins, "Sir Laurence Olivier," *Genesis* Magazine (January, 1973): p. 56.

27. *Time* magazine (December 29, 1975): p. 58.

28. Harris, *All the Stage Is His World*.

29. Kenneth Tynan, *The Sound of Two Hands Clapping* (New York: Holt, Rinehart and Winston, 1975), p. 140.

30. Jack L. Jorgens, *Shakespeare on Film* (Bloomington, Ind. and London: Indiana University Press, 1977), p. 194.

31. Pauline Kael, *Kiss Kiss Bang Bang* (Boston: Little Brown and Co., 1968), p. 213.

32. Thomas Lask, "With Olivier in the Cast, Can You Fail?," *New York Times*.

33. Robert L. Daniels, "Zeffirelli: From Romeo to St. Francis," Englewood, N. J.: *North Jersey Suburbanite* (May 9, 1973).

34. Letter to the author from Olivier, February 5, 1970.

35. Leonard Mosley, *Battle of Britain, The Making of a Film* (New York: Ballantine Books, 1969), p. 198.

36. George Curry, *Copperfield '70* (New York: Ballantine Books, 1970), p. 77.

37. Kenneth L. Geist, *Pictures Will Talk, The Life and Films of Joseph L. Mankiewicz* (New York: Charles Scribner's Sons, 1978), p. 379.

38. William Barclay, *Jesus of Nazareth* (London: Fount Paperbacks, William Collins, Sons and Co. Ltd., 1977), p. 114.

39. Curtis Bill Pepper, "Talking with Olivier," *New York Times Magazine* (March 25, 1979), p. 18.

Olivier on Television

1. Cecil Smith, "Natalie on a Hot Tin Roof," New Jersey *Bergen Record* (December 5, 1976).

2. Neil Hickey, "It's the Most Beautiful Work I've Ever Had Anything to do With," *TV Guide* (October 21, 1978).

Music from the Films of Laurence Olivier

1. Mark Evans, *Soundtrack: The Music of the Movies* (New York: Hopkinson and Blake, 1975), p. 87.

Bibliography

Agee, James. *Agee on Film, Reviews and Comments.* Boston: Beacon Press, 1964.

Atkinson, Brooks. *Broadway.* New York: Macmillan and Co., 1970.

Barclay, William. *Jesus of Nazareth.* London: Fount Paperbacks, William Collins, Sons and Co., Ltd., 1977.

Barker, Felix. *The Oliviers.* Philadelphia & New York: J. B. Lippincott, 1953.

Bayer, William. *The Great Movies.* New York: Grosset and Dunlap, 1973.

Behlmer, Rudy, ed. *Memo from David O. Selznick.* New York: Viking Press, 1972.

Burton, Hal, ed. *Great Acting.* New York: Hill and Wang, 1966.

Caillou, Alan. *Khartoum.* New York: Signet Books, New American Library, 1966.

Cottrell, John. *Laurence Olivier.* Englewood Cliffs, N.J.: Prentice-Hall, Inc., 1975.

Crowther, Bosley. *The Great Films, Fifty Golden Years of Motion Pictures.* New York: G. B. Putnam's Sons, 1967.

Curry, George. *Copperfield '70, The Story of the Making of a Film.* New York: Ballantine Books, 1970.

Dent, Alan. *Vivien Leigh—A Bouquet.* London: Hamish Hamilton, 1969.

Dunbar, Janet. *Flora Robson.* London: George G. Harrap and Co. & Curtis Brown Ltd., 1961.

Evans, Mark. *Soundtrack: The Music of the Movies.* New York: Hopkinson and Blake, 1975.

Findlater, Richard. *The Player Kings.* New York: Stein and Day, 1971.

Gassner, John and Nichols, Dudley, eds. *Twenty Best Film Plays.* New York: Crown Publishers, 1943.

Geist, Kenneth L., *Pictures Will Talk, The Life and Films of Joseph L. Mankiewicz.* New York: Charles Scribner's Sons, 1978.

Goldman, William. *William Goldman's Story of A Bridge Too Far.* New York: Dell Publishing Co., 1977.

Gottfried, Martin. *Opening Nights.* New York: G. P. Putnam's Sons, 1963.

Gourlay, Logan, ed. *Olivier.* New York: Stein and Day, 1973.

Guthrie, Tyrone. *A Life in the Theatre.* New York: McGraw Hill Book Co. Inc., 1959.

Halliwell, Leslie. *The Filmgoer's Companion.* New York: Hill and Wang, 1965.

Harwood, Ronald. *Sir Donald Wolfit.* London: Secker and Warburg, 1971.

Hawkins, Jack. *Anything for a Quiet Life.* New York: Stein and Day, 1974.

Howard, Leslie Ruth. *A Quite Remarkable Father.* New York: Harcourt, Brace and Co., 1959.

Hoyt, Edwin P., *Marilyn, The Tragic Venus.* New York: Duell, Sloan and Rearce, 1965.

Jorgens, Jack J. *Shakespeare on Film*. Bloomington, Ind. and London: Indiana University Press, 1977.

Kael, Pauline. *I Lost It at the Movies*. Boston: Little, Brown and Co., Atlantic Press, 1965.

————. *Kiss Kiss Bang Bang*. Boston: Little, Brown and Co., Atlantic Press, 1968.

Kauffman, Stanley. *World on Film*. New York: Harper and Row, 1958.

Kulik, Karol. *Alexander Korda, The Man Who Could Work Miracles*. London: W. H. Allen and Co., 1975.

Lasky, Jesse L., Jr. with Pat Silver. *Love Scene, The Story of Laurence Olivier and Vivien Leigh*. New York: Thomas Y. Crowell, 1978.

Manvell, Roger, *New Cinema in Britain*. New York and London: Studio Vista, Dutton Paperback, 1969.

————. *Shakespeare and the Film*. London: J. M. Dent and Sons, Ltd., 1971.

Minney, R. J. *The Films of Anthony Asquith*. South Brunswick, N. J. and New York: A. S. Barnes and Co., 1975.

Morely, Sheridan. *A Talent to Amuse, A Biography of Noel Coward*. Garden City, N. Y.: Doubleday and Company, Inc., 1969.

Mosley, Leonard. *Battle of Britain, The Making of a Film*. New York: Ballantine Books, 1969.

Olivier, Laurence and Saint-Denis, Michael. *Five Seasons of the Old Vic Theatre Company*. London: Saturn Press, 1950.

Osborne, Robert. *Academy Awards Illustrated*. Hollywood: Marvin Miller Enterprises, 1965.

Pointer, Michael, Cataloger. *Public Life of Sherlock Holmes*. New York: Drake Publishers Inc., 1975.

Pratt, William. *Scarlet Fever, The Ultimate Pictorial Treasury of "Gone With the Wind"*. New York: Macmillan Publishing Co., Inc., 1977.

Priestley, J. B. *Particular Pleasures*. New York: Stein and Day, 1975.

Preminger, Otto. *Preminger—An Autobiography*. New York: Doubleday and Co., 1977.

Schumach, Murray. *The Face on the Cutting Room Floor*. New York: William Morrow and Co., 1964.

Seldes, Marian. *The Bright Lights, A Theatre Life*. Boston: Houghton Mifflin Company, 1978.

Taylor, John Russell, ed. *Graham Greene on Film, Collected Film Criticism 1935–1940*. New York: Simon and Schuster, 1972.

Trewin, J. C. *Robert Donat*. London: Heinemann, 1968.

Tynan, Kenneth. *Curtains*. New York: Antheneum, 1961.

————. *The Sound of Two Hands Clapping*. New York: Holt, Rinehart and Winston, 1975.

Ustinov, Peter. *Dear Me*. Boston: Little Brown and Co., Atlantic Press, 1977.

Whitehead, Peter and Bean, Robin, comp. *Olivier/Shakespeare*. London: Lorrimer Films Ltd., 1966.

Wilcox, Herbert. *Twenty-Five Thousand Sunsets, The Autobiography of Herbert Wilcox*. South Brunswick, N. J. and New York: A. S. Barnes and Co., 1967.

Young, William C. *Famous Actors and Actresses on the American Stage*. New York: R. R. Bowker Co., 1975.

Zierold, Norman. *Garbo*. New York: Stein and Day, 1969.

Index